CATALYST   the prentice hall custom laboratory program for chemistry

Tim Thomas

Chem 225

PEARSON
Custom Publishing

PEARSON
Prentice Hall

Director of Database Publishing: Michael Payne
Executive Marketing Manager: Nathan L. Wilbur
Operations Manager: Eric M. Kenney
Development Editor: Emily A. Colangelo

Cover Art: Courtesy of Photodisc, Age Fotostock America, Inc. and Photo Researchers.

This special edition published in cooperation with Pearson Custom Publishing.

Printed in the United States of America.

Please visit our web site at *www.prenhall.com/catalyst*

Attention bookstores: For permission to return unused stock, call 800-428-4266.

ISBN-13: 978-0-536-94370-5   ISBN-10: 0-536-94370-2

PEARSON CUSTOM PUBLISHING
75 Arlington St., Suite 300
Boston, MA 02116

Laboratory Safety: General Guidelines

1. Notify your instructor immediately if you are pregnant, color blind, allergic to any insects or chemicals, taking immunosuppressive drugs, or have any other medical condition (such as diabetes, immunologic defect) that may require special precautionary measures in the laboratory.

2. Upon entering the laboratory, place all books, coats, purses, backpacks, etc. in designated areas, not on the bench tops.

3. Locate and, when appropriate, learn to use exits, fire extinguisher, fire blanket, chemical shower, eyewash, first aid kit, broken glass container, and cleanup materials for spills.

4. In case of fire, evacuate the room and assemble outside the building.

5. Do not eat, drink, smoke, or apply cosmetics in the laboratory.

6. Confine long hair, loose clothing, and dangling jewelry.

7. Wear shoes at all times in the laboratory.

8. Cover any cuts or scrapes with a sterile, waterproof bandage before attending lab.

9. Wear eye protection when working with chemicals.

10. Never pipet by mouth. Use mechanical pipeting devices.

11. Wash skin immediately and thoroughly if contaminated by chemicals or microorganisms.

12. Do not perform unauthorized experiments.

13. Do not use equipment without instruction.

14. Report all spills and accidents to your instructor immediately.

15. Never leave heat sources unattended.

16. When using hot plates, note that there is no visible sign that they are hot (such as a red glow). Always assume that hot plates are hot.

17. Use an appropriate apparatus when handling hot glassware.

18. Keep chemicals away from direct heat or sunlight.

19. Keep containers of alcohol, acetone, and other flammable liquids away from flames.

20. Do not allow any liquid to come into contact with electrical cords. Handle electrical connectors with dry hands. Do not attempt to disconnect electrical equipment that crackles, snaps, or smokes.

21. Upon completion of laboratory exercises, place all materials in the disposal areas designated by your instructor.

22. Do not pick up broken glassware with your hands. Use a broom and dustpan and discard the glass in designated glass waste containers; never discard with paper waste.

23. Wear disposable gloves when working with blood, other body fluids, or mucous membranes. Change gloves after possible contamination and wash hands immediately after gloves are removed.

24. The disposal symbol indicates that items that may have come in contact with body fluids should be placed in your lab's designated container. It also refers to liquid wastes that should not be poured down the drain into the sewage system.

25. Leave the laboratory clean and organized for the next student.

26. Wash your hands with liquid or powdered soap prior to leaving the laboratory.

27. The biohazard symbol indicates procedures that may pose health concerns.

The caution symbol points out instruments, substances, and procedures that require special attention to safety. These symbols appear throughout this manual.

Measurement Conversions

Metric to American Standard	American Standard to Metric
Length	
1 mm = 0.039 inches	1 inch = 2.54 cm
1 cm = 0.394 inches	1 foot = 0.305 m
1 m = 3.28 feet	1 yard = 0.914 m
1 m = 1.09 yards	1 mile = 1.61 km
Volume	
1 mL = 0.0338 fluid ounces	1 fluid ounce = 29.6 mL
1 L = 4.23 cups	1 cup = 237 mL
1 L = 2.11 pints	1 pint = 0.474 L
1 L = 1.06 quarts	1 quart = 0.947 L
1 L = 0.264 gallons	1 gallon = 3.79 L
Mass	
1 mg = 0.0000353 ounces	1 ounce = 28.3 g
1 g = 0.0353 ounces	1 pound = 0.454 kg
1 kg = 2.21 pounds	

Temperature

To convert temperature:

$$^{\circ}C = \frac{5}{9}(F - 32)$$

$$^{\circ}F = \frac{9}{5}C + 32$$

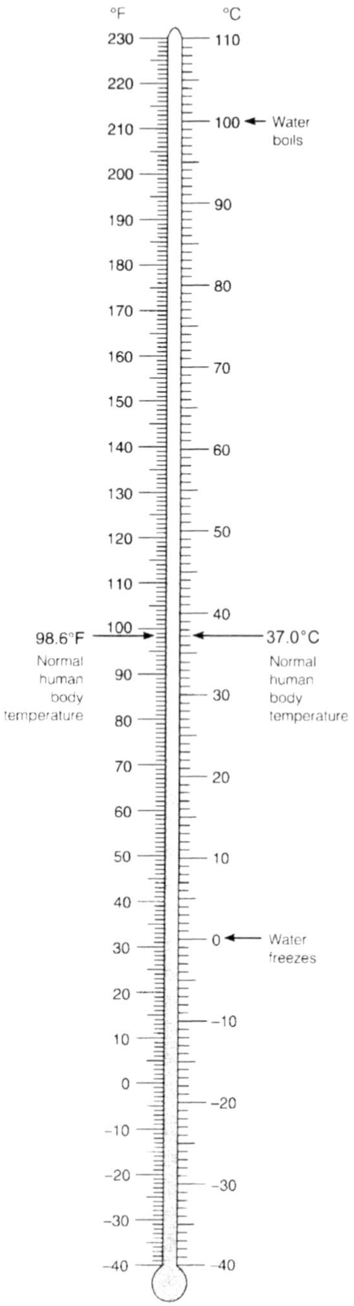

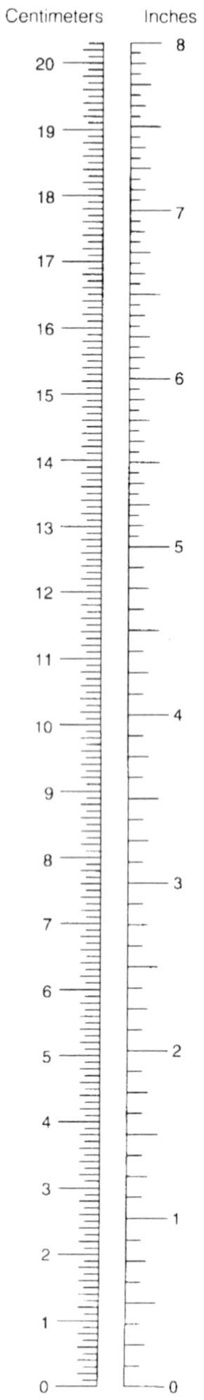

°F

230
220
210 — 100 ◄ Water boils
200
190 — 90
180
170 — 80
160
150 — 70
140 — 60
130
120 — 50
110
100 — 40
90 — 37.0°C Normal human body temperature
80 — 30
70 — 20
60
50 — 10
40
30 — 0 ◄ Water freezes
20
10 — −10
0
−10 — −20
−20
−30 — −30
−40 — −40

98.6°F — 100 Normal human body temperature

°C

Centimeters

20
19
18
17
16
15
14
13
12
11
10
9
8
7
6
5
4
3
2
1
0

Inches

8
7
6
5
4
3
2
1
0

Contents

2-Chloro-2-Methylpropane

Octenes

DETAILED TABLE OF CONTENTS

Multiscale Operational Organic Chemistry by John W. Lehman

The Operations

A. Basic Operations

Cleaning and Drying Glassware

Cleaning Glassware

Clean glassware is essential for good results in the organic chemistry laboratory. Even small amounts of impurities can sometimes inhibit chemical reactions, catalyze undesirable side reactions, and invalidate the results of chemical tests or rate studies. Always clean your dirty glassware at the end of each laboratory period or as soon as possible after the glassware is used. That way, your glassware should be clean and dry for the next experiment, and you will be ready to start working when you arrive. If you wait too long to clean glassware, residues may harden and become more resistant to cleaning agents; they may also attack the glass itself, weakening it and making future cleaning more difficult. It is particularly important to wash out strong bases such as sodium hydroxide promptly, because they can etch the glass permanently and cause glass joints to "freeze" tight. When glassware has been thoroughly cleaned, water applied to its inner surface should wet the whole surface and not form droplets or leave dry patches. Used glassware that has been scratched or etched may not wet evenly, however.

You can clean most glassware adequately by vigorous scrubbing with hot water and a laboratory detergent such as Alconox, using a brush of appropriate size and shape to reach otherwise inaccessible spots. A plastic trough or another suitable container can serve as a dishpan. A tapered centrifuge-tube brush can be used to clean conical vials as well as centrifuge tubes. A nylon mesh scrubber is useful for cleaning spatulas, stirring rods, beakers, and the outer surfaces of other glassware. Pipe cleaners or cotton swabs can be used to clean narrow funnel stems, eyedroppers, Hickman still side ports, etc.

Organic residues that cannot be removed by detergent and water will often dissolve in organic solvents, such as technical-grade acetone. (Never use reagent-grade solvents for washing.) Use organic solvents sparingly and recycle them after use, as they are much more costly than water. Be certain that acetone is completely removed from glassware before you return it to a lab kit, because it will dissolve the foam liner. After washing, always rinse the glassware thoroughly with water (a final distilled-water rinse is a good idea) and check it to see if the water wets its surface evenly. If it doesn't pass this test, scrub it some more or use a cleaning solution such as Nochromix.

Drying Glassware

The easiest (and cheapest) way to dry glassware is to let it stand overnight in a position that allows easy drainage. You can dry the outer surfaces of glassware with a soft cloth, but don't dry any surfaces that will be in contact with chemicals this way, because of the possibility of contamination. If a piece of glassware is needed shortly after washing, drain it briefly to remove excess water. Then rinse it with one or two small portions of wash acetone and dry it in a stream of clean, dry air or put it in a drying oven for a few minutes. Compressed air from an air line contains pump oil, moisture and dirt, so don't use it directly from the line for drying. It can be cleaned and dried as described in OP-24a. Remember that you don't need to dry glassware completely if it will contain water or an aqueous solution during the experiment. Just let it drain for a few minutes before you use it.

Glassware that is to be used for a moisture-sensitive reaction (such as a Grignard reaction) must be dried thoroughly before use. If possible, clean the glassware during the previous lab period, let it dry overnight or longer, then dry it in an oven set at about 110°C for 20–30 minutes. Assemble the apparatus and attach one or more drying tubes (see OP-24) as soon as possible after oven drying; otherwise, moisture will condense inside it as it cools. If the glassware must be cleaned the same day as it is used, rinse it with acetone after washing and flush it with clean, dry air before you put it in the oven. You can also dry glassware by playing a "cool" Bunsen burner flame over the surface of the assembled apparatus, but this practice should never be used in laboratories where volatile solvents, such as ethyl ether, are in use. It should be done only with the instructor's permission and according to his or her directions.

Take Care! Use tongs or heat-resistant gloves when handling hot glass.

Using Specialized Glassware

OPERATION **2**

Most ground-joint glassware used in organic chemistry is of the straight, standard-taper type with rigid joints. The size of a tapered joint is designated by two numbers, such as 19/22 (for typical standard scale glassware) or 14/10 (for typical microscale glassware), in which the first number is the diameter at the top of the joint and the second is the length of the taper, measured in millimeters. The glassware in a commercial organic lab kit, or its equivalent purchased as separate parts, can be used to construct apparatus for many different laboratory operations. Setups for the various operations are illustrated in the appropriate operation descriptions in this book.

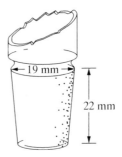

Figure A1 19/22 standard-taper joint

 Lubricating Joints

For some operations, such as vacuum distillation, certain glass joints should be lubricated with a suitable ground-glass joint grease. For most other operations, particularly with microscale equipment, lubrication of glass joints is unnecessary and may be undesirable. Your instructor should inform you if lubrication will be necessary. To lubricate a ground-glass joint, apply a thin layer of joint grease completely around the top half of the inner (male) joint. Do not lubricate the outer (female) joint. Be careful to keep grease away from the open end of the joint, where it may contact and contaminate your reaction mixture or product. When you assemble the components, press the

The Operations

outer and inner joints together firmly, with a slight twist, to form a seal around the entire joint, with no gaps. Grease should never extend beyond the joint inside the apparatus.

After disassembling the apparatus, remove the grease completely by using a suitable organic solvent. Petroleum-based greases are easily removed with petroleum ether or hexanes; silicone greases can be removed by thorough cleaning with dichloromethane. An inner joint can be cleaned by wrapping a small amount of cotton loosely around the end of an applicator stick, dipping it in the solvent, and wiping the joint with the moist cotton.

Take Care! Keep flames away from petroleum ether and hexanes. Avoid contact with dichloromethane and do not breathe its vapors.

Assembling Standard Scale Glassware

Standard-taper joints are rigid, so a setup using standard scale glassware must be assembled carefully to avoid strain that can result in breakage. First, place the necessary clamps and rings at appropriate locations on the ring stand (use two ring stands for distillation setups). Then assemble the apparatus *from the bottom up, starting at the heat source.* Position the heat source on a ring or other support, so that it can be removed easily when the heating period is over; otherwise, it may continue to heat a reaction mixture or an empty distilling flask even after it is switched off, causing a danger of breakage, tar formation, or even an explosion. Clamp the reaction flask or boiling flask securely at the proper distance from the heat source.

As you add other components, clamp them to the ring stand(s), but do not tighten the clamp jaws completely until all of the components are in place and aligned properly. Use as many clamps as are necessary to provide adequate support for all parts of the apparatus. A vertical setup, such as the one for addition under reflux [OP-11], requires at least two clamps for security because if the setup is bumped, the clamp holding the reaction flask may rotate and deposit your glassware on the lab bench—usually with very expensive consequences. Some vertical components, such as Claisen connecting tubes, need not be clamped if they are adequately supported by the component below. Nonvertical components, such as distilling condensers, should be clamped; otherwise they may be accidentally dislodged and fall. Distillation receivers, which may need to be replaced during a distillation, should be supported by a ring and wire gauze or another suitable support. To clamp condensers and other components at an angle to a ring stand, an adjustable clamp with a wing nut on the shaft is required. This wing nut is tightened after the apparatus is aligned.

Some joints, such as the joint that connects a condenser to a vacuum adapter, tend to separate easily, so they should be held together with joint clips or strong rubber bands. For example, a vacuum adapter can be secured to a condenser by stretching a rubber band around the tubulation on both, or by snapping a joint clip around the joint rim. Condensers and vacuum adapters should never be allowed to hang unsupported, even momentarily while you are assembling the apparatus.

When the clamps have been positioned so that all glass joints come together without applying excessive force, seat the joints (with a slight twist, if necessary) and tighten all the clamps. Examine all joints for gaps, then check to make sure that the apparatus is held securely by the clamp jaws and that the clamp holders are secured tightly to the ring stand(s).

Figure A2 summarizes the steps followed in assembling one kind of ground-glass apparatus. Most of the glassware setups you will be using are less complex than the one illustrated.

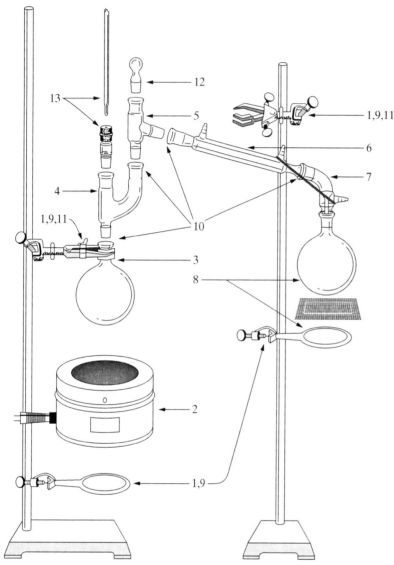

Steps

1 Position clamps, rings.

2 Position heat source.

3 Secure boiling flask (clamp tightly).

4, 5 Add Claisen, three-way connecting tubes.

6 Clamp condenser in place.

7 Attach vacuum adapter with rubber band or spring clamp.

8 Attach receiving flask, support with ring and wire gauze.

9 Readjust all clamps to align.

10 Press joints together.

11 Tighten clamps.

12 Add stopper.

13 Add thermometer adapter and position thermometer.

Figure A2 Steps in the assembly of standard scale ground-glass apparatus

Assembling Microscale Glassware

Microscale glassware comes in a variety of configurations. Most undergraduate microscale laboratory courses use glassware of the kind developed and tested by students at Bowdoin and Merrimack Colleges under the direction of Professors Dana W. Mayo and Ronald M. Pike. There are variations in the construction of this type of glassware, but the components are usually held

The Operations

together by plastic compression caps. Such microscale components are connected with standard-taper joints, just as for standard scale equipment, but a compression cap and O-ring are used to give a tight, greaseless seal. You can assemble such a joint as illustrated in Figure A3 for a conical vial and a water-cooled condenser. First, put a compression cap, threaded side down, over the male (outer) joint of the condenser. Hold it in place as you roll an O-ring over the joint onto the clear part of the glass. Make sure the entire O-ring is above the ground joint, then release the cap, which should be held in place by the O-ring. Now insert the male joint of the condenser into the female (inner) joint of the conical vial and screw the cap over the threads at the top of the vial, tightly enough so that the outer joint cannot be rotated around the inner joint. Be careful, because screwing it down too tightly may break the threads or cause strains in the glass that will lead to eventual breakage. Other microscale components, such as Claisen connecting tubes, drying tubes, and Hickman stills, can be connected to conical vials and microscale reaction flasks to perform a wide variety of laboratory operations, such as distillation (Figure E11) and addition under reflux (Figure B13). All of the components are connected by compression caps, as shown by the appropriate illustrations in the operation descriptions.

Unlike standard scale apparatus, microscale apparatus can be assembled on the bench top and *then* clamped to a ring stand, often with a single microclamp, rather than being assembled from the bottom up on one or more ring stands. Since the reaction vessel (flask or conical vial) is not going to fall off the joint it is connected to, it need not be clamped. Instead, you can clamp the apparatus higher up—on a condenser, for example—to provide a more stable assembly.

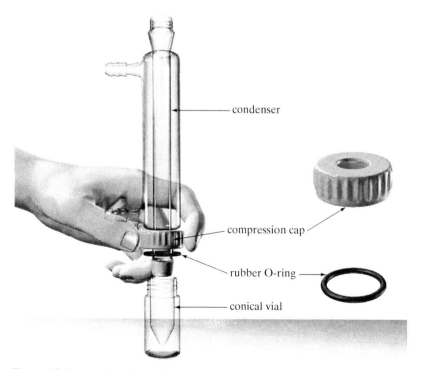

Figure A3 Connecting microscale components

Be sure that the microclamp is held securely to the ring stand and that the clamp jaws are tightened securely around the apparatus, so that it doesn't wobble or fall to the bench and break.

 ### Disassembling Glassware

Disassemble (take apart) ground-joint glassware promptly after use, as joints that are left coupled for extended periods of time may freeze together and become difficult or impossible to separate without breakage. Ground joints can usually be separated by pulling the components apart with a twisting motion. For microscale glassware, unscrew the compression cap completely before you separate the joints. The cap and O-ring can be left in place unless your instructor indicates otherwise. If a joint is frozen, you can sometimes loosen it by tapping it gently with the wooden end of a spatula or by applying steam to the joint while rotating the apparatus slowly, then pulling the components apart with a twisting motion. If this doesn't work, consult your instructor. Clean [OP-1] the glassware thoroughly and return each component to its proper location in the lab kit or to the stockroom.

Take Care! The glass may break, so protect your hands with heavy gloves.

Using Glass Rod and Tubing   OPERATION **3**

Glass connecting tubes, stirring rods, and other simple glass items are required for certain operations in organic chemistry. Soft-glass rod and tubing can be worked easily with a Bunsen burner, but borosilicate glass (Pyrex, Kimax, etc.) requires the hotter flame provided by a Meker-type burner or an oxygen torch. To distinguish borosilicate from soft glass, dip the glass into anhydrous glycerol; borosilicate glass will seem to disappear in the liquid, because it has nearly the same refractive index as glycerol (1.475).

Cutting Glass Rod and Tubing

Glass rods and tubes are *cut* by scoring them at the desired location and snapping them in two. Score the rod or tube by drawing a sharp triangular file (or other glass-scoring tool) across the surface at a right angle to the axis of the tubing. Often, only a single stroke is needed to make a deep scratch in the surface; don't use the file like a saw. To cut a thin, fragile glass tube, such as a melting-point tube or the capillary tip of a Pasteur pipet, it is best to use a special glass scorer, but a sharp triangular file may work if applied carefully so as not to crush the glass. Moisten the scratch with water or saliva. Using a towel or gloves to protect your hands, place your thumbs about 1 cm apart on the side opposite the scratch and, while holding the glass firmly in both hands, press forward against the glass with your thumbs as you rotate your wrists outward (Figure A4).

Working Glass Rod and Tubing

The cut ends of a glass rod or tube should always be *fire-polished* to remove sharp edges and prevent accidental cuts. To fire-polish a glass rod or tube, hold it at a 45° angle to a burner flame (see OP-7 for directions on using a burner)

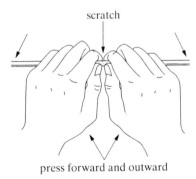

scratch

press forward and outward

Figure A4 Breaking glass tubing

The Operations

and rotate its cut end slowly in the flame until the edge becomes rounded and smooth (Figure A5).

To round the end of a glass rod, rotate the rod in a burner flame, holding it at a 45° angle with its tip at the inner blue cone of the flame. The end should be hemispherical in shape, not rounded only at the edges and flat on the bottom.

To flatten one end of a glass rod, rotate it with its tip at the inner blue cone of the flame until it is incandescent and very soft, but not starting to bend. Then press the softened end straight down onto a hard surface, such as the base of a ring stand. The flattened end should be about twice the diameter of the rod.

To seal one end of a glass tube, hold the tube at a 45° angle to the burner and rotate its open end at the inner blue cone of the flame until the soft edges come together and eventually merge. Remove the tube from the flame as soon as it is closed and immediately blow into the open end to obtain a sealed end of uniform thickness. Let the tube cool to room temperature. Then check it for leaks by connecting the open end to an aspirator or vacuum line with a length of rubber tubing and placing the closed end in a test tube containing a small amount of dichloromethane. (**Take Care!** Avoid contact with dichloromethane and do not breathe its vapors.) If the tube is not properly sealed, the liquid will leak into it when you apply suction. To seal the end of a thin, fragile tube, such as a melting-point capillary, rotate its open end in the *outer* edge of the flame.

To bend glass tubing, first place a flame spreader on the barrel of a Bunsen burner (or use a Meker-type burner). Hold the tubing over the burner flame parallel to the long axis of the flame spreader and rotate it constantly at a slow, even rate until it is nearly soft enough to bend under its own weight (Figure A6). (The flame will turn yellow as the glass begins to soften.) Remove the hot tubing from the flame and immediately bend it to the desired shape with a firm, even motion and a minimum of force (if much force is required, the glass is not soft enough). Bend it in a vertical plane, with the ends up and the bend at the bottom; the bend should follow a smooth curve with no constrictions.

Take Care! Don't burn yourself on the hot end of a glass rod or tube, or lay the glass on combustible materials.

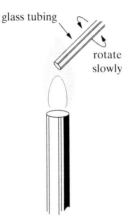

glass tubing
rotate slowly

Figure A5 Fire-polishing

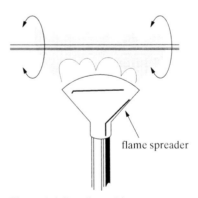

flame spreader

Figure A6 Bending tubing

Inserting Glass Items into Stoppers

Safety Notes

Improper insertion of glass tubing is one of the most frequent causes of laboratory accidents. The resulting cuts and puncture wounds can be very severe, requiring medical treatment and sometimes causing the victim to go into shock. Thermometers are particularly easy to break, especially at the scored immersion line.

Sometimes you may have to insert a glass tube through a hole bored in a cork or a rubber stopper. To bore a hole in a solid stopper, obtain a *sharp* cork borer that is slightly smaller in diameter than the object to be inserted in the stopper.

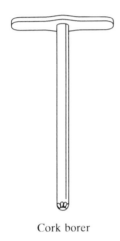

Cork borer

Lubricate its cutting edge with a small amount of glycerine, then *twist* it through the stopper using a minimum of force (don't try to "punch" out the hole). Rotate the borer and stopper in opposite directions, checking the alignment frequently to make sure that the borer is going in straight. When the borer is about halfway through, twist it out and start boring from the opposite end of the stopper until the holes meet. You can remove the plug left inside the cork borer with a rod that comes with a set of cork borers.

To insert a length of glass tubing into a rubber stopper, or a thermometer into a rubber thermometer adapter cap, first lubricate the hole lightly with glycerol or another suitable lubricant; water may work if the hole is not too tight. You can use a cotton swab or an applicator stick to apply the lubricant evenly. Protect your hands with gloves or a towel, then grasp the tube (or thermometer) close to the stopper (or thermometer adapter cap) and twist it through the hole with firm, steady pressure. Do not hold the tube too far from the stopper or the glass may break and lacerate your hand. Apply force directly along the axis of the tube, as any sideways force may cause it to break. Using excessive force or forcing glass through a hole too small for it can also cause it to break. After the tube or thermometer is correctly positioned, rinse off any glycerol with water.

To remove a glass tube from a stopper or a thermometer from a thermometer adapter cap, wet the part of the glass that will pass through the stopper (or use glycerol if necessary), protect your hands with gloves or a towel, and twist the glass out with a firm, continuous motion. Hold the tube or thermometer close to the stopper or cap and avoid applying any sideways force that could cause it to break. If you can't remove a glass tube by this method, obtain a cork borer of a size that will just fit around the tube and twist it gently through the stopper until the glass can be removed.

A microscale thermometer adapter uses an O-ring rather than a rubber cap to hold the thermometer in place.

The Operations

Weighing

Most modern chemistry laboratories are equipped with electronic balances that display the mass directly, without any preliminary adjustments. If you will be using a different type of balance, your instructor will demonstrate its operation. For microscale experiments, chemicals should be weighed on balances that measure at least to the nearest milligram (0.001 g). For standard scale experiments, balances that measure to the nearest centigram (0.01 g) are acceptable for most purposes, but milligram balances are preferable. Most products obtained from a preparation are transferred to vials or other small containers, which should be *tared*—weighed empty—and then reweighed after the product has been added. As a rule, the container should be weighed with its cap and label on and this *tare mass* recorded.

Figure A7 An electronic balance

A balance is a precision instrument that can easily be damaged by contaminants, so avoid spilling chemicals on the balance pan or on the balance itself. If spillage does occur, clean it up immediately. If you spill a corrosive liquid or solid on any part of the balance, notify your instructor as well. Before you leave the balance area, replace the caps on all reagent bottles, return them to their proper locations if you obtained them elsewhere, and see that the area around the balance is clean and orderly.

Weighing Solids

Solids can be weighed in glass containers (such as vials or beakers), in aluminum or plastic weighing dishes, or on glazed weighing papers. In standard scale work, solid reactants are usually weighed on glazed paper or in weighing dishes and then transferred to the reaction flask. In microscale work, it is best to weigh solid reactants directly into the reaction vessel to avoid losses in transfer. A round-bottom flask or pear-shaped flask should be supported in a beaker or on a cork ring for weighing. Hygroscopic solids, those that absorb moisture from the atmosphere, should be weighed in screw-cap vials or other containers that can be capped immediately after the solid is added. Filter paper and other absorbent papers should not be used for weighing, since a few particles will always remain in the fibers of the paper.

To weigh a sample of solid that is in a tared container, set the digital readout to zero by pressing the appropriate button, then place the container on the balance pan. Be sure that the draft shield (if there is one) is in place, then read the mass of the container and its contents from the digital display. Wait until the reading remains constant, then record the mass in your laboratory notebook, including all digits after the decimal point. For example, if the balance reads 3.610 g, do not record the mass as 3.61 g, because zeroes following the decimal point are significant. Then subtract the tare mass to obtain the mass of the solid.

To weigh a sample of solid that is not in a tared container, place a weighing container on the balance pan, press the tare button to zero the digital display, and transfer the solid to the weighing container. With the draft shield in place, wait until the reading has stabilized and then read the mass of the sample directly from the digital display.

To measure out a specific quantity of a solid, such as a solid reactant, place a weighing container on the balance pan and press the tare button to zero the digital display. Then use a spatula or scoopula to add the solid in small portions until the desired mass appears on the digital display. With the draft shield in place, wait until the reading has stabilized and then read the mass of the sample directly from the digital display. Ordinarily you need not measure out the exact mass specified in the procedure (or calculated as directed in the prelab assignment), but try not to deviate from the specified or calculated mass by more than 2% or so, especially for a limiting reactant. Since the theoretical yield of a preparation is based on the actual mass of a starting material, always use your measured mass, not the calculated or specified mass, for stoichiometric calculations.

For example, if a procedure requires 0.250 g of a limiting reactant, you should measure out between 0.245 g and 0.255 g of the reactant.

Weighing Liquids

Organic liquids should be weighed in screw-cap vials or other closed containers to prevent damage to the balance from accidental spillage and losses by evaporation. If liquid must be added to or removed from a weighed container, the container should be removed from the balance pan first.

To measure the mass of a liquid sample in a tared or untared container, follow the directions for solids, but be sure to keep the container capped while it is on the balance pan. When using a tared container, subtract the tare mass to obtain the mass of the liquid.

To measure out a specific mass of a liquid from a reagent bottle, you should first measure the approximate quantity of the liquid by volume and then weigh that quantity accurately in an appropriate closed container. For example, if you need 3.71 g of 1-butanol ($d = 0.810$ g/mL) for an experiment, measure [OP-5] about 4.6 mL (3.71 g $\div$ 0.810 g/mL) of the liquid by volume into a tared container, then cap and weigh the container and liquid. If the measured mass is not close enough to 3.71 g, add or remove liquid with a clean Pasteur pipet or medicine dropper.

For microscale work, it is best to weigh liquid reactants in the reaction vessel, such as a conical vial or round-bottom flask. A round-bottom flask should be supported in a beaker or on a cork ring for weighing. Measure the calculated volume of the liquid with a graduated syringe, automatic pipet, or measuring pipet. Then transfer the liquid to the container, cap it, and record the mass of the container and liquid.

Take Care! Be careful not to spill liquids on the balance pan. If you do, clean up the spill immediately and inform your instructor.

The Operations

Measuring Volume

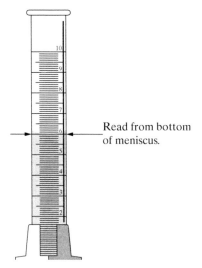

Read from bottom
of meniscus.

Figure A8 Reading the volume contained in a graduated cylinder—in this case, 6.0 mL

Figure A9 A bottle-top dispenser

A convenient homemade pipetting bulb is described in J. Chem. Educ. **1974**, *51*, 467.

Several different kinds of volume-measuring devices are used in the undergraduate organic chemistry laboratory. Relatively large volumes of liquids are measured using graduated cylinders whose capacity usually varies from 10 mL to 100 mL. Smaller volumes can be measured using various kinds of pipets and syringes. Reagent bottles containing liquids may be provided with bottle-top dispensers that measure out a preset volume of the liquid. For some of the experiments in this book, you will use a buret or a volumetric flask; their use is described in most general chemistry laboratory manuals.

Graduated Cylinders

Graduated cylinders are not highly accurate, but in standard scale work they are often used to measure specified quantities of solvents and wash liquids or even some liquid reactants that are used in excess. The liquid volume should always be read from the bottom of the liquid meniscus, as shown in Figure A8.

Bottle-Top Dispensers

A typical adjustable bottle-top dispenser (Figure A9) has a movable plunger that pumps liquid into a glass cylinder, from which it is dispensed through a discharge tube. Its vertical components are usually surrounded by a protective sleeve, which is raised to fill the cylinder and lowered to dispense the liquid. The dispenser is screwed onto a bottle containing the liquid and can be adjusted to dispense a specified volume of liquid, which is read from a scale on the sleeve. Before its initial use, the dispenser must be *primed* by pumping it several times to fill the cylinder and discharge tube and to expel any air bubbles.

To use the dispenser, first check to see that there are no air bubbles in the dispensing tube (if there are, reprime the dispenser or inform your instructor). Then hold your container underneath the discharge tube and raise the sleeve as high as it will go. Release the sleeve so that it drops by gravity, then push it down gently until it moves no farther. Touch the tip of the discharge tube to an inside wall of your container to remove the last drop of liquid. If the liquid is the limiting reactant for a preparation, you should then weigh it accurately as described in OP-4.

Measuring and Volumetric Pipets

A *measuring pipet* has a graduated scale and is used to measure liquid volumes within a range of values; for example, a typical 1-mL measuring pipet can measure volumes up to 1.00 mL to the nearest 0.01 mL. A *volumetric pipet* measures only a single volume, but is more accurate than a measuring pipet. Suction is required to draw the liquid into a measuring or volumetric pipet, but you should never pipet liquids by mouth because of the danger of ingesting toxic or corrosive liquids. A pipet pump is a simple and convenient suction device for filling such pipets. Other pipet fillers such as large rubber bulbs can also be used.

To use a measuring pipet with a pipet pump of the type shown in Figure A10, first see that the plunger is as far down as it will go. Then insert the wide (untapered) end of the pipet firmly into the opening at the bottom of the pump.

Place the tip of the pipet in the liquid and rotate the thumbwheel back toward you with your thumb until the liquid meniscus rises a few millimeters above the zero graduation mark, being careful not to draw any liquid into the pump itself. Slowly rotate the thumbwheel away from you until the meniscus drops just to the zero mark. Measure the desired volume of liquid into a clean container by placing the pipet tip over the container and rotating the thumbwheel away from you until the meniscus drops to the graduation mark corresponding to the desired volume. If the pipet is one dedicated for use with a particular reagent bottle, the excess liquid can be drained into the bottle by depressing the pump's quick-release lever (if it has one) or rotating the thumbwheel away from you as far as it will go. Otherwise, the liquid should be drained into another container or disposed of as directed by your instructor.

To use a volumetric pipet, obtain a bulb-type pipet filler or a pipet pump with a quick-release lever that allows the liquid to drain by gravity. Use the bulb or pump to fill the volumetric pipet to its calibration mark, hold the pipet tip over a receiving container, and let the liquid drain out until only a small amount of liquid is left in the tip. Do not force this liquid into the receiving container, since it is accounted for when the pipet is calibrated.

Automatic Pipets

Automatic pipets (also called pipetters) provide a quick, convenient way of delivering the same volume of liquid with a high degree of reproducibility. Most automatic pipets measure comparatively small volumes of liquids and are therefore most useful for microscale experiments. A variable-volume automatic pipet can be set to a specified volume within a certain range of volumes, such as 20–200 μL (0.020–0.200 mL). The volume is displayed on a digital display or an analog scale, usually in microliters (μL). To prevent contamination, liquid is drawn into a disposable tip and never inside the pipet itself. Whenever the pipet is used for a different liquid, the volume is reset (if necessary) and a new pipet tip is installed. The instructor or a lab assistant will ordinarily set the volume of an automatic pipet and designate it for a specific liquid. Do *not* try to reset the volume or use it for a different liquid without explicit permission from your instructor.

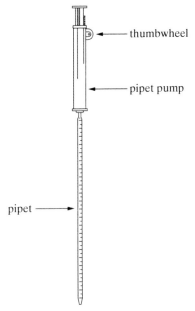

Figure A10 Pipet pump and measuring pipet

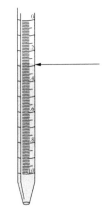

Figure A11 Reading the volume delivered from a measuring pipet—in this case, 0.30 mL

Figure A12 An automatic pipet

The Operations

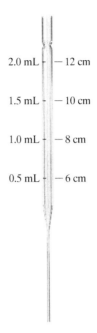

2.0 mL — 12 cm

1.5 mL — 10 cm

1.0 mL — 8 cm

0.5 mL — 6 cm

Figure A13 A calibrated Pasteur pipet

plunger

barrel

needle

Figure A14 A syringe

To use an automatic pipet, depress the plunger to the first *detent* (stop) position, when you will feel resistance to farther movement. Insert the tip into the designated liquid to a depth of about 1 cm or less. Slowly release the plunger to draw liquid into the pipet tip. Place the tip inside the receiving container and depress the plunger to the first detent position, pause a second or so, then push the plunger down to the second detent position and touch the tip to the inner wall of the receiving container to expel the last drop of liquid.

Calibrated Pasteur Pipets

A calibrated Pasteur pipet can be used to measure approximate volumes of liquids such as washing and extraction solvents. To calibrate the pipet, measure 0.50 mL of water into a conical vial or small test tube using a measuring pipet or other accurate measuring device, carefully draw all of the liquid into the Pasteur pipet so that there are no air bubbles in the tip (if necessary, squeeze the bulb *gently* to expel the air), and mark the position of the meniscus with an indelible glass-marking pen. Expel all of the water and repeat this operation using 1.00 mL of water, and other volumes if desired. Additional Pasteur pipets of the same type can be calibrated roughly by aligning them with the calibrated pipet and marking them at the same locations. A quicker, but less accurate, way to calibrate a short (5.75-inch) Pasteur pipet is to use a ruler to mark lines 6 cm, 8 cm, 10 cm, and 12 cm from the narrow (capillary) tip of the pipet. These lines mark volumes of approximately 0.5 mL, 1.0 mL, 1.5 mL, and 2.0 mL. Make sure that the capillary tip is intact; if part of it has broken off, this calibration method will not work. For measuring volatile liquids, a filter-tip pipet (see OP-6) that has been calibrated should work better than an ordinary calibrated pipet.

To use a calibrated pipet, first attach a latex rubber bulb to its wide end. Hold the pipet vertically over the liquid to be measured, squeeze the bulb to expel some of the air (ideally, an amount of air nearly equal to the volume of liquid required), and insert the tip in the liquid. Then release the bulb until the liquid meniscus is at the level of the appropriate calibration mark, quickly move the pipet tip into position over the receiving container, and squeeze the bulb to expel all of the liquid. It takes practice to transfer the liquid without losing some in the process, so read OP-6 for additional tips about the use of Pasteur pipets.

Syringes

Syringes are used to measure and deliver small volumes of liquid, often by inserting the needle through a rubber septum. Such syringes are used to inject liquid samples into a gas chromatograph and (in some microscale experiments) to add liquid reagents to a reaction mixture during the reaction. To use a syringe, fill it by placing the needle tip in the liquid and slowly pulling out the plunger until the barrel contains a little more than the required volume of liquid. (**Take Care!** Don't stick yourself with the needle!) If there are air bubbles in the liquid, try to get rid of them by holding the syringe vertically with the needle up and tapping the barrel with your fingernail, or by expelling the liquid and filling the syringe again, more slowly. Then hold the syringe with the needle pointed upward and slowly push in the plunger to eject the excess liquid (collect it for disposal if requested) until the bottom of the liquid column is at the appropriate graduation mark. Wipe off the tip of the needle with a tissue, place the needle tip into the receiving vessel or through the septum, and expel the liquid by gently pushing the plunger in as far as it will go. Clean the syringe immediately after use by flushing it repeatedly with a soap solution or an appropriate solvent, such as acetone. If you use soap for washing, rinse the syringe thoroughly with water. Dry the syringe by pumping the plunger several times to expel excess solvent. Then remove the plunger to let the barrel dry. If the syringe it to be used again shortly, you can dry it by drawing air through the barrel with an aspirator or a vacuum line.

Take Care! Don't bend the plunger.

The plastic 1-mL syringes provided in some microscale lab kits are subject to contamination and are not compatible with certain organic solvents. For some volume-measuring applications, the barrel of the syringe can be connected to the wide end of a clean Pasteur pipet with a small length of tubing, so that the measured volume of liquid is drawn into the Pasteur pipet rather than the body of the syringe (see *J. Chem. Educ.* **1993**, *70*, A311).

Making Transfers   OPERATION **6**

In many organic syntheses, losses during transfers constitute a substantial part of the total product loss, so they can have a major impact on your yield. Such losses can occur whenever you transfer a liquid or solid from one container to another, whether the original container is a stock bottle, reaction flask, beaker, or funnel. Making complete transfers is particularly important in microscale work, where losing just a few crystals of a solid product or a drop of a liquid product may reduce your percent yield significantly.

 Transferring Solids

Bulk solids (such as those from a lab stock bottle) can be transferred from one container to another using spatulas of various shapes and sizes. For standard scale work, a scoopula is preferred because it is curved to help keep the solid from sliding off. A flat-bladed spatula will also work, but unless you are careful, some of the solid may spill over its sides. For microscale work, the U-shaped or V-shaped end of a Hayman-type microspatula (see Figure A15) can be used to transfer solids. Small amounts of solids can also be transferred with a plastic microscoop, made by cutting a 1-mL automatic pipet tip in half.

Solids can be conveniently transferred to small containers, such as test tubes and storage vials, using a folded weighing paper as a makeshift funnel. If the solid to be transferred is in a square plastic weighing dish, hold opposite corners of the dish between your thumb and middle finger and bend the dish to form a spout from which you can pour it or scrape it out. During such transfers, be sure to place the receiving container on another square of weighing paper or in a weighing dish, so that any solid that misses the container can be recovered. If the solid you are transferring sticks to the sides of its container (such as a reaction vial or Buchner funnel), use a flexible flat-bladed spatula or microspatula to scrape as much as you can off the sides. When you need to transfer the last traces of a solid, you can dissolve the residual solid

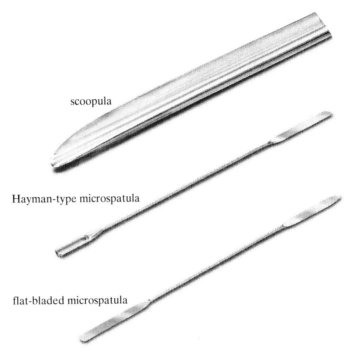

scoopula

Hayman-type microspatula

flat-bladed microspatula

Figure A15 Spatulas for transferring solids

in a volatile solvent, make the transfer, and evaporate the solvent as described next for liquid transfers.

Transferring Liquids

In standard scale work, liquid transfers are usually accomplished by simply pouring the liquid from its original container into a graduated cylinder or another container. Various kinds of pipets and dispensers [OP-5] are used for some liquid transfers.

In microscale work, most liquids (especially liquid reactants and products) should *not* be poured, because too much liquid will adhere to the inside of the original container and be lost. Instead, liquids are transferred using pipets or syringes. A Pasteur pipet fitted with a latex rubber bulb (Figure A16) is often used for such transfers. Highly volatile liquids, such as dichloromethane and diethyl ether, tend to partially vaporize (especially on a warm day or when the pipet is warmed by your hand), causing some of the liquid to spurt out of the tip of the pipet. You may be able to avoid this problem by drawing in and expelling the liquid several times to fill the pipet with solvent vapors before you use it for the transfer. Alternatively, you can use a *filter-tip pipet.*

To make a filter-tip pipet, obtain a *very* small wisp of clean cotton, roll it into a loose ball, and use a straight length of thin (20 gauge) copper wire to push it past the narrow neck of a 5.75-inch Pasteur pipet into its capillary end. Hold the pipet with the capillary tip pointed up as you use the wire to push the cotton as close to the end of the pipet as you can (see Figure A16).

Pipets and syringes are a common cause of contamination, so never allow a liquid to be sucked into a rubber bulb or pipet pump, and clean [OP-1] all pipets and syringes thoroughly after use.

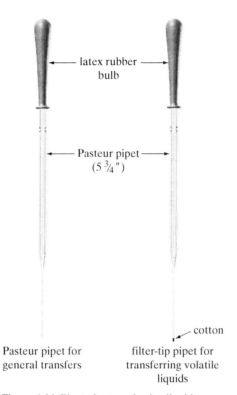

Pasteur pipet for
general transfers

filter-tip pipet for
transferring volatile
liquids

cotton

Figure A16 Pipets for transferring liquids

If the cotton ball is too large, it will get hoplessly stuck in the capillary and you will have to start over with another pipet and cotton ball. You may have to poke the cotton plug repeatedly with the wire to get it in place; the capillary is very fragile so be careful you don't break it. Mayo and Pike, et al. [*Microscale Techniques for the Organic Laboratory,* 2nd. ed. New York: Wiley, 2000] recommend that the cotton plug in a filter-tip pipet be washed with 1 mL of methanol and 1 mL of hexanes and then dried before use, but this measure should be necessary only when the liquid transferred must be very pure and dry (when in doubt, follow your instructor's recommendation).

A filter-tip pipet is useful for transferring all types of liquids, not just volatile ones, because the cotton plug helps remove solid impurities from the liquid, if any are present. It also gives you better control over the transfer process, reducing the likelihood that some of your product will drip onto the bench top on the way to the collecting container. The main disadvantages of the traditional filter-tip pipet are that (1) it takes some time and practice to prepare one properly, (2) the cotton plug in an improperly prepared pipet may be so tight as to impede liquid flow or so loose that it won't stay in place, and (3) it may be difficult to get the cotton plug out without breaking the fragile tip. An alternative is to cut off [OP-3] most of the capillary tip of a 5.75-inch Pasteur pipet, leaving a stub about 5 mm long, and use the method described above to push a wisp of cotton to the end of the shortened tip. A shortened filter-tip pipet is particularly useful for transferring hot recrystallization [OP-25] solutions.

The Operations

A 1-mL (or smaller) syringe of the kind that comes with some microscale lab kits can also be used for microscale liquid transfers. It is particularly useful for transferring liquids to or from containers that are sealed with septum caps to keep out air or moisture. The syringe needle is carefully pushed through the septum and the plunger is pulled (or pushed) far enough to withdraw (or deliver) the desired volume of liquid. See OP-5 for additional information about the use and care of syringes.

When you are transferring a liquid from one container to another, you can avoid losses by keeping the containers as close together as possible. For example, if you are transferring a liquid from a conical vial to a screw-cap storage vial, hold the vials together in the same hand with their mouths at the same level. Then use your free hand to make the transfer. That way, any dripping liquid should be caught by one or the other container rather than ending up on the bench top. Even after a careful transfer, an appreciable amount of liquid may remain behind in the original container. You can recover that liquid by adding a small amount of volatile solvent to the original container, tilting and rotating the container to wash all of the liquid off its sides, transferring the resulting solution to the receiving container, and evaporating [OP-16] the solvent with a stream of dry air or nitrogen. The volatile solvent must be one in which the liquid is appreciably soluble. Dichloromethane and ethyl ether are suitable solvents for most organic liquids.

B. Operations for Conducting Chemical Reactions

Heating

a. Heat Sources

Many kinds of heating devices are available for such applications as heating reaction mixtures, evaporating volatile solvents, and carrying out distillations. The choice of a heat source for a particular application depends on such factors as the temperature required, the flammability of a liquid being heated, the need for simultaneous stirring, and the cost and convenience of the heating device. Of the heat sources described here, heating mantles, steam baths, and oil baths are used mostly for standard scale work, while hot plates, heating blocks, sand baths, and hot water baths are used mostly for microscale work. But some heat sources, such as hot water baths, are useful for both standard scale and microscale work, so select the heat source that is most appropriate for the task at hand.

Heating Mantles. A heating mantle is generally used to heat a round-bottom flask during a reaction or distillation. It is always used in conjunction with a voltage-regulating or time-cycling ("on–off") heat control to vary its heat output. A mantle can be used with a magnetic stirrer (see OP-10), and its heat output can be varied over a wide range, but its operating temperature cannot be monitored with a thermometer. Certain heating mantles, such as Thermowell ceramic flask heaters, are designed to heat round-bottom flasks over a range of sizes. For example, a 100-mL Thermowell mantle can be used to heat 25-mL, 50-mL, and 100-mL round-bottom flasks efficiently. Most other mantles are designed for a specific flask size, so a 100-mL fiberglass heating mantle should be used only to heat a 100-mL round-bottom flask; the mantle will not heat efficiently and could even burn out if used with a flask of another size. Don't turn on an empty heating mantle or use it to heat an empty flask, because that might burn out its heating element. If you spill any chemicals into the well of a heating mantle, particularly if it is hot, notify your instructor immediately.

To operate a heating mantle, first support it on a ring support, a lab jack, or a set of wood blocks so that it can be lowered and removed quickly if the heating rate becomes too rapid. Clamp the flask in place so that it is in direct contact with the well of the heating mantle. If you are heating a small flask in a larger mantle, filling the well with glass wool up to the flask's liquid level may help distribute the heat more evenly (this is said to be unnecessary with a Thermowell mantle). See that the heat control unit is set to zero, then plug the mantle into it—*never* directly into an electrical outlet—and adjust the heat control dial until the desired rate of heating is attained. Note that the dial controls only the rate of heating and cannot be set to a specific temperature. Because a heating mantle responds slowly to changes in the control setting, it is easy to overshoot the desired temperature by turning the control too

The Operations

Figure B1 Heating mantle and heat control

high at the start. If this occurs, lower the mantle so that it is no longer in contact with the flask, reduce the dial setting, and allow sufficient time for the temperature to drop before raising the mantle again. Further adjustments may be needed to maintain heating at the desired rate. When you are done heating, lower the mantle, adjust the heat control dial to its lowest or "off" setting, and let the mantle cool down before you unplug it and return it to its original location.

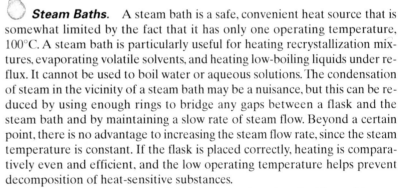

Steam Baths. A steam bath is a safe, convenient heat source that is somewhat limited by the fact that it has only one operating temperature, 100°C. A steam bath is particularly useful for heating recrystallization mixtures, evaporating volatile solvents, and heating low-boiling liquids under reflux. It cannot be used to boil water or aqueous solutions. The condensation of steam in the vicinity of a steam bath may be a nuisance, but this can be reduced by using enough rings to bridge any gaps between a flask and the steam bath and by maintaining a slow rate of steam flow. Beyond a certain point, there is no advantage to increasing the steam flow rate, since the steam temperature is constant. If the flask is placed correctly, heating is comparatively even and efficient, and the low operating temperature helps prevent decomposition of heat-sensitive substances.

To operate a steam bath, first obtain two lengths of rubber tubing, attach one to the steam bath's *water outlet* tube and the other to the steam valve over the sink, and place the open ends of both rubber tubes in the sink. (If your steam bath has no water outlet tube, you will have to turn off the steam periodically to empty it of water.) Remove inner rings from the steam bath, leaving enough rings to safely support the container you wish to heat (unless it is supported by a clamp), but providing a large enough opening so that the steam will contact most of the container's base. If the container is a round-bottom flask that is clamped to a ring stand, remove enough rings so that the flask can be lowered through the rings to about its midpoint, leaving the smallest possible gap between the inner ring and the flask.

Directing the steam into the sink drain, open the steam valve fully until little or no water drips from the end of the rubber tube. Close the steam

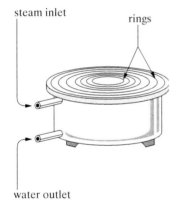

Figure B2 Steam bath

Take Care! Avoid contact with the steam, which can cause serious thermal burns.

valve, connect it to the steam bath's *steam inlet* tube, then open it just enough to maintain the desired rate of heating with the container in place. You can adjust the heating rate somewhat by adding or removing rings, raising or lowering a clamped flask, and changing the steam flow rate. When you are done heating, turn off the steam valve completely and let the steam bath cool down. Then remove the rubber tubes, drain any water that remains in the steam bath, and put it and the rubber tubes back where you found them. (Don't leave rubber tubing in the sink!)

Oil Baths. An oil bath can supply uniform heating and precise temperature control, reducing the likelihood of decomposition and side reactions caused by local overheating, and its operating temperature can be measured easily with a thermometer. But oil baths are messy to work with and difficult to clean. They can also cause dangerous fires or severe burns. You should never heat an oil bath above the flash point of the heating oil, since above this temperature, the vapors of the oil can be ignited by a spark or burner flame. Hot oil can cause severe injury if accidentally spilled on the skin—the oil, which is difficult to remove and slow to cool, remains in contact with the skin long enough to produce deep burns. Water should be kept away from hot oil baths, since it causes dangerous splattering. Oil that contains water should not be used until the water is removed, and a bath liquid that is dark and contains gummy residues should be replaced.

Most oil fires can be extinguished by dry-chemical fire extinguishers or powdered sodium bicarbonate.

Mineral oil is probably the most commonly used oil bath liquid, but it presents a potential fire hazard and is hard to clean up. High molecular weight polyethylene glycols, such as Carbowax 600, are water soluble, which makes cleanup much easier, and can be used at comparatively high temperatures without appreciable decomposition. Some silicone oils can be used at even higher temperatures, but they are considerably more expensive. Flash points and other information about selected oil bath liquids are given here. Note that flash points may vary with composition; check the label or ask your instructor if you are not sure about the flash point of a specific oil bath liquid.

An oil bath can be heated by a coil of resistance wire, a power resistor, a Calrod heating element, or some other device that can be safely immersed in the bath liquid. (Hot plates are also used, but they may cause a fire if the oil spills onto the hot surface.) The output of the heating element is controlled by a variable transformer, and the temperature of the bath is measured with a thermometer suspended in the liquid. A large porcelain casserole makes a convenient bath container, since it is less easily broken than a glass container and has a handle for convenient placement and removal.

To use an oil bath, first place it on a lab jack, a set of wood blocks, or some other support that will allow it to be lowered quickly when necessary. Do not set it on a ring support, because of the danger of spilling hot oil when the ring is raised or lowered. See that the apparatus containing the reaction flask or boiling flask is clamped securely to a ring stand. Then loosen (at the ring stand) the clamp holding the flask and lower the flask into the bath so that the liquid level inside it is 1–2 mm below the oil level. Clamp a thermometer so that its bulb is immersed in the oil but does not touch anything else in the oil bath. Drop in a stir bar, if desired, and use it to stir the bath gently; a smaller stir bar can be used to stir the flask contents (see Figure B3). Switch on the variable transformer and adjust it until the desired temperature is obtained, then

Oil bath liquids
Mineral oil
    Flash point ~190°C, but varies
    with composition
    Potential fire hazard

Glycerol
    Flash point 160°C
    Water soluble, viscous

Dibutyl phthalate
    Flash point 171°C
    Viscous at low temperatures

Triethylene glycol
    Flash point 165°C
    Water soluble

Polyethylene glycols (Carbowaxes)
    Flash point varies with molecular
    weight
    Water soluble; some are solids at
    room temperature

Silicone oil, high temperature
    Flash point 315°C, usable range
    −40°C–230°C
    Expensive; decomposition
    products are very toxic

The Operations

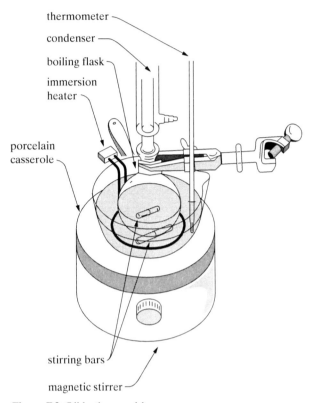

Figure B3 Oil bath assembly

Take Care! If the oil bath liquid starts smoking, discontinue heating and use fresh oil or an oil bath liquid with a higher flash point.

Take Care! Keep flames away from petroleum ether. Avoid contact with and inhalation of dichloromethane.

readjust it as needed to maintain that temperature. When you are done heating, turn off the heat and allow the oil bath to cool nearly to room temperature before you remove it. Transfer the oil to an appropriate container for reuse. Clean the bath container using a suitable solvent, such as petroleum ether for mineral oil, dichloromethane for silicone oil, or water for glycerol and polyethylene glycol.

Burners. Bunsen-type burners are simple and convenient to operate, but they present a serious risk of fire in an organic chemistry lab, in which highly flammable solvents are often used. For that reason, burners should be used mainly for operations that cannot be conducted with flameless heat sources, such as bending and fire-polishing glass tubing.

Safety Notes

Always check to see that there are no flammable liquids in the vicinity before you light a burner. Never use a burner to heat a flammable liquid in an open container. Never leave a burner flame unattended; it may go out and cause an explosion due to escaping gas.

To operate a typical burner with a needle valve at the base, connect it to a gas outlet with a rubber hose and make sure that the gas valve at the outlet is turned off. Close the needle valve on the burner by rotating the knurled wheel clockwise until you feel resistance (don't close it tightly), then open it a turn or two. Open the gas valve and—without delay—ignite the burner with a burner lighter. If it doesn't light, rotate the barrel of the burner clockwise (or close the sleeve-type regulator) and try again. When the burner is lit, adjust the needle valve and rotate the barrel or sleeve to obtain a flame of the desired size and intensity. Rotating the barrel counterclockwise or opening the sleeve regulator to introduce more air produces a hotter, bluer flame. If you are using a burner to heat a nonflammable liquid in a beaker or other container, place the container on a ring support using a ceramic-centered wire gauze to spread out the flame and prevent superheating. The ring support should be positioned so that the bottom of the wire gauze is at the top of the inner blue cone of the flame, where it is hottest.

Hot Plates. A hot plate can be used to heat most liquids in flat-bottomed containers, such as Erlenmeyer flasks or beakers. It should *not* be used to heat low-boiling, flammable liquids that could splatter on the hot surface and ignite, or to heat round-bottom flasks directly. Hot plates can also be used to heat water baths, oil baths, sand baths, and aluminum heating blocks while conducting chemical reactions and distillations. Hot plates with built-in magnetic stirrers [OP-10] are often used for reactions that require simultaneous stirring and heating.

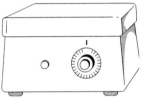

Figure B4 Hot plate

A hot plate is plugged into an electrical outlet and operated with a dial that controls the rate of heating. Tongs, heat-resistant gloves, or other insulating materials should be kept handy so that you can quickly remove the container being heated when necessary. For example, a rectangle of paper toweling can be folded lengthwise several times and looped around the neck of a hot Erlenmeyer flask to remove it from a hot plate. If you are using a hot plate with a sand bath or an aluminum block, it is a good idea to prepare a calibration curve by measuring the equilibrium temperature at each dial setting (wait 10–15 minutes for the temperature to equilibrate at each setting) and plotting the temperature against the dial setting. Then you can adjust the hot plate for the desired operating temperature when you use the same sand bath or aluminum block again. Note that the volume of sand in a sand bath must be kept constant in order for the calibration to be valid.

Hot Water Baths. Hot water baths are useful for heating low-boiling reaction mixtures, evaporating [OP-16] volatile solvents, and in other applications that require gentle heating. Although special metal water baths that resemble steam baths are available, a beaker can be used for most purposes. A typical hot water bath for microscale work is illustrated in Figure B5. Note that the water should fill the water-bath container about three-fourths full when the container being heated is immersed in it. The usual function of the air condenser shown is to return solvent vapors to a boiling reaction mixture (this process is described in OP-7c), but it also makes a convenient "handle" that can be used to lower or raise the container being heated and keeps it from tipping over in the water bath.

If a specific bath temperature is required, heat the water bath on a hot plate or hot plate–stirrer and adjust the heat setting until the specified temperature is reached. Monitor the bath temperature [OP-9] using a thermometer clamped with its bulb beneath the water surface and at the same

The Operations

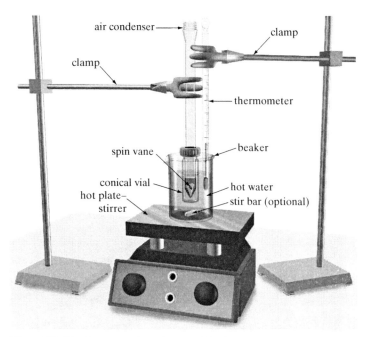

Figure B5 Heating a reaction mixture with a hot water bath

level as the mixture you are heating. The thermometer bulb should not touch the beaker or the container being heated. If the bath temperature rises above the specified value by 5°C or more, withdraw some of the bath water and replace it by an equal volume of cold water. A 10-mL pipet equipped with a pipet pump can be used for this purpose. For most purposes, the bath temperature can be allowed to vary by ±5°C or so from the specified value. If a boiling-water bath is required, add boiling chips or a stir bar to the water before you heat it to boiling. A stir bar is desirable even when the water is not boiling, as it ensures more uniform heat distribution.

If precise temperature control is not necessary, you can fill a beaker with preheated water from a hot water tap or another source and adjust the temperature by adding hot or cold water. As the bath cools, withdraw some of the bath water and replace it by fresh heated water.

Heating Blocks. Aluminum heating blocks with holes or wells designed to accommodate small test tubes, round-bottom flasks, reaction vials, and similar containers can be used for microscale reactions and recrystallizations. The aluminum block is heated on a hot plate or hot plate–stirrer, usually with a thermometer to monitor the temperature. A nonmercury glass thermometer or a digital or dial thermometer with a metal probe should be used if available. A glass thermometer should be secured by a three-finger clamp on a ring stand and *carefully* lowered into a small hole (one drilled in the face of the block to accommodate it) until its bulb just rests on the bottom of the hole. Do this before you begin heating the block, or the thermometer bulb may break. The metal probe of a bimetallic dial thermometer can be inserted into a small hole drilled in one corner of some heating blocks.

As a rule, the temperature of an aluminum block should be *at least* 20°C higher than the temperature you wish to attain in a conical vial or other con-

Take Care! A hot aluminum block looks just like a cold one, so never touch an aluminum block unless you are sure it is cold.

Take Care! If the bulb of a mercury thermometer breaks, especially in a heated block, it will release toxic mercury vapors into the atmosphere. Notify your instructor at once.

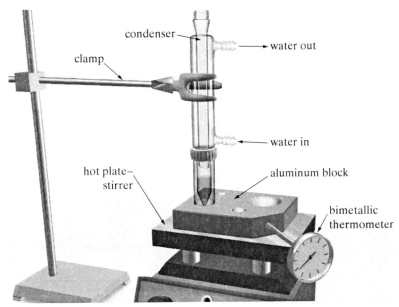

Figure B6 Heating a reaction mixture with an aluminum block

tainer, because the temperature inside the container is invariably lower than the block temperature. For example, if you want to boil a reaction mixture in which water is the solvent, first raise the block temperature to 120°C. If the reaction mixture does not boil when the block is at that temperature, increase the temperature gradually until it does boil. Because a heating block takes some time to reach a desired temperature, start heating it well before it will be needed, using a calibration curve (if you have prepared one) to select an appropriate heat setting. Place the container to be heated in a well of the appropriate size and adjust the temperature as necessary. Standard-taper glassware setups should be clamped to a ring stand, but a small test tube, Craig tube, or similar item can be supported adequately by the walls of its well. You can control the heating rate to some extent by raising and lowering a container in its well without changing the heat setting. If you need to reduce the temperature quickly, as when a recrystallization mixture threatens to boil over, raise the container out of its well first, *then* lower the heat setting or clamp the container at a higher level.

A hot plate–stirrer can be used for the simultaneous heating and stirring [OP-10] of a reaction mixture in a heating block. Copper heats and cools much faster than aluminum, so copper heat-transfer plates have been developed for use in microscale laboratories. These plates are not commercially available, but they can easily be fabricated [Mayo, D.W., et al. *Microscale Techniques for the Organic Laboratory*, 2nd ed. New York: Wiley, 2000].

Sand Baths. A typical sand bath consists of a flat-bottomed container, such as a cylindrical crystallization dish, that has been filled with fine sand to a depth of 10–15 mm. (Using a deeper sand layer may overload and damage a hot plate's heating element, especially at high temperatures.) Like an aluminum heating block, such a sand bath is heated on a hot plate or hot plate–stirrer, using a thermometer to monitor its temperature. When necessary, the heating can be made more uniform and a higher temperature can

Take Care! Don't touch a sand bath or its container unless you are sure it is cold.

The Operations

be attained at a given heat setting by covering the bath container with aluminum foil. Holes must be cut in the foil to accommodate the thermometer and the container being heated. Although sand can be heated to a very high temperature, the glass container of a sand bath may break if it is heated much above 200°C. A convenient sand bath that is usable at high temperatures can be constructed by partly filling the ceramic well of a 100-mL Thermowell heating mantle with sand.

Sand baths heat and cool more slowly than aluminum blocks, but it is easier to observe changes in a reaction mixture and to swirl or shake a mixture in a sand bath. A sand bath also provides a temperature gradient, with lower temperatures near the top of the sand layer and higher temperatures near the bottom. Thus, it not necessary to control the measured temperature of a sand bath precisely, since you can vary the amount of heat applied to a container by varying its depth in the sand bath. For example, you can bring a reaction mixture to the boiling point quickly by immersing its container deep in the sand, then raise the container just enough to keep it boiling gently.

To use a sand bath, first clamp a thermometer to a ring stand and lower it deeply enough into the sand so that its bulb is completely covered but is not touching the bath container. Try to place the thermometer bulb at the same depth in the sand each time, because the temperature reading will vary with its depth. Begin heating the sand bath well before it will be needed, using a calibration curve (if you have prepared one) to select an appropriate heat setting. Position the container being heated, using clamps to support it if necessary, with its bottom immersed in the sand.

Other Heat Sources. Heating devices such as infrared heat lamps and electric forced-air heaters (heat guns) can be used in some heating applications. A heat lamp plugged into a variable transformer provides a safe

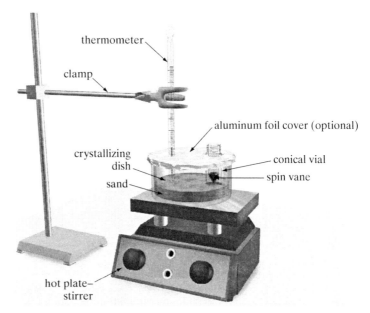

Figure B7 Heating a reaction mixture with a sand bath

and convenient way to heat comparatively low-boiling liquids. The boiling flask is usually fitted with an aluminum foil heat shield to concentrate the heat on the reaction mixture.

Figure B8 Heat lamp

b. Smooth Boiling Devices

When a liquid is heated at its boiling point, it may erupt violently as large bubbles of superheated vapor are discharged from the liquid; this phenomenon is called *bumping*. A porous object, such as a boiling chip, prevents bumping by providing nucleating sites on which smaller bubbles can form. Boiling chips (also called boiling stones) are made from pieces of alumina, marble, glass, Teflon, and other materials. Boiling chips made of Teflon or another chemically resistant material should be used for heating strongly acidic or alkaline mixtures, since ordinary boiling chips may break down in such mixtures. Wooden applicator sticks can be broken in two and the broken ends used to promote smooth boiling in nonreactive solvents; they should not be used in reaction mixtures because of the possibility of contamination. Boiling chips are not needed when a liquid being heated is stirred at a moderate rate with a magnetic stir bar or spin vane, because stirring [OP-10] causes turbulence that breaks up the large bubbles responsible for bumping.

Unless you are instructed differently, you should always add one or more boiling chips to any liquid or liquid mixture that will be boiled without stirring, such as a liquid to be distilled or a reaction mixture to be heated under reflux (see section **c** below). One or two small boiling chips is usually sufficient for microscale work; several boiling chips should be used for standard scale work. It is important to add boiling chips *before* heating begins, because the liquid may froth violently and boil over if you add them when it is hot. If you let a boiling liquid cool below its boiling point, add a fresh boiling chip if you then reheat it, because liquid fills the pores of a boiling chip and reduces its effectiveness when boiling stops.

c. Heating Under Reflux

Most organic reactions are carried out by heating the reaction mixture to increase the reaction rate. The temperature of a reaction mixture can be controlled in several ways, the simplest and most convenient being to use a reaction solvent that has a boiling point within the desired temperature range for the reaction. Sometimes a liquid reactant may itself be used as the solvent. The reaction is conducted at the boiling point of the solvent, using a *condenser* to return all of the solvent vapors to the reaction vessel so that no solvent is lost. This process of boiling a reaction mixture and condensing the solvent vapors back into the reaction vessel is known as *heating under reflux* (or more informally as "refluxing"), where the word reflux refers to the "flowing back" of the solvent. Usually a reaction time is specified for a reaction conducted under reflux. That time should be measured from the time the reaction mixture begins to boil, *not* from the time heating is begun.

Several different kinds of condensers are available. A *water-cooled condenser* consists of two concentric tubes, with cold tap water circulating through the outer tube and solvent vapors from a reaction mixture rising up the inner tube. The water cools the walls of the inner tube, cooling the vapors

Do not mistake a jacketed distilling column for a standard scale condenser; the condenser has a smaller diameter.

The Operations

and causing them to condense to liquid droplets that flow back into the reaction vessel. The West condenser provided in standard scale lab kits can be used for this purpose. An *air condenser* is ordinarily a single tube whose walls transfer heat to the surrounding air, cooling the vapors of high-boiling liquids enough to condense them. For standard scale work, a distilling column is sometimes used as an air condenser. As a rule, air condensers can be used with liquids that boil at 150°C or above, or with small amounts of lower-boiling liquids that are heated gently. Air condensers are sometimes used with aqueous solutions, because the loss of water vapor into the laboratory air does not present a safety hazard, but when in doubt, it is best to use a water-cooled condenser for its more efficient cooling action.

Figure B9 shows a standard scale apparatus for heating under reflux, with a round-bottom flask and West condenser. Figure B10A shows a microscale reflux apparatus with a round-bottom flask and a water-cooled condenser, and Figure B10B illustrates one with a conical vial and an air condenser. Either type of condenser can be used with either kind of reaction vessel, however.

A reflux apparatus consisting of a cold-finger condenser (a water-cooled tube) inserted through a notched rubber stopper into a test tube is convenient for some small-scale reactions, such as those used in qualitative analysis. If you have such a condenser, your instructor can show you how to use it.

General Directions for Heating Under Reflux

Safety Notes

Never heat the reaction flask before the condenser water is turned on; solvent vapors may escape and cause a fire or health hazard.

 Standard Scale

Equipment and Supplies

> heat source
> round-bottom flask
> West condenser
> boiling chips or stir bar
> 2 lengths of rubber tubing

Position the heat source at the proper location on or near a ring stand so that it can be quickly removed if the flask should break or the reaction become too vigorous. Select a round-bottom flask of a size such that the reactants fill it about half full or less. For example, if the total volume of the reaction mixture will be 22 mL, use a 50-mL round-bottom flask. Clamp this *reaction flask* securely to the ring stand at the proper location in relation to the heat source. Transfer [OP-6] the reactants and any specified solvent to the reaction flask. Solids should be added through a powder funnel or with a weighing dish or a square of weighing paper, and liquids should be added through a stemmed funnel. Add a few boiling chips or a magnetic stir bar (see OP-10) and mix the reactants by swirling or stirring. Insert a West condenser into the flask, making sure the joint is tight. Put a clamp near the top

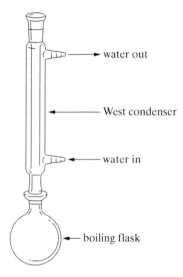

water out

West condenser

water in

boiling flask

Figure B9 Standard scale apparatus for heating under reflux

of the condenser to keep the apparatus from toppling over if it is jarred, but don't tighten its jaws completely.

Connect the water inlet (the lower connector) on the condenser jacket to a cold water tap with a length of rubber tubing, and run another length of tubing from the water outlet (the upper connector) to a sink drain, making sure that it is long enough to prevent splashing when the water is turned on. If the rubber tubing slips off when pulled with moderate force, replace it by tubing of smaller diameter, or secure it with wire or a tubing clamp. Turn on the water carefully so that the condenser jacket slowly fills with water from the bottom up, and adjust the water pressure so that a narrow stream flows from the outlet. The flow rate should be just great enough to (1) maintain a continuous flow of water in spite of pressure changes in the water line and (2) keep the condenser at the temperature of the tap water during the reaction. Excessively high water pressure may force the tubing off the condenser and spray water on you and your neighbors.

If you are using a stir bar, begin stirring at a moderate rate. Turn on the heat source and adjust it to keep the solvent boiling gently, measuring the reaction time from the time that boiling begins. At this time, a continuous stream of bubbles should emerge from the liquid. If the liquid bubbles violently or froths up, reduce the heating rate. Reflux has begun when liquid begins to drip into the flask from the condenser. The vapors passing into the condenser will then form a *reflux ring* of condensate that should be clearly visible. Below this point, solvent will be seen flowing back into the flask; above it, the condenser should be dry. If the reflux ring rises more than halfway up the condenser, reduce the heating rate or increase the water flow rate to prevent the escape of solvent vapors.

At the end of the reaction period, turn off the heat source and remove it from contact with the flask. Let the apparatus cool; then turn off the condenser water, and pour the reaction mixture into a container suitable for the

The Operations

next operation. Clean [OP-1] the reaction flask as soon as possible so that residues do not dry on the glass.

Summary

1 Position heat source.
2 Clamp flask over heat source.
3 Add solvent and reactants.
4 Add boiling chips or a stir bar.
5 Insert reflux condenser, clamp in place, and attach tubing.
6 Turn on condenser water and adjust flow rate.
7 Start heating, adjust heat until reaction mixture boils gently.
8 Check position of reflux ring, readjust water flow or heating rate as necessary.
9 Turn off and remove heat source, let flask cool, transfer reaction mixture.
10 Disassemble and clean apparatus.

 ## Microscale

Equipment and Supplies

heat source
conical vial or round-bottom flask
air condenser or water-cooled condenser
boiling chip(s) or stirring device
2 lengths of rubber tubing (for water-cooled condenser only)

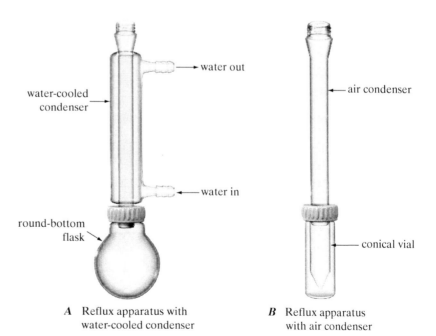

A Reflux apparatus with water-cooled condenser

B Reflux apparatus with air condenser

Figure B10 Microscale apparatus for heating under reflux

For the *reaction vessel*, select a conical vial or round-bottom flask of a size such that the reactants fill it about half full or less. For example, if the total volume of the reaction mixture will be 2.1 mL, use a 5-mL conical vial rather than a 3-mL vial. Transfer [OP-6] the reactants and any specified solvent to the reaction vessel. It is best to weigh limiting reactants directly into the reaction vessel. Add a boiling chip or a magnetic stirring device (see OP-10) and mix the reactants by swirling or stirring. Attach an appropriate reflux condenser to the reaction vessel, making sure that the compression cap is screwed on securely (see OP-2). Clamp the apparatus to a ring stand and lower it into a heating device, such as an aluminum block or sand bath.

If you are using an air condenser, go to the next paragraph. If you are using a water-cooled condenser, connect the water inlet (the lower connector) on the jacket to a cold water tap with a length of rubber tubing, and run another length of tubing from the water outlet (the upper connector) to a sink, making sure that it is long enough to prevent splashing when the water is turned on. If the rubber tubing slips off when pulled with moderate force, replace it with tubing of smaller diameter, or secure it with wire or a tubing clamp. Turn on the water carefully so that the condenser jacket slowly fills with water from the bottom up, and adjust the water pressure so that a narrow stream flows from the outlet. The flow rate should be just great enough to (1) maintain a continuous flow of water in spite of pressure changes in the water line and (2) keep the condenser at the temperature of the tap water during the reaction. Excessively high water pressure may force the tubing off the condenser and spray water on you and your neighbors.

If you are using a stirring device, begin stirring at a moderate rate. Adjust the heat setting or the depth of the reaction vessel in the heat source to keep the solvent boiling gently, measuring the reaction time from the time that boiling begins. At this time, a continuous stream of bubbles should emerge from the liquid. If the liquid bubbles violently or froths up, reduce the heating rate. If there is sufficient liquid in the reaction vessel, its vapors should form a *reflux ring* of condensate in the condenser. Below this point, solvent will be seen flowing back into the reaction vessel; above it, the condenser should be dry. If the reflux ring rises more than halfway up the condenser, reduce the heating rate or increase the water flow rate (for a water-cooled condenser) to prevent the escape of solvent vapors.

At the end of the reaction period, turn off the heat source and raise the apparatus on the ring stand. When the reaction vessel has cooled nearly to room temperature, turn off the condenser water (if used). Unless the next operation will be carried out in the reaction vessel, transfer its contents to a container suitable for that operation. Clean [OP-1] the reaction vessel as soon as possible, so that residues do not dry on the glass.

Summary

1. Transfer reactants and solvent to reaction vessel.
2. Add boiling chip or a stirring device.
3. Attach reflux condenser.
4. Clamp apparatus over heat source.
   IF an air condenser is being used, GO TO 7.
5. Attach tubing to condenser.
6. Turn on condenser water and adjust flow rate.
7. Adjust heat so that reaction mixture boils gently.
8. Readjust water flow or heating rate as necessary.
9. Turn off heat source, let reaction vessel cool, and transfer reaction mixture.
10. Disassemble and clean apparatus.

The Operations

<table>
<tr><td>OPERATION **8**</td><td># Cooling</td></tr>
</table>

Some reactions proceed too violently to be conducted safely at room temperature, or involve reactants or products that decompose at room temperature. In such cases, the reaction mixture is cooled with some kind of cold bath, which can be anything from a beaker filled with cold water to an electrically refrigerated device. Cold baths are also used to increase the yield of crystals from a reaction mixture or recrystallization mixture and for other purposes.

A setup like the one shown in Figure B5 for a hot water bath can also be used for a cold bath. A cold bath can be prepared using any suitable container, such as a beaker of suitable size, a crystallization dish, an evaporating dish, or a pair of nested Styrofoam cups. A beaker can be wrapped with glass wool and placed inside a larger beaker to keep it cold longer, if necessary.

A number of cooling fluids and mixtures are used for cold baths. A mixture of ice (or snow) and tap water can be used for cooling in the 0–5°C range. The ice should be finely divided, and enough water should be present to just cover the ice, since ice alone is not an efficient heat-transfer medium. An ice–salt bath consisting of three parts of finely crushed ice or snow with one part sodium chloride can attain temperatures down to −20°C, and mixtures of $CaCl_2 \cdot H_2O$ containing up to 1.4 g of the calcium salt per gram of ice or snow can provide temperatures down to −55°C. In practice, these minimum values may be difficult to attain; the actual temperature of an ice–salt bath depends on such factors as the fineness of the ice and salt and the insulating ability of the container. Temperatures down to −75°C can be attained by mixing small chunks of dry ice with acetone, ethanol, or another suitable solvent in a vacuum-jacketed container such as a Dewar flask.

Temperatures below −40°C cannot be measured using a mercury thermometer, because mercury freezes at that temperature.

Take Care! Never handle dry ice with your bare hands.

General Directions for Cooling

Equipment and Supplies

> cold bath container
> cooling fluid (or mixture)
> thermometer

Obtain a suitable cold bath container and fill it with the cooling fluid to a level depending on the size of the container to be cooled. When this container is immersed in the cold bath, the cooling fluid should fill the cold bath container about three-fourths full. Clamp a thermometer [OP-9] so that its bulb is entirely immersed in the cooling fluid, but not touching either container. Lower the container to be cooled into the cooling bath so that the liquid level in that container is below the cooling-fluid level. If possible, attach the container to an air condenser and clamp the condenser to a ring stand. Otherwise, either clamp the top of the container to a ring stand or hold it in your hand so that it does not tip over in the cold bath. Keep the contents of the cold bath mixed by occasional stirring or swirling. The contents of the container being cooled can also be swirled or stirred for more efficient cooling. Replace any ice that melts to keep the temperature in the desired range.

Temperature Monitoring

In the organic chemistry lab, thermometers are used to monitor the temperatures of heating devices, cooling baths, reaction mixtures, distillations, and for many other purposes. Such thermometers should have a range of at least -10 to $260°C$, and a wider range is desirable for some purposes. Most broad-range glass thermometers contain mercury, which is toxic and presents a safety hazard if a thermometer is broken, but broad-range non-mercury thermometers are also available. Short glass thermometers (about 15 cm long) are available for microscale work, and bimetallic thermometers with metal probes can be used to measure the temperatures of some heating devices.

You can monitor the temperature of a liquid or heating medium (such as sand) using a thermometer clamped with its bulb entirely immersed in the liquid or heating medium. It should be held in place by a three-fingered clamp or a special thermometer clamp, or inserted into a stopper that is held by a utility clamp. The thermometer should not touch the side or bottom of the container or any apparatus that is placed inside the container. For the most accurate temperature readings, a thermometer should be *calibrated* and an *emergent stem correction* applied as described in Operation 30, but this is generally not necessary for routine temperature monitoring.

To monitor the temperature of a reaction mixture that will be stirred [OP-10] in an open container, such as an Erlenmeyer flask, clamp a thermometer so that its bulb is completely immersed in the mixture, but does not contact the stirring device (a large stir bar could break the thermometer bulb). If a magnetic stirrer is not available, you may have to hold the thermometer inside the reaction vessel as it is being swirled or shaken. Do this by holding the neck of the flask and nesting the thermometer stem in the "vee" between your thumb and index finger, so that the bulb of the thermometer is held securely inside the flask and continuously immersed in the liquid. With a little practice, you should be able to mix the contents of the flask quite vigorously without damage to the thermometer. If continuous mixing is not necessary, you can insert the thermometer each time you stop shaking or swirling the reaction flask, read it when the temperature has stabilized, then remove it and resume mixing. Never use the thermometer itself for stirring, because the bulb is fragile and breaks easily.

You will ordinarily need a thermometer adapter to monitor the temperature of an operation (such as distillation) conducted in a jointed glassware setup. Be certain that the thermometer adapter, when inserted in the apparatus, does not create a closed system. For example, never place a thermometer adapter assembly on top of a reflux condenser that is attached directly to a round-bottom flask, because heating such a system may cause it to shatter. For a standard scale operation, carefully insert the bulb of the thermometer through the rubber cap of the thermometer adapter, using an appropriate lubricant (see OP-3); then secure the adapter in the appropriate joint on the apparatus and carefully raise or lower the thermometer so that the bulb is positioned correctly. To prevent accidental breakage, it is best to remove the thermometer assembly from the apparatus before repositioning the thermometer. To use a microscale thermometer adapter, first place a small rubber O-ring around the thermometer (the O-ring should come with the adapter). Secure the adapter in the appropriate joint on the apparatus, insert the thermometer (bulb end down) through the adapter, and adjust the position of the thermometer bulb by moving the O-ring up or down. Then use the adapter's threaded cap to secure the thermometer assembly to the apparatus.

OPERATION **10**

Mixing

Reaction mixtures are frequently stirred, shaken, or agitated in some other way to promote efficient heat transfer, prevent bumping, increase contact between the components of a heterogeneous mixture, or mix in a reactant as it is being added. If the reaction is being carried out in an Erlenmeyer flask, mixing can be accomplished by manual shaking and swirling or by using a stirring rod. A motion combining shaking with swirling is more effective than swirling alone. If the apparatus is not too unwieldy and the reaction time is comparatively short, ground-glass assemblies can sometimes be manually shaken for adequate mixing. This is most easily done by clamping the assembly *securely* to a ring stand and carefully sliding the base of the ring stand back and forth. But when more efficient and convenient mixing is required, particularly over a long period of time, it is necessary to use some kind of magnetic or mechanical stirring device. Mechanical stirrers, which utilize a motor that turns a shaft connected to a stirring paddle, are seldom used in undergraduate organic chemistry labs, so they will not be described here.

Mixing is used at other times than during reactions. For example, large quantities of liquids can be dried [OP-22] by swirling the liquid with a drying agent in an Erlenmeyer flask. This increases the amount of contact between the liquid and particles of the drying agent, increasing drying efficiency. Microscale quantities are often dried by stirring the liquid with the drying agent in a conical vial. Such stirring can be carried out by placing the pointed end of a flat-bladed microspatula in the bottom of the vial and twirling it. Similarly, the rounded end of a flat-bladed microspatula can be twirled inside a Craig tube or small test tube to stir recrystallization solutions and other mixtures.

Magnetic Stirring. A magnetic stirrer consists of an enclosed unit containing a motor attached to a bar magnet, which is underneath a metal or ceramic platform. As the bar magnet rotates, it in turn rotates a Teflon-coated stirring magnet—a *stir bar*—inside a container placed on or above the platform. Since no moving parts extend outside of the stirrer, a reaction assembly that is to be stirred magnetically can be completely enclosed if necessary. The rate of stirring is controlled by a dial on the magnetic stirrer. For efficient stirring, the vessel containing the stirring device should be positioned near the center of the stirring unit and as close to its platform as practicable.

Magnetic stirrers can be used in conjunction with heating mantles, oil baths, steam baths, and other heat sources that are constructed of nonferrous materials. A hot plate–stirrer resembles a magnetic stirrer except that it has two dials, one to control the heating unit and the other to control the

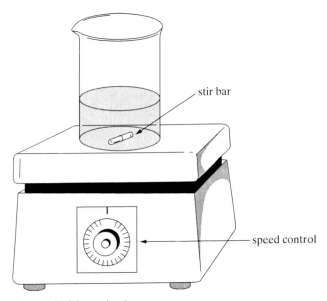

Figure B11 Magnetic stirrer

stirrer. Hot plate–stirrers can be used to heat and stir flat-bottomed containers such as Erlenmeyer flasks directly, but they are also used in conjunction with heating devices that require an external heat source, such as aluminum blocks, hot water baths, and sand baths. Figure B5 shows a hot plate–stirrer being used to heat a hot water bath and stir both the bath liquid and a reaction mixture at the same time.

A hot plate–stirrer is nearly indispensable in the microscale laboratory. The stirring device can be either a *spin vane*, which is used in conical vials, or a small stir bar, which is used in round-bottom flasks, Erlenmeyer flasks, beakers, and other vessels with flat or gently rounded bottoms. Because the magnetic bar in a spin vane is located near the top of the vane, it is quite distant from the platform, so the spin vane may not rotate properly unless it is centered correctly and the stirring rate is relatively low. If necessary, you can use a small stir bar to stir the contents of a conical vial. At low speeds, the stir bar wobbles around in the conical end of the vial and doesn't stir very efficiently, but at higher speeds, it should spin horizontally in the wider part of the vial and create a vortex that promotes efficient mixing.

General Directions for Stirring a Reaction Mixture

Set the heating device (heating mantle, aluminum block, sand bath, etc.) directly on the stirrer or hot plate–stirrer and place a stir bar or spin vane in the reaction vessel in place of boiling chips (the stirring action prevents bumping). Position the reaction vessel as close to the center of the stirring unit's platform as possible. If you are using a stir bar to stir a heating bath as well, it should be larger than the one in the reaction mixture. Start the stirrer and turn on the cooling water for the reflux condenser (if you are using one) before you begin heating. Adjust the stirrer dial carefully to obtain an appropriate stirring rate. If the stirring rate is too high or the reaction vessel

The Operations

is not positioned correctly, the stirring device will flop around erratically rather than rotate smoothly. If that happens, reset the stirrer dial to a low value and increase it gradually until a suitable rate is attained, or reposition the reaction vessel to bring it closer to the top and center of the stirring unit's platform. High stirring rates may be needed for heterogeneous reaction mixtures, such as those involving two immiscible solvents, but in most cases a moderate stirring rate is suitable.

OPERATION **11**

Addition of Reactants

In many organic preparations, the reactants are not all combined at the start of the reaction. Instead, one or more of them is added during the course of the reaction. This is necessary when the reaction is strongly exothermic or when one of the reactants must be kept in excess to prevent side reactions. Solids can be divided into small portions that are added at regular intervals. For standard scale work, liquids are added in portions or drop by drop using a separatory funnel or a specialized addition funnel. For microscale work, liquids are generally added using a syringe or Pasteur pipet.

 Standard Scale Addition

An addition funnel is provided with a pressure-release tube to equalize the pressure in the reaction vessel and addition funnel, allowing its contents to flow freely into the reaction vessel. When such addition funnels are not available, a separatory funnel will work, but an opening must be left at the top for air to enter. Otherwise, the liquid outflow will create a vacuum in the separatory funnel and the flow will eventually stop. If a reaction is run in an open container, such as an Erlenmeyer flask, the addition funnel can simply be clamped to a ring stand above the flask, which is shaken and swirled during the addition. For a reaction conducted under reflux, see the general directions for standard scale addition that follow.

 Microscale Addition

Small amounts of reactants can be added to a reaction mixture through the reflux condenser using a long (9-inch) Pasteur pipet, or directly into the reaction vessel (when there is no condenser) using a short Pasteur pipet. When an addition must be made over an extended period, it is more convenient to use a syringe, which is filled with a measured amount of the liquid to be added, then inserted through a septum so that its needle is directly over the reaction mixture. A Teflon-lined septum (the kind that fits inside a compression cap) may not remain airtight after it is punctured by a syringe needle, so if you are using such a septum, try to find an intact septum or one that has already been punctured but still fits tightly around the syringe needle. (Your instructor may want you to use a punctured one to keep the others intact.) A rubber septum should remain airtight even after it has been punctured by a syringe needle. Remember that a syringe needle is very sharp (unless it has been blunted to prevent injury) and may be contaminated with dangerous biological or chemical substances, so be careful not to stick yourself or anyone else with it.

General Directions for Addition Under Reflux

 Standard Scale

Equipment and Supplies

> boiling flask
> Claisen adapter
> separatory–addition funnel
> West condenser
> stopper (can be omitted for most aqueous solutions or other nonvolatile liquids)

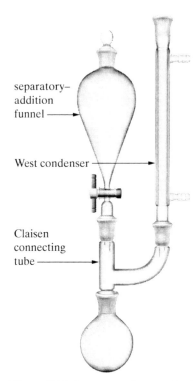

Figure B12 Apparatus for standard scale addition under reflux

Assemble the apparatus shown in Figure B12, placing the separatory–addition funnel on the straight arm of the Claisen adapter so that it is directly over the reaction flask.

Make sure the stopcock is closed; then place the liquid to be added in the separatory–addition funnel and the other reactants in the reaction flask. Unless the liquid in the separatory–addition funnel must be protected from atmospheric moisture, place a strip of filter paper between its ground-glass joint and the stopper. If the liquid is moisture sensitive, insert a drying tube [OP-24] filled with drying agent in the top of the funnel. Add the liquid either in portions or continuously, as directed in the experiment. For portionwise addition, add small portions of the liquid at regular intervals by opening the stopcock momentarily, with shaking or magnetic stirring to mix the reactants. For continuous addition, open the stopcock just far enough so that the liquid drips or drizzles slowly into the reaction flask, and adjust the stopcock position to provide the desired rate of addition. Continuous addition is usually carried out dropwise (drop by drop), with magnetic stirring or periodic shaking to keep the reactants mixed.

The apparatus can be modified to provide for temperature monitoring or mechanical stirring if a three-necked flask is available. In the latter case, one neck of the flask is used for the addition funnel, one for the reflux condenser, and the third for another function.

 Microscale

Equipment and Supplies

> reaction vessel (conical vial or boiling flask)
> Claisen adapter
> septum cap
> air condenser or water-cooled condenser
> syringe

The Operations

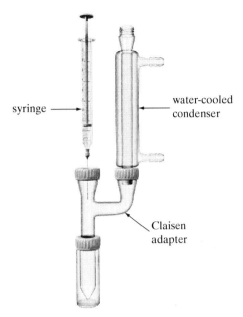

Figure B13 Apparatus for microscale addition under reflux

Assemble the apparatus illustrated in Figure B13 by inserting a Claisen adapter in the reaction vessel and attaching an appropriate reflux condenser to its long arm and a septum cap to its short, straight arm. Fill the syringe with the desired volume of the liquid to be added (see OP-5). Hold the syringe vertically with its needle pointing down and carefully insert the needle through the septum. Add the liquid in small portions during the reaction, as directed in the experiment, by depressing the plunger. If necessary, remove the syringe to refill it, then immediately replace it on the apparatus. When the addition is complete, remove the syringe and clean it (see OP-5) immediately.

C. Separation Operations

Gravity Filtration

Filtration is used for two main purposes in organic chemistry: (1) to remove solid impurities from a liquid or solution, and (2) to separate an organic solid from a reaction mixture or a crystallization solvent. *Gravity filtration* is generally used for the first operation and *vacuum filtration* [OP-13] for the second. *Centrifugation* [OP-14] can be used for either. In a gravity filtration, the liquid component of a liquid–solid mixture drains through a filtering medium (such as cotton or filter paper) by gravity alone, leaving the solid on the filtering medium. The filtered liquid, called the *filtrate*, is collected in a flask or another container. Gravity filtration is often used to remove drying agents from dried organic liquids or from solutions, and solid impurities from hot recrystallization solutions.

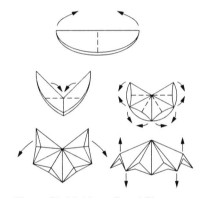

Figure C1 Making a fluted filter paper

 ### Standard Scale Gravity Filtration

Standard scale gravity filtration of organic liquids can be carried out using a funnel with a short, wide stem (such as a powder funnel) and a relatively fast, fluted filter paper. Ordinary filter paper can be fluted (folded) as shown in Figure C1, but commercial fluted filter papers are available from chemical supply houses. Glass wool is sometimes used for very fast filtration of coarse solids. A thin layer of glass wool is placed inside the cone of a short-stemmed funnel, covering the outlet hole, and the mixture to be filtered is poured directly onto the glass wool. Because fine particles will pass through, this method is most often used for prefiltration of mixtures that will be filtered again.

 ### Microscale Gravity Filtration

Small amounts of solid–liquid mixtures (~ 10 mL or less) can be filtered using a *filtering pipet:* a Pasteur pipet containing a small plug of cotton or glass wool (see Figure C3). A filtering pipet is usually made with a standard $5\frac{3}{4}$-inch Pasteur pipet. For filtering hot recrystallization [OP-25] solutions, it is preferable to use a shortened filtering pipet made by cutting off [OP-3] most of the capillary tip; otherwise, crystals may form in the narrow tip and block the liquid flow. A glass-wool plug can be used when large particles are being removed or when the mixture being filtered contains an acid or other substance that may react with cotton. Glass wool does not filter out fine particles, so cotton is preferred for most applications. Very fine particles may pass through cotton also; a filtering pipet containing a 20-mm layer of chromatography-grade alumina or silica gel on top of a cotton plug can be used to remove such particles from a mixture.

A microscale gravity filter with a larger capacity can be constructed by cutting the rounded top off the bulb of a plastic Beral-type pipet and packing

The Operations

some cotton or glass wool in its neck (see *J. Chem. Educ.* **1993**, *70*, A204). The plastic may not be compatible with some organic solvents, however.

A filter-tip pipet, prepared as described in OP-6, can also be used to filter small amounts of liquids. This technique is not really gravity filtration but it accomplishes the same purpose, removing a solid from the liquid being filtered. It has the disadvantage that some solid may adhere to the cotton and be transferred to the collecting container. When the solid particles are quite coarse, such as the granules of sodium sulfate used for drying, you may be able to use a Pasteur pipet without a filter tip. Use the pipet tip to push aside any solid that is in the way, then hold it flat against the bottom of the container as you draw liquid into it.

General Directions for Gravity Filtration

 ## Standard Scale

Equipment and Supplies

> powder funnel
> fluted filter paper
> bent wire or paper clip
> Erlenmeyer flask or other collecting container

If you are filtering the solid–liquid mixture into a narrow-necked container, such as an Erlenmeyer flask, support the funnel on the neck of the flask with a bent wire or a paper clip between them to provide space for pressure equalization (see Figure C2). Alternatively, you can support the funnel in a ring or funnel support positioned directly over the collecting container. Open the fluted filter paper to form a cone and insert it snugly into the funnel, trying to avoid flattening out any of its folds. Add the mixture fast enough to keep the filter paper cone two-thirds full or more throughout the filtration, but don't let it rise above the top of the filter paper. If the mixture contains a considerable amount of finely divided solid, let the solid settle and *decant* (pour out) the liquid carefully onto the filter paper so that most of the solid remains behind until the end of the filtration. Otherwise, the pores of the filter paper may become clogged and slow down the filtration. If you are filtering a solution, use a small amount of the appropriate pure solvent (the one that is in the solution) to rinse the flask containing the solid left behind after decanting; then pour this solvent onto the filter paper and let it drain into the filtrate. If there is much solid on the filter paper, wash it by stirring the solvent gently as it drains, but be careful not to tear the filter paper with the stirring rod. This washing will reduce losses due to adsorption of dissolved organic materials on the solid.

 ## Microscale

Equipment and Supplies

> 2 $5\frac{3}{4}$-inch Pasteur pipets
> rubber bulb (2-mL capacity)
> cotton (or glass wool)
> applicator stick or stirring rod
> collecting containers

Figure C2 Apparatus for standard scale gravity filtration

fluted filter paper

powder funnel

bent wire

collecting flask

Unless you need to save the solid as well as the filtrate, there is no need to transfer all of the solid to the filter paper.

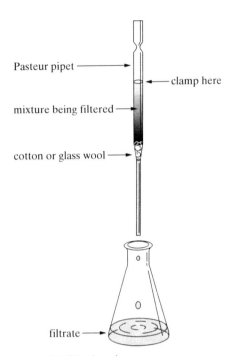

Pasteur pipet

clamp here

mixture being filtered

cotton or glass wool

filtrate

Figure C3 Filtering pipet

Roll a small amount of cotton (or glass wool) between your fingers to form a loose ball, and insert it in the top of a $5\frac{3}{4}$-inch Pasteur pipet (or a Beral-type pipet with the top cut off). Then use a small stirring rod or a wooden applicator stick to push it down the pipet, forming a cotton plug that ends about where the capillary section of the pipet begins, as shown in Figure C3. Don't pack it too tightly because that will slow down the filtration. Clamp the resulting filtering pipet vertically over a small beaker. Rinse it with a suitable solvent (usually the solvent present in the mixture being filtered) by using a second Pasteur pipet to transfer about 0.5 mL of the solvent to the top of the filtering pipet, letting it drain, and using a rubber bulb to force any remaining solvent through. Replace the beaker by another collecting container, such as a conical vial or a small flask, and use the second Pasteur pipet to transfer the mixture being filtered, in several portions if necessary, to the top of the filtering pipet. Let the liquid drain by gravity into the collecting container. If the filtration rate is very slow, you can use a pipet pump (see OP-5) to apply a gentle, constant pressure to the top of the filtering pipet, depressing the quick-release lever (if it has one) before you remove the pipet. (Don't use excessive pressure because it may force particles into the filtrate.) Unless you are filtering a neat (undiluted) liquid, rinse the filtering pipet with a small amount of the previous rinse solvent and let it drain into the filtrate.

General Directions for Filtration with a Filter-Tip Pipet

Construct a filter-tip pipet as described in OP-6 and rinse it with a suitable solvent (usually the solvent present in the mixture being filtered) by drawing in about 1 mL of the solvent and slowly ejecting it into a waste con-

The Operations

tainer. Use the pipet and attached bulb to draw up liquid from the mixture being filtered and transfer it to a suitable collecting container, leaving the solid behind in the original container, until all of the liquid has been transferred. To avoid transferring adherent solid along with the liquid, try to keep the pipet's tip away from the solid when you draw liquid into it. To transfer the last few drops of liquid, push the solid aside with the tip of the pipet and hold the tip flat against the bottom of the original container as you withdraw the liquid.

OPERATION **13**

Vacuum Filtration

Vacuum filtration (also called suction filtration) provides a fast, convenient method for isolating a solid from a solid–liquid mixture or for removing impurities from large quantities of a liquid. In a typical standard scale vacuum filtration, a circle of filter paper is laid flat on a perforated plate inside a porcelain *Buchner funnel*, which is attached by an airtight connector to a heavy walled *filter flask* having a sidearm on its neck (see Figure C4). The filter flask's sidearm is connected to a vacuum line or to the sidearm of a *water aspirator* by a short length of heavy-walled rubber tubing. In the water aspirator, a rapid stream of water passes by a small hole leading to the sidearm, creating a vacuum there and in the attached filter flask, and exits into a sink. An aspirator should always be run "full blast," because its efficiency decreases and the likelihood of water backup increases at lower flow rates. When the mixture being filtered is poured into the Buchner funnel, the liquid is forced through the paper by the unbalanced external pressure and collects in the filter flask, while the solid remains on the filter paper as a compact *filter cake*.

Small quantities of solids can be filtered by essentially the same method using a *Hirsch funnel* supported on a small filter flask or a sidearm test tube (see Figure C5). This apparatus is suitable for many of the microscale experiments in this book and can be used for some standard scale experiments

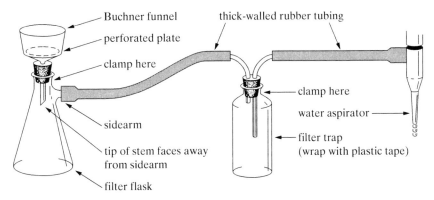

Figure C4 Apparatus for standard scale vacuum filtration

as well. A porcelain Hirsch funnel contains an integral peforated plate about 1–2 cm in diameter; plastic Hirsch-type funnels with separate fritted disks are also available. Hirsch funnels require very small filter paper circles. These are available commercially, but they can also be cut from ordinary filter paper using a sharp cork borer on a flat cutting surface, such as the bottom of a large cork. For a porcelain Hirsch funnel, the filter paper should be about equal in size to the perforated plate or slightly smaller, but large enough to completely cover all of the holes.

Filter Traps and Cold Traps. You should ordinarily connect a *filter trap* between the filter flask (or sidearm test tube) and a water aspirator to keep water from backing up into the flask when the water pressure changes, as it often does. Using a filter trap is most important when the filtrate is to be saved, because any backup will contaminate the filtrate, but it's a good idea to use the trap for all vacuum filtrations. A suitable filter trap can be constructed by wrapping a thick-walled Pyrex jar with transparent plastic tape (to reduce the chance of injury in case of implosion) and inserting a rubber stopper fitted with connecting tubes, as described in Minilab 1. If you are using a vacuum line connected to a central mechanical vacuum pump, it may be necessary to use a *cold trap* to protect the pump from solvent vapors that might damage it (your instructor will inform you if it is necessary to use a cold trap). A filter trap can function as a cold trap if it is immersed in an appropriate cold bath [OP-8].

Filtering Media. Because of the external pressure on the mixture being filtered, solid particles are more likely to pass through the filter paper than with gravity filtration, so a slower (finer grained) grade of filter paper should be used. An all-purpose filter paper, such as Whatman #1, is adequate for filtration of most solids. When filtering finely divided solids from a liquid, it is sometimes necessary to use a *filtering aid* (such as Celite) to keep the solid from plugging the pores in the filter paper. The filtering aid is mixed with a solvent to form a slurry (a thick suspension), which is poured into the filter under vacuum until a bed about 2–3 mm thick has been deposited. The solvent is then removed from the filter flask before continuing with the filtration. This technique cannot be used when the solid is to be saved, since it would then be contaminated with the filtering aid.

Washing. Unless otherwise instructed, you should *wash* the solid on the filter paper with an appropriate solvent, usually the same as the one from which it was filtered. To reduce losses, the wash solvent should be cooled in ice water. For example, if the solid was filtered from an aqueous solution, use cold distilled water as the wash solvent. If it was filtered from a mixture of solvents, as in a mixed-solvent recrystallization [OP-25c], you can use the component of that mixture in which the solid is least soluble. Sometimes a solid is washed with a lower-boiling solvent to help it dry faster. The wash solvent must be miscible with the solvent from which the solid was filtered, and the solid should not be appreciably soluble in it. Thus, a solid filtered from toluene might be washed with low-boiling petroleum ether.

Drying. A solid that has been collected by vacuum filtration is usually *air-dried* after the last washing by leaving it on the filter for a few minutes

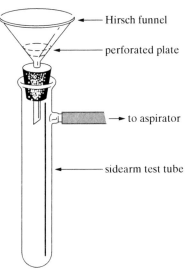

Figure C5 Apparatus for small-scale vacuum filtration with sidearm test tube

The Operations

with the vacuum turned on. The vacuum draws air through the solid, which increases the drying rate. If the solid is still quite wet, you can place a *rubber dam* (a thin, flexible rubber sheet) or a sheet of plastic wrap over the mouth of the funnel. The vacuum should cause the sheet to flatten out on top of the filter cake, forcing water out of it. Unless the solid was filtered from a low-boiling solvent, it will require further drying by one of the methods described in OP-23.

 General Directions for Vacuum Filtration

Equipment and Supplies

Buchner funnel or Hirsch funnel
filter flask (or sidearm test tube)
1-hole rubber stopper or neoprene adapter
filter trap
filter paper
thick-walled rubber tubing
flat-bottomed stirring rod (optional)
flat-bladed spatula
wash solvent

Replace the term "filter flask" by "sidearm test tube" if you are using the latter.

Clamp the filter flask and trap (if you are using one) securely to a ring stand and connect them to an aspirator or vacuum line as shown in Figure C4. Use thick-walled rubber tubing for all connections. If you are using a water aspirator, connect the longer glass tube in the filter trap (the tube that extends farther into the trap) to the aspirator and the shorter glass tube to the filter flask. If you are using a vacuum line and are required to use a cold trap, connect the cold trap to the vacuum line and filter flask and place it inside a cooling bath as directed by your instructor. Insert a Buchner or Hirsch funnel into the filter flask, using a neoprene filter flask adapter or a snug-fitting rubber stopper to provide a tight seal. Obtain a circle of filter paper of the correct diameter and place it inside the funnel so that it covers all of the holes in the perforated plate, but does not fit too snugly; it should not extend up the sides of the funnel.

Moisten the filter paper with a few drops of the solvent that is present in the mixture being filtered, or one that is miscible with it. Open the aspirator tap or vacuum-line valve as far as it will go. Direct the water stream from an aspirator into a large beaker or another container to prevent splashing (don't attach rubber tubing to the aspirator outlet to reduce splashing, because it will also reduce the aspirator's effectiveness). If the volume of the filtration mixture is greater than the capacity of the funnel, add it in portions, keeping the funnel nearly full throughout. If the solid is finely divided, let it settle before you decant the liquid into the funnel, and transfer the bulk of the solid near the end of the filtration. Stir or swirl the filtration mixture near the end of the filtration to get most of the solid onto the filter. Transfer any remaining solid to the filter paper with a flat-bladed spatula, using a small amount of the filtrate or some cold wash solvent to facilitate the transfer. Leave the vacuum on until only an occasional drop of liquid emerges from the stem of the funnel. Then turn off the vacuum if you are using a filter trap. If you are not using a trap, disconnect the rubber tubing at the vacuum source before you turn off the vacuum.

Add enough previously chilled wash solvent to cover the solid. Being careful not to disturb the filter paper, stir the mixture *gently* with a spatula or a flat-bottomed stirring rod until the solid is suspended in the liquid. (For microscale work, stirring is often omitted because of the likelihood of product loss.) Without delay, turn the vacuum on to drain the wash liquid. For standard scale work, the washing step can be repeated with another portion of chilled wash solvent, but one portion is usually adequate for microscale work. Work quickly to avoid dissolving an appreciable amount of solid in the wash solvent. After the last washing, leave the vacuum on for 3–5 minutes to air-dry the solid on the filter and make it easier to handle. Run the tip of a small flat-bladed spatula around the circumference of the filter paper to dislodge the *filter cake* (the compressed solid on the filter paper), then invert the funnel carefully over a square of glazed paper, a watch glass, a weighing dish, or another suitable container to remove the filter cake and filter paper. Use your spatula to scrape any particles remaining on the funnel into the container. The filtrate should be disposed of as specified by the experiment directions or your instructor, and the solid should be dried by one of the methods described in OP-23. To reduce losses, dry the filter paper along with the filter cake and scrape off any additional solid after it is dry, being careful not to scrape any filter paper fibers into your product.

Rule of Thumb: Use 1–2 mL of wash solvent per gram of solid unless directed otherwise.

Summary

1 Assemble apparatus for vacuum filtration.
2 Position and moisten filter paper, turn on vacuum.
3 Add filtration mixture to funnel.
4 Transfer any remaining solid to funnel.
5 Wash solid on filter with cold solvent.
6 Air-dry solid on filter paper.
7 Transfer solid to container, remove filtrate from filter flask.
8 Disassemble and clean apparatus.

Centrifugation   OPERATION **14**

Centrifugation is used to separate different phases from one another by centrifugal force. When a mixture in a *centrifuge tube* is whirled around a circular path at high speed, the denser phase (often a solid) is forced to the bottom of the tube, leaving the other phase on top. In the microscale laboratory, centrifugation is often used to collect solids that have crystallized from solution in a *Craig tube*. Centrifugation may also be used to separate a finely divided solid from a liquid or to separate two immiscible liquids sharply during an extraction [OP-15] operation.

The Operations

 ## General Directions for Centrifugation

Equipment and Supplies

benchtop centrifuge
two centrifuge tubes
Pasteur pipet (optional)
flat-bladed spatula (optional)

To carry out the centrifugation of a mixture containing a solid, first transfer the mixture to a centrifuge tube. (If you are using a Craig tube, see OP-25.) A conical centrifuge tube with a capacity of 15 mL should be suitable. Obtain an empty matched centrifuge tube and add enough water to it so that the two tubes have approximately equal masses. Usually you can estimate the amount of water needed by volume, but you may have to weigh the tubes to ensure proper balance. Alternatively, find another student who is doing the same operation and use his or her centrifuge tube to balance your own (label the tubes so you don't mix them up). Place the two centrifuge tubes directly opposite one another in the rotor of the centrifuge; they fit into tube wells, which are often cushioned to reduce breakage. Close the centrifuge lid, set the centrifuge's timer (if it has one) to 3–5 minutes, and start the centrifuge. If the centrifuge rattles loudly or stops before the time is up, the tubes are not balanced properly. Balance them and try again. When the time is up (or when you stop the centrifuge), the rotor will slowly come to a stop. Wait until its

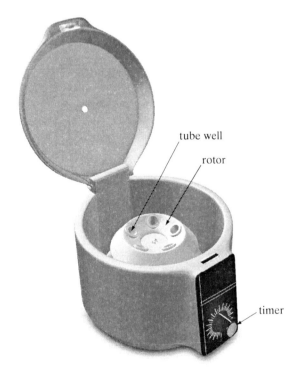

tube well

rotor

timer

Figure C6 A benchtop centrifuge

whirring sound has stopped, open the lid, and remove the centrifuge tubes. Carefully decant (pour out) the liquid or remove it with a Pasteur pipet, leaving the solid behind. If you are saving the solid, use the pointed end of a flat-bladed spatula to remove it.

If you are centrifuging a mixture of two immiscible liquids, separate the liquids after centrifugation by removing the lower layer with a Pasteur pipet as described in OP-15.

Summary

1 Transfer mixture to centrifuge tube.
2 Balance second centrifuge tube against the first.
3 Place balanced tubes in opposite tube wells.
4 Run centrifuge 3–5 minutes.
5 Let centrifuge stop, remove tubes.
6 Remove liquid layer and solid (or second liquid layer) separately.

Extraction   OPERATION **15**

If you shake a bromine/water solution with a portion of dichloromethane, the red-brown color of the bromine fades from the water layer and appears in the dichloromethane layer as you shake. These color changes show that the bromine has been transferred from one solvent into another. The process of transferring a substance from a liquid or solid mixture to a solvent is called *extraction*, and the solvent is called the *extraction solvent*. The extraction solvent is usually a low-boiling organic solvent that can then be evaporated [OP-16] to isolate the desired substance. In organic chemistry, extraction is used (1) to separate a desired organic substance from a reaction mixture or some other mixture, or (2) to remove impurities from a desired organic substance, which is usually dissolved in an organic solvent. The second process is described in OP-21, "Washing Liquids."

a. Liquid–Liquid Extraction

Principles and Applications

Liquid–liquid extraction is based on the principle that if a substance is soluble to some extent in two immiscible liquids, it can be transferred from one liquid to the other by shaking the two liquids together. For example, acetanilide is partly soluble in both water and ethyl ether. If a solution of acetanilide in water is shaken with a portion of ethyl ether, some of the acetanilide will be transferred to the ether layer. The ether layer, being less dense than water, separates above the water layer and can be removed and replaced with another portion of ether. When the fresh ether is shaken with the aqueous solution, more acetanilide passes into the new ether layer. This new layer can then be removed and combined with the first. By repeating this process enough times, virtually all of the acetanilide can be transferred from the water to the ether.

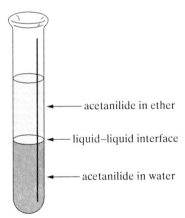

— acetanilide in ether

— liquid–liquid interface

— acetanilide in water

Figure C7 Distribution of a solute between two liquids

The ability of an extraction solvent, S_2, to remove a solute A from another solvent, S_1, depends on the partition coefficient (K) of solute A in the two solvents, as defined in Equation **1**

$$K = \frac{\text{concentration of A in } S_2}{\text{concentration of A in } S_1} \qquad \textbf{(1)}$$

In the example of acetanilide in water and ethyl ether, the partition coefficient is given by

$$K = \frac{[\text{acetanilide}]_{\text{ether}}}{[\text{acetanilide}]_{\text{water}}}$$

The larger the value of K, the more solute will be transferred to the ether layer with each extraction, and the fewer portions of ether will be required for essentially complete removal of the solute. A rough estimate of K can be obtained by using the ratio of the solubilities of the solute in the two solvents—that is,

$$K \sim \frac{\text{solubility of A in } S_2}{\text{solubility of A in } S_1}$$

This approximate relationship can be helpful in choosing a suitable extraction solvent.

Extraction Solvents

Most extraction solvents are organic liquids that are used to extract nonpolar and moderately polar solutes from aqueous solutions, but water and aqueous solutions are sometimes used to extract polar solutes from organic solutions. For example, dilute aqueous NaOH can be used to extract carboxylic acids from organic solvents by first converting them to carboxylate salts, which are much more soluble in water and less soluble in organic solvents than the original carboxylic acids.

$$\text{RCOOH} + \text{NaOH} \longrightarrow \text{RCOO}^-\text{Na}^+ + \text{H}_2\text{O}$$

If the carboxylic acid is sufficiently insoluble in water, it can be recovered by acidifying the aqueous extract to precipitate the acid, which is then recovered by vacuum filtration [OP-13]. Similarly, dilute aqueous HCl is used to extract basic solutes, such as amines, from organic solvents by first converting the amines to ammonium salts.

$$\text{RNH}_2 + \text{HCl} \longrightarrow \text{RNH}_3^+ + \text{Cl}^-$$

A good *organic* extraction solvent should be immiscible with water, dissolve a wide range of organic substances, and have a low boiling point so that it can be removed by evaporation after the extraction. The substance being extracted should be more soluble in the extraction solvent than in water; otherwise, too many steps will be required to extract it.

Ethyl ether and dichloromethane (methylene chloride) are the most commonly used organic extraction solvents. Ethyl ether has a very low boiling point ($34.5°C$) and can dissolve both polar and nonpolar organic compounds, but it is extremely flammable and tends to form explosive peroxides on standing. Dichloromethane is more dense than water, which can simplify the extraction process, and it is not flammable. Dichloromethane has a tendency to form emulsions, which can make it difficult to separate cleanly, and it must be handled with caution because it is a suspected carcinogen. These and other extraction solvents and their properties are listed in Table C1. Organic extraction solvents that have densities less than that of water (1.00 g/mL) will separate as the top layer during the extraction of an aqueous solution; extraction solvents having densities greater than that of water will separate as the bottom layer.

Table C1 Properties of commonly used extraction solvents

Solvent	b.p., °C	d, g/mL	Comments
water	100	1.00	for extracting polar compounds, generally using a reactive solute such as NaOH or HCl
ethyl ether	34.5	0.71	good general solvent; absorbs some water; very flammable
dichloromethane	40	1.34	good general solvent; suspected carcinogen
toluene	111	0.87	for extracting aromatic and nonpolar compounds; difficult to remove
petroleum ether	~35-60	~0.64	for extracting nonpolar compounds; very flammable
hexane	69	0.66	for extracting nonpolar compounds; flammable

Potential hazards should be considered in selecting and using an extraction solvent. Precautions must be taken with all organic solvents to minimize contact and inhalation of vapors. Solvents such as benzene, trichloromethane (chloroform), and tetrachloromethane (carbon tetrachloride) should not be used in an undergraduate laboratory because of their toxicity and carcinogenic potential. Flames must not be allowed in the laboratory when highly flammable solvents, such as ethyl ether and petroleum ether, are in use.

Experimental Considerations

Extraction Methods. A standard scale liquid–liquid extraction is ordinarily carried out in a *separatory funnel*, which has a stopcock in its stem. This makes it possible to drain the lower layer into a separate container, leaving the upper layer behind in the separatory funnel. Separatory funnels are very expensive and break easily. Never prop a separatory funnel on its base; support it on a ring or some other stable support. If your separatory funnel has a glass stopcock, lubricate it by applying thin bands of stopcock grease on both sides, leaving the center (where the drain hole is located) free of grease to prevent contamination (see Figure C8). A glass stopcock is secured to the separatory funnel by a compression clip or a rubber ring, which should be tight enough to keep it from leaking. A Teflon stopcock (which should *not* be lubricated) is secured by a Teflon washer, rubber ring, and Teflon nut, in that order. The nut is screwed in just tightly enough to prevent leakage and allow the stopcock to turn without excessive force.

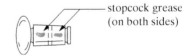
stopcock grease (on both sides)

Figure C8 Lubricating a glass stopcock

The Operations

A screw-cap centrifuge tube is preferable, since it is less likely to leak than one having a snap-on cap.

In the microscale laboratory, an extraction is usually performed by shaking the liquids in a conical vial or conical centrifuge tube and separating them with a Pasteur pipet. A 5-mL conical vial can be used with liquid volumes up to ~4 mL and a 15-mL centrifuge tube with liquid volumes up to ~12 mL. A conical vial may leak if the Teflon liner is damaged or the rim of the vial is chipped, so shake some water in the capped vial to check for leaks before using the vial for an extraction. Do this for a centrifuge tube also, and replace the cap if it leaks. The layers are ordinarily separated by removing the *lower* layer with a Pasteur pipet and transferring it to another container. This way, the interface between the layers is at the narrowest part of the container when the last of the lower layer is removed, making a sharp separation possible. It takes some practice and a steady hand to remove all of the bottom layer without including any of the top layer, but it is important that you learn how to do so; otherwise, you will lose part of your product or the product will be contaminated with material from the layer being extracted. Accurate separation is most important for the last extraction step, because any extraction solvent that is not recovered during earlier extraction steps can be recovered in the last one. Most extraction solvents have a high vapor pressure, which can cause them to spurt out of the tip of a Pasteur pipet during transfer. Product loss due to spurting can be reduced or prevented by (a) making sure that the extraction solvent, the liquid being extracted, and the Pasteur pipet are at room temperature or below, (b) rinsing the Pasteur pipet with the extraction solvent two or three times to fill it with solvent vapors just before use, and (c) using a filter-tip pipet.

Volume of Extraction Solvent. The volume of extraction solvent and the number of extraction steps are sometimes specified in an experimental procedure. If they are not, use a volume of extraction solvent about equal to the volume of liquid being extracted, divided into at least two portions. For example, extract 12 mL of an aqueous solution with two successive 6-mL (or three 4-mL) portions of ethyl ether. Note that it is more efficient to use several small portions of extraction solvent rather than one large portion of the same total volume.

Rule of Thumb: Total volume of extraction solvent ≈ volume of liquid being extracted.

Emulsions. Under some conditions, the liquid layers do not separate sharply, either because an *emulsion* forms at the interface between the two liquids or because droplets of one liquid remain in the other liquid layer. Emulsions can often be broken up by using a wooden applicator stick to stir the liquids gently at the interface or by mixing in some saturated aqueous sodium chloride solution (or enough solid NaCl to saturate the aqueous layer) and then allowing the extraction container (separatory funnel, conical vial, centrifuge tube, etc.) to stand open and undisturbed for a time. A wooden applicator stick can be used to help consolidate the liquid layers by rubbing or stirring any liquid droplets that form on the sides or bottom of the extraction container, and to remove small amounts of insoluble "gunk" that sometimes form near the interface. Larger amounts of insoluble material can be removed by filtering [OP-12] the mixture through a loose pad of glass wool in a powder funnel or filtering pipet.

An emulsion usually contains microscopic droplets of one liquid suspended in another.

Saving the Right Layer. Occasionally, a student who has completed an extraction will inadvertently discard the layer that contains the product and have to repeat the experiment from the beginning. The most important rule to remember when doing an extraction is to *always keep both layers until you are certain which layer contains the desired product.* The safest policy is to keep both layers until you have actually isolated the product from one of them, but you can usually determine which is the right layer before that. In most extractions, the product is extracted from an aqueous solution into an organic solvent, such as dichloromethane or diethyl ether. If you make careful observations when you add the extraction solvent, you can usually tell whether it sinks below the aqueous layer or floats on top of it. Since dichloromethane ($d = 1.33$ g/mL) is more dense than water, it should ordinarily form the lower layer when it is used to extract an aqueous solution. Likewise, ethyl ether ($d = 0.713$ g/mL) is less dense than water and will form the upper layer with an aqueous solution. However, aqueous solutions are more dense than pure water and a very concentrated aqueous solution (10 M NaOH, for example) may be even more dense than dichloromethane. If you are not sure which layer is the aqueous one, add a drop or two of water to a drop or two of each layer separately. The layer in which the water dissolves is the aqueous layer.

General Directions for Extraction

 Standard Scale

Equipment and Supplies

separatory funnel with stopper
ring stand
support for separatory funnel
extraction solvent
graduated cylinder
wooden applicator stick
2 flasks

Support a separatory funnel on a ring of suitable diameter or another appropriate support. Close the stopcock by turning the handle to a horizontal position, and add the liquid to be extracted through the top of the separatory funnel, preferably through another funnel (avoid getting either liquid on the glass joint). The liquid should be at room temperature (or below) to prevent vaporization of a volatile extraction solvent. Measure the required volume of extraction solvent using a graduated cylinder (the exact volume is not crucial), and pour it into the funnel. The total volume of both liquids should not exceed three-quarters of the funnel's capacity; if it does, obtain a larger separatory funnel or carry out the extraction in two or more steps, using a fraction of the liquid in each step.

Moisten the stopper with water and insert it firmly. Then pick up the funnel in both hands and partly invert it, with your right hand holding the stopcock (or your left hand, if you are a southpaw) and the first two fingers of your left hand holding the stopper in place (see Figure C9). *Vent* the separatory funnel by slowly opening the stopcock to release any pressure buildup. Be sure that the outlet of the funnel is above the liquid level and that its stem is pointed away from you and your neighbors when you are venting it. Close the stopcock, shake or swirl the funnel gently for a few seconds, and then vent it again (be sure the funnel is inverted). Shake the funnel more vigorously (but

If you use a metal ring as a support, cushion it with three short lengths of split rubber tubing to prevent damage to the separatory funnel.

The Operations

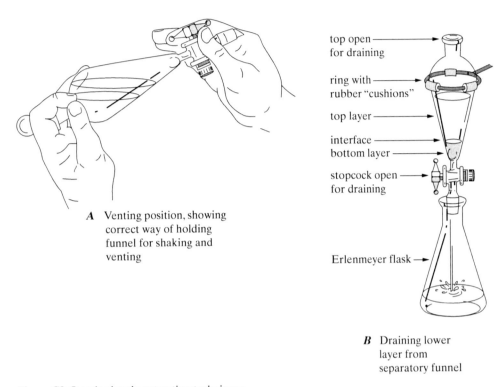

A Venting position, showing
correct way of holding
funnel for shaking and
venting

top open
for draining

ring with
rubber "cushions"

top layer

interface
bottom layer

stopcock open
for draining

Erlenmeyer flask

B Draining lower
layer from
separatory funnel

Figure C9 Standard scale extraction techniques

not too vigorously if the solvent tends to form emulsions), with occasional venting, for 2–3 minutes. A combined shaking and swirling motion is more efficient than swirling alone. Venting should not be necessary after there is no longer an audible hiss of escaping vapors when the stopcock is opened.

Replace the funnel on its support, remove the stopper, and allow the funnel to stand until there is a sharp dividing line between the two layers. If an emulsion forms, try to break it up as described previously. Drain the bottom layer into an Erlenmeyer flask (flask **A**) by opening the stopcock fully; partly close it to slow the drainage rate as the interface approaches the bottom of the funnel. When the interface just reaches the outlet, quickly close the stopcock to separate the layers cleanly. Follow method **1** if the extraction solvent is *more* dense than the liquid being extracted (forming the lower layer), and method **2** if it is *less* dense than the liquid being extracted (forming the upper layer).

1 Extract the liquid that remains in the separatory funnel (the original top layer) with a fresh portion of the same extraction solvent; then drain the bottom layer as before and combine it with the first extract in **A**. Repeat the process, as necessary, with fresh extraction solvent. After the last extraction is finished and the bottom layer has been drained, pour the top layer out of the *top* of the separatory funnel into a separate container (**B**) and retain it for later disposal.

2 Pour the liquid that remains in the separatory funnel (the original top layer) out of the *top* of the separatory funnel into a separate container (flask **B**). Then return the liquid in **A** to the separatory funnel and

extract it with a fresh portion of extraction solvent. Again drain the bottom layer into **A** and pour the top layer into **B**. Repeat the process, as necessary, with fresh extraction solvent, combining the extracts in **B**. Retain the liquid in flask **A** for later disposal.

Summary

1 Add liquid to be extracted to separatory funnel.
2 Add extraction solvent, stopper funnel, invert, and vent.
3 Shake and swirl funnel, with venting, to extract solute into extraction solvent.
4 Remove stopper, let layers separate.
5 Drain lower layer into flask **A**.
   IF extraction solvent forms lower layer, GO TO 6.
   IF extraction solvent forms upper layer, GO TO 7.
6 Stopper flask **A**.
   IF another extraction step is needed, GO TO 2.
   IF extraction is complete, empty and clean separatory funnel; STOP.
7 Pour upper layer into flask **B** and stopper it.
   IF another extraction step is needed, return contents of **A** to separatory funnel, GO TO 2.
   IF extraction is complete, clean separatory funnel; STOP.

 ## Microscale

Equipment and Supplies

   conical vial or centrifuge tube with cap
   support for extraction container
   2 Pasteur pipets with bulbs, one calibrated
   extraction solvent
   wooden applicator stick
   1 or 2 containers (conical vials, screw-cap vials, test tubes, etc.)

Depending on the amount of liquid to be extracted, obtain a 3-mL or 5-mL conical vial with a compression cap and unperforated septum or a 15-mL conical centrifuge tube with a screw cap. Check the extraction container for leaks. To keep the container from tipping over, place a conical vial in a small beaker or a centrifuge tube in a test-tube rack or other suitable support. Add the liquid to be extracted, which should be at room temperature or below. If its volume is less than 1 mL, it is advisable to add enough of a suitable solvent (usually water) to give it a total volume of at least 1 mL. Use a calibrated Pasteur pipet (or other measuring device) to add a measured portion of extraction solvent, and cap the container tightly. Shake the extraction container gently at first, and unscrew the cap slightly after 5–10 shakes to release any pressure inside the container. Tighten the cap and shake the mixture more vigorously at least 100 times, but remember that excessively vigorous shaking may cause an emulsion to form. (Alternatively, you can use a spin vane to stir the contents of a conical vial vigorously for at least 1 minute, or use a vortex mixer as directed by your instructor.) Loosen the cap and let the mixture stand until there is a sharp interface between the layers. Use a wooden applicator stick to help consolidate the layers if necessary. If you are using

The Operations

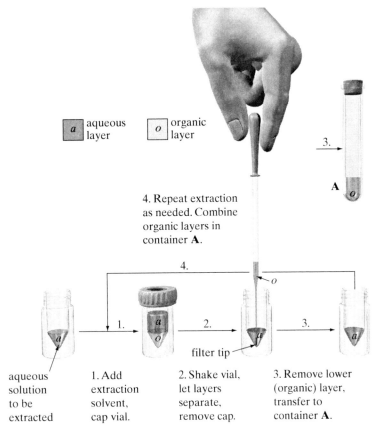

4. Repeat extraction
as needed. Combine
organic layers in
container **A**.

a | aqueous
layer

o | organic
layer

aqueous
solution
to be
extracted

1. Add
extraction
solvent,
cap vial.

2. Shake vial,
let layers
separate,
remove cap.

filter tip

3. Remove lower
(organic) layer,
transfer to
container **A**.

Figure C10 Microscale extraction using an extraction solvent more dense than the liquid being extracted

a centrifuge tube, it can be spun in a centrifuge [OP-14] to facilitate layer separation. If an emulsion forms, try to break it up as described previously. Follow method **1** (illustrated in Figure C10) if the extraction solvent is *more* dense than the liquid being extracted (forming the lower layer), and method **2a** (illustrated in Figure C11) or **2b** if it is *less* dense than the liquid being extracted (forming the upper layer). Method **2b** can be used only if all of both liquid layers will fit into the Pasteur pipet. Although this method requires fewer transfers than **2a**, it is more difficult to perform proficiently.

1 Squeeze the bulb of a Pasteur pipet to expel air, and insert the pipet vertically so that its tip just touches the bottom of the "vee" in the conical extraction container. Slowly withdraw the *bottom* (organic) layer, taking care not to mix the layers, and transfer it to a suitable container (container **A**). Add another measured portion of pure extraction solvent to the liquid remaining in the extraction container and shake to extract it as before, transferring the extract (the bottom layer) to **A**. Repeat the process if necessary, combining all of the extracts in **A**. Retain the liquid in the extraction container for later disposal.

*The kind of container you use for **A** depends on the next operation (washing, drying, etc.) that you will use.*

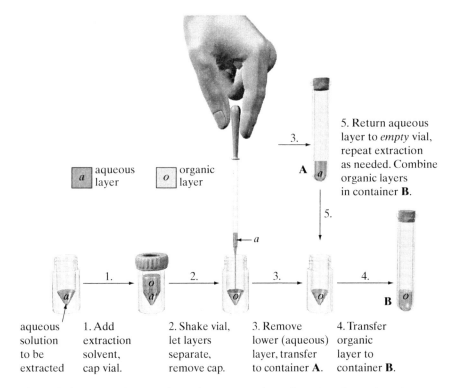

a | aqueous layer

o | organic layer

5. Return aqueous layer to *empty* vial, repeat extraction as needed. Combine organic layers in container **B**.

aqueous solution to be extracted

1. Add extraction solvent, cap vial.

2. Shake vial, let layers separate, remove cap.

3. Remove lower (aqueous) layer, transfer to container **A**.

4. Transfer organic layer to container **B**.

Figure C11 Microscale extraction using an extraction solvent less dense than the liquid being extracted

2a Squeeze the bulb of a Pasteur pipet to expel air, and insert the pipet vertically so that its tip just touches the bottom of the "vee" in the conical extraction container. Slowly withdraw the *bottom* (aqueous) layer, taking care not to mix the layers, and transfer it to a test tube or other small container (**A**). Transfer the contents of the extraction container to another container (**B**) and return the contents of **A** to the extraction container (see Figure C11). Add another measured portion of pure extraction solvent and extract as before, transferring the lower layer to **A** and combining the upper layer with the extract in **B**. If another extraction is necessary, return the contents of **A** to the extraction container and repeat the process. Retain the liquid in **A** for later disposal.

*The kind of container you use for **B** depends on the next operation (washing, drying, etc.) that you will use.*

2b (For small amounts of liquid.) Slowly draw all of *both* liquid layers into the Pasteur pipet (avoid drawing in much air), and wait until a sharp interface forms between the layers; then carefully return the bottom layer to the empty extraction container and transfer the top layer to a suitable container (**A**). Add another measured portion of pure extraction solvent to the liquid in the extraction container and extract it as before, returning the bottom layer to the empty extraction container and transferring the top layer to **A**. Repeat this process for any subsequent extractions, combining all of the extracts in **A**. Retain the liquid in the extraction container for later disposal.

The Operations

Summary

1 Add liquid to be extracted to extraction container.
2 Add extraction solvent, cap tightly, shake gently, vent.
3 Shake to extract solute into extraction solvent.
4 Loosen cap, let layers separate.
5 Uncap extraction container, transfer lower layer to container **A**.
  IF extraction solvent forms lower layer, GO TO 6.
  IF extraction solvent forms upper layer, GO TO 7.
6 Cap container **A**.
  IF another extraction step is needed, GO TO 2.
  IF extraction is complete, STOP.
7 Transfer upper layer to container **B** and cap it.
  IF another extraction step is needed, transfer contents of container **A** to extraction container, GO TO 2.
  IF extraction is complete, clean up, STOP.

b. Salting Out

Adding an inorganic salt (such as sodium chloride or potassium carbonate) to an aqueous solution containing an organic solute usually reduces the solubility of the organic compound in the water, and thus promotes its separation. This *salting out* technique is often used to help separate an organic liquid from its aqueous solution or to increase the amount of an organic solute transferred from the aqueous to the organic layer during an extraction. Usually enough of the salt is added to saturate the aqueous solution, which is stirred or shaken to dissolve the salt. The mixture is filtered by gravity if any undissolved salt remains, then transferred to a separatory funnel, conical vial, or other suitable container for separation or extraction.

c. Liquid–Solid Extraction

Natural products and other solid mixtures may contain components that can be extracted from the solid with a liquid solvent.

A simple technique for standard scale liquid–solid extraction is to mix the solid intimately with an appropriate solvent using a flat-bottomed stirring rod or a flexible flat-bladed spatula in a beaker, and separate the extract by gravity filtration [OP-12] or vacuum filtration [OP-13], repeating the process as many times as necessary. The mixing should be as thorough as possible. Press down or crush the solid in contact with the solvent with the flat end of the stirring rod or spatula to extract as much of the desired component as you can. After each filtration, return any solid that collects on the filter to the beaker for the next extraction. Combine the liquid extracts in a single collecting container.

A microscale liquid–solid extraction can be carried out by shaking the solid with the extraction solvent in a centrifuge tube, then using a flat-bladed microspatula to crush and rub the solid against the sides of the tube, repeating the shaking and crushing sequence several times. The mixture can then be centrifuged and the extract decanted into a suitable container. Alternatively, a filter-tip pipet can be used to separate the extract from the solid residue. Extraction of the residue in the centrifuge tube can then be repeated as necessary.

Evaporation

Evaporation is the conversion of a liquid to vapor at or below the boiling point of the liquid. Evaporation can be used to remove a volatile solvent, such as ethyl ether or dichloromethane, from a comparatively involatile liquid or solid. Complete solvent removal is used to isolate an organic solute after such operations as extraction [OP-15] or column chromatography [OP-18]. Partial solvent removal, or *concentration*, can be used to bring a recrystallization solution to its saturation point (see OP-25).

Experimental Considerations

Because of possible health and fire hazards, you should never evaporate an organic solvent by heating an open container outside a fume hood. Even when using the method described here, you should know and allow for the hazards associated with each solvent. In standard scale work, solvents are generally evaporated under vacuum, while in microscale work, they are more often evaporated using a stream of dry air or nitrogen, but there are exceptions to these rules. For example, the standard scale apparatus shown in Figure C12C can be adapted for microscale use by using a 10-mL round-bottom flask and a microscale thermometer adapter.

Relatively large quantities of solvents, including high-boiling solvents, can be removed by simple distillation [OP-27] or vacuum distillation. This procedure is often used to concentrate a solution that is then evaporated further by one of the methods described later. In microscale work, for example, a solution may be concentrated to a volume of 0.5–1.0 mL by distillation into a Hickman still and the remaining solvent evaporated under a stream of dry air or nitrogen. Commercial *flash evaporators* are used to evaporate solvents rapidly under reduced pressure, but they are seldom available in undergraduate organic chemistry labs because of their high cost.

Moderate to large quantities of solvent can be evaporated under vacuum using one of the setups pictured in Figure C12. The test tube or flask containing the liquid to be evaporated is heated [OP-7a] gently with a hot water bath or steam bath, and an aspirator or vacuum line is used to reduce the pressure inside the apparatus, increasing the evaporation rate. Swirling or stirring the solution continuously during evaporation speeds up the process and reduces foaming and bumping. Magnetic stir bars, because they tend to retain some of the residue, are not recommended for microscale evaporation unless the residue will later be dissolved in another solvent or undergo an operation requiring magnetic stirring.

Evaporation under vacuum requires constant attention, because excessive heat or a sudden pressure decrease may cause liquid to foam up and out of the container. One way to control the vacuum and reduce the likelihood of boilover is to replace the stopper shown in Figure C12B with a Hirsch funnel assembly. If you hold your thumb over the holes in the porcelain plate of the Hirsch funnel, you can decrease the internal pressure by pressing down with your thumb or increase the pressure by raising it.

A trap similar to the one pictured in Figure C4 of OP-13 should be interposed between the evaporation container and the aspirator to collect the

The Operations

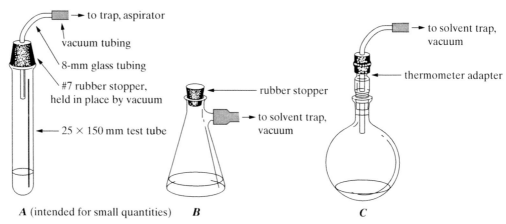

A (intended for small quantities) **B** **C**

Figure C12 Apparatus for evaporation under vacuum

evaporated solvent, which should then be returned to a solvent recovery container. To recover a low-boiling solvent, such as ethyl ether, you should immerse the solvent trap in an appropriate cold bath [OP-8].

Small quantities of a volatile solvent can be evaporated by passing a slow stream of dry air or nitrogen over a solution. Nitrogen is preferred because the oxygen in air may react with easily oxidized solutes, but clean, dry air is suitable for most purposes. The gas stream sweeps solvent molecules away from the surface of the liquid, accelerating the evaporation rate. Evaporation cools the remaining liquid, however, so heating is needed to maintain a rapid evaporation rate and to prevent condensation of water vapor in the product. This operation must be carried out under a fume hood to keep solvent vapors out of the laboratory. Your laboratory may have a hood with an "evaporation station" where a number of Pasteur pipets are attached to a source of dry air or nitrogen and supported above a large hot plate. The solution to be evaporated is placed in a conical vial (or another suitable container), which is heated gently in a hot water bath or warm sand bath while a stream of the dry gas is directed over the surface of the liquid (see Figure C13A). The bath temperature should be about 5–10°C below the boiling point of the solvent so that the solvent evaporates rapidly without boiling.

It is possible to use an aluminum block or hot plate as the heat source, but you must be very careful to avoid overheating, which may cause the residue to decompose. The evaporation container should never be placed directly on the hot surface; instead, clamp it above the hot surface at a level that will allow evaporation without boiling the solvent.

An aluminum block or similar heat source can be used safely to *concentrate* solutions by boiling, because decomposition is unlikely while some of the solvent remains. Twirling the end of a microspatula in the solution helps prevent bumping and boilover. Figure C13B illustrates the concentration of a recrystallization [OP-25] solution in a Craig tube.

To avoid transfers in microscale work, it is advisable to carry out an evaporation in the container that will be used in the next step, if possible. For example, if a substance in solution is to be purified by distillation, evaporate the solvent in the conical vial from which the residue will be distilled. If that vial is not large enough to hold all of the liquid, you can carry out the evaporation in stages by adding one portion of the liquid, evaporating most of it, and then adding the next portion, etc. If the residue will be the final product from a preparation, you can carry out the evaporation in a tared storage vial.

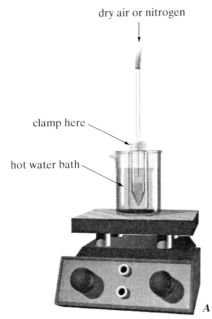

A Evaporation under a stream of dry air or nitrogen

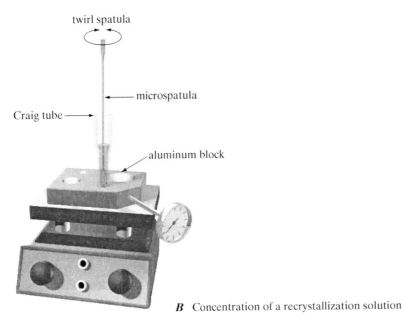

B Concentration of a recrystallization solution

Figure C13 Apparatus for microscale evaporation

The Operations

 General Directions for Evaporation Under Vacuum

Equipment and Supplies

evaporation container (Figure C12)
rubber tubing
solvent trap
aspirator
heat source

Assemble one of the setups pictured in Figure C12, using heavy-walled rubber tubing that will not collapse under vacuum. Be sure to check all glassware for cracks, star fractures, and other imperfections that might cause them to implode under vacuum. Add the solution to be evaporated, stopper the evaporation container, and connect the apparatus to a solvent trap and the trap to a vacuum source. Turn on the vacuum and heat the evaporation container gently over a steam bath or in a hot water bath [OP-7a], swirling it throughout the evaporation to minimize foaming and bumping. (In some cases, the liquid can be stirred magnetically [OP-10].) Adjust the steam flow rate or water bath temperature to attain a satisfactory rate of evaporation; the liquid may boil gently, but should not foam up. Be ready to remove the evaporation container from the heat source immediately if it starts to foam up; otherwise, your product may be carried over to the solvent trap.

If you are using a steam bath, wear gloves or use a towel to protect your hands.

Continue evaporating until all of the solvent has been removed. At this point, boiling will stop, the volume of the residue (which may be a solid or liquid) will not decrease with time, and the odor of the solvent will be gone. When evaporation appears complete, discontinue heating. Break the vacuum by detaching the vacuum hose, opening the pressure-release valve on the trap (if it has one), or sliding the stopper off the mouth of the test tube (for apparatus **A**); then turn off the vacuum source. If you are not certain that all of the solvent has evaporated, dry the outside of the evaporation container to remove moisture from the heating bath, weigh it, and resume evaporation for a few minutes; then dry and weigh it again. Repeat this process as necessary until the mass no longer decreases significantly between weighings.

If you need to only concentrate the solution, stop the evaporation when sufficient solvent has been removed.

Let the evaporation container cool down before you remove the residue. If the residue is a solid, transfer it with a flat-bladed spatula. You can transfer the last traces of residue by rinsing the container with a small amount of volatile solvent (such as diethyl ether or dichloromethane) and allowing the solvent to evaporate under a hood or in a stream of dry air or nitrogen. Place the solvent from the trap in a solvent recovery container.

Summary

1 Assemble apparatus for solvent evaporation.
2 Add liquid, stopper evaporation container, connect to trap and vacuum source.
3 Turn on vacuum.
4 Apply heat with swirling or stirring until evaporation is complete.
5 Discontinue heating, turn off vacuum.
6 Transfer residue and recover solvent.
7 Disassemble and clean apparatus.

General Directions for Evaporation with Dry Air or Nitrogen

Equipment and Supplies

> evaporation container (conical vial, etc.)
> Pasteur pipet, rubber tubing
> drying tube with drying agent (optional)
> hot water bath, sand bath, or other heating device
> hot plate

The liquid to be evaporated should be in a tared conical vial or other container suitable for evaporation. If an evaporation station is not available, prepare a suitable gas-drying tube [OP-24], and then connect one end to an air line and the other end to a Pasteur pipet (the gas delivery pipet) using short lengths of rubber tubing. If dry nitrogen is available, omit the drying tube. Clamp a gas delivery pipet (your own or one from an evaporation station) vertically above the heat source. Heat the hot water bath or sand bath to a temperature about 5–10°C below the solvent's boiling point and immerse the evaporation vial in it. Holding the vial in your hand provides more control over the evaporation rate, but clamping or otherwise securing it in the bath can help prevent accidental spillage. Position the gas delivery pipet so that its tip is 1–2 cm above the surface of the liquid in the vial, and *slowly* adjust the flow rate so that the gas distorts the surface of the liquid, but causes no splashing. As necessary, adjust the heating rate, the position of the vial, or the position of the gas delivery pipet, so that the solvent evaporates quite rapidly but the liquid does not boil appreciably or foam up. If you are holding the vial in your hand, swirl it gently to increase the evaporation rate and help prevent boilover.

To avoid the likelihood of product loss, you can adjust the gas flow rate using a vial of water or solvent.

When the volume of residue in the evaporation vial remains constant for a minute or more (or if the residue is a dry solid), remove the vial from the heat source, clean or dry the outside of the vial, and weigh it when it has cooled. Then hold it under the gas stream for another minute or so and reweigh it. If the masses are essentially identical, evaporation is complete; if not, continue evaporating until the mass no longer decreases significantly between weighings. If the residue is a solid that is to be transferred to another container, transfer it using a flat-bladed microspatula. You can transfer the last traces of residue by rinsing the container with a small amount of volatile solvent (such as diethyl ether or dichloromethane) and allowing the solvent to evaporate under a hood or in a stream of dry air or nitrogen.

Summary

1 Transfer liquid being evaporated to evaporation vial.
2 Place vial in heated water bath or sand bath.
3 Position gas delivery pipet over liquid and adjust gas flow.
4 Apply gentle heat until evaporation is complete.
5 Transfer residue, if necessary.
6 Clean apparatus.

The Operations

Steam Distillation

Distillation of a mixture of two (or more) immiscible liquids is called *codistillation*. When one of the liquids is water, the process is usually called *steam distillation*. *External steam distillation* is carried out by passing externally generated steam (as from a steam line) into a boiling flask containing the organic material (see Figure C14). The vaporized organic liquid is carried over into a receiver with the condensed steam. *Internal steam distillation* can be carried out by boiling a mixture of water and an organic material in a distillation apparatus (see Figure C15), causing vaporized water (steam) and organic liquid to distill into a receiver. This is the method generally used for microscale steam distillation.

Both kinds of steam distillation are used to separate organic liquids from reaction mixtures and natural products, leaving behind high-boiling residues such as tars, inorganic salts, and other relatively nonvolatile components. Steam distillation is particularly useful for isolating the essential oils of plants from various parts of the plant. For example, clove oil can be steam-distilled from clove buds. Steam distillation is not useful for the final purification of a liquid, however, because it cannot effectively separate components with similar boiling points.

Principles and Applications

If you are not familiar with the principles of distillation, see OP-25.

When a *homogeneous mixture* of two liquids is distilled, the vapor pressure of each liquid is lowered by an amount proportional to the mole fraction of the other liquid present. This usually results in a solution boiling point that is somewhere between the boiling points of the separate components. For example, a solution containing equal masses of cyclohexane (b.p. = 81°C) and toluene (b.p. = 111°C) boils at 90°C.

When a *heterogeneous mixture* of two immiscible liquids, A and B, is distilled, each liquid exerts its vapor pressure more or less independently of the other. The total vapor pressure over the mixture (P) is thus approximately equal to the sum of the vapor pressures that would be exerted by the separate pure liquids $(P_A^\circ$ and $P_B^\circ)$ at the same temperature.

$$P \approx P_A^\circ + P_B^\circ$$

This has several important consequences. First, the vapor pressure of a mixture of immiscible components will be *higher* than the vapor pressure of its most volatile component. Because raising the vapor pressure of a liquid or a liquid mixture lowers its boiling point, the boiling point of the mixture will be *lower* than that of its most volatile (lowest boiling) component. Because the vapor pressure of a pure liquid is constant at a constant temperature, the vapor pressure of the mixture of liquids will be constant as well. Thus, the boiling point of the mixture will remain constant throughout its distillation as long as each component is present in significant quantity.

For example, suppose that you are distilling a mixture of the immiscible liquids toluene and water at standard atmospheric pressure (760 torr, 101.3 kPa). The mixture will start to boil when the sum of the vapor pressures of the two liquids is equal to the external pressure, 760 torr. This occurs at 85°C, where the vapor pressure of water is 434 torr and that of toluene is 326 torr. Because the vapor pressures of the two components are additive, the mixture distills well below the normal boiling point of either toluene (b.p. = 111°C) or water. According to Avogadro's law, the number of moles of a component in a mixture of ideal gases is proportional to its partial pressure in the mixture, so the mole fraction of toluene in the vapor should be about 0.43 (326/760) and that of water should be about 0.57 (434/760). (These calculations are approximate because the vapors are not ideal gases.) In other words, about 43 percent of the molecules in the vapor are toluene molecules. Because toluene (M.W. = 92) molecules are heavier than water (M.W. = 18) molecules, they make a greater contribution to the total mass of the vapor. In 1.00 mol of vapor, there will be 0.43 mol of toluene and 0.57 mol of water, so the mass of toluene in the vapor will be about 40 g (0.43 mol × 92 g/mol), and the mass of water will be about 10 g (0.57 mol × 18 g/mol). The mass of one mole of the vapor is thus about 50 g, of which toluene makes up 40 g, or 80%. The liquid that collects in the receiver during a distillation—the *distillate*—is merely condensed vapor, so distilling a mixture of toluene and water will yield a distillate that contains about 80% toluene, by mass.

Because of its comparatively low molecular weight and its immiscibility with many organic compounds, water is nearly always one of the liquids used in a codistillation involving an organic liquid. The organic liquid must be insoluble enough in water to form a separate phase, and it cannot react with hot water or steam. As shown in Table C2, the higher the boiling point of the organic liquid, the lower will be its proportion in the distillate, and the closer the mixture boiling point will be to 100°C.

Table C2 Boiling points and compositions of heterogeneous mixtures with water (component B)

Component A	b.p. of A	b.p. of A/B mixture	Mass % of A in distillate
toluene	111°	85°	80%
chlorobenzene	132°	90°	71%
bromobenzene	156°	95°	62%
iodobenzene	188°	98°	43%
quinoline	237°	99.6°	10%

Because the distillation boiling point is never higher than 100°C at 1 atm—well below the normal boiling points of most water-immiscible organic liquids—thermal decomposition of the organic component is minimized.

 External Steam Distillation

Externally generated steam is preferred for many codistillations, especially those involving solids or low-boiling liquids, because external steam produces a rapid distillation rate and helps prevent bumping caused by solids and tars. The steam is usually obtained from a steam line; if another kind of steam generator is to be used, your instructor will show you how to use it. A *steam trap* is used to remove condensed water and foreign matter, such as grease or rust, from externally generated steam. A steam trap that includes a valve for draining off excess water, such as the one illustrated in Figure C14, works best. With other kinds of traps, distillation may have to be interrupted periodically to drain the trap.

The boiling flask should be large enough so that the liquid will not fill it much more than half full throughout the distillation. Some steam will condense during the distillation, raising the water level in the boiling flask; during an extended distillation, excessive water can be removed by external heating, if necessary. A Claisen adapter is used to help prevent mechanical transfer of liquids or particles from the boiling flask to the receiver. A thermometer can be used to indicate when most of the desired component has distilled, as the vapor temperature should rise to 100°C at that point. It is not useful when the component boils around 200°C or higher, because the temperature will be close to 100°C throughout the distillation. The distillation should be carried out rapidly to reduce condensation in the boiling flask and to compensate for the large volume of water-laden distillate that may have to be collected to yield much of the organic component. Because of the rapid distillation rate and the high heat content of steam, efficient condensing is essential. The vacuum adapter should be cool to the touch throughout the distillation, and no steam should escape from its outlet.

General Directions for External Steam Distillation

 Standard Scale

Equipment and Supplies

heat source
ring stand, rings, clamps
rubber tubing
steam delivery tube
large round-bottom flask
Claisen adapter
still head (connecting adapter)
thermometer (optional)
thermometer adapter (optional) or stopper
West condenser
vacuum adapter
receiving flask
steam trap (bent adapter, two-hole rubber stopper,
   bent glass tubes, rubber tubing, screw clamp)

Assemble the apparatus pictured in Figure C14, using a large round-bottom boiling flask and, as the steam delivery tube, a 6-mm o.d. (outer diameter) glass tube extending to within about 0.5 cm of the bottom of the flask. Position the boiling flask high enough so that external heat can be applied, if necessary. Connect the steam delivery tube to a bent glass tube on the steam trap, which should be clamped to a ring stand over a beaker, and see that the screw clamp on the steam trap is closed. Add the organic mixture and a small amount of water (unless the mixture already contains water) to the boiling flask, which should be no more than one-third full at the start. Turn on the condenser water so that it flows at a comparatively rapid rate. (Be sure that

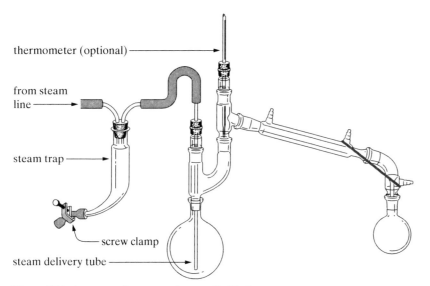

thermometer (optional)

from steam line

steam trap

screw clamp

steam delivery tube

Figure C14 Apparatus for external steam distillation

the condenser hoses are tight!). Connect a rubber hose to the steam valve over the sink and turn on the steam, directing it into the sink, until only a little water drips from the end of the hose. Turn off the steam and connect the hose to the other bent tube on the steam trap.

Turn on the steam cautiously, and after distillation begins, adjust the steam flow to maintain a rapid rate of distillation. Check the vacuum adapter periodically; if it becomes warm, and especially if vapor begins to escape from its outlet, you should (a) turn down the steam, (b) increase the cooling-water flow rate, or (c) cool the receiver in an ice/water bath. Check the connection between the condenser and still head frequently to make sure that no vapor is escaping; this joint sometimes separates because of the violent action of the steam (you can use a joint clip to prevent this). Drain the trap periodically to remove condensed water. If the boiling flask begins to fill up excessively (it should not be much more than half full), heat it with a steam bath or other heat source to reduce condensation. If you must interrupt the distillation for any reason, open the steam-trap valve (or raise the steam delivery tube out of the liquid) *before* you turn off the steam; otherwise, liquid in the boiling flask may back up into the steam line.

When the distillate appears clear *and* the temperature is near 100°C (if you used a thermometer), collect and examine a few drops of fresh distillate on a watch glass. Continue distilling if the fresh distillate is cloudy, contains oily droplets, or has a pronounced odor; and collect and examine more distillate at 5- or 10-minute intervals. When the distillate is water-clear and you are certain the distillation is complete, open the steam-trap valve fully (or raise the steam delivery tube out of the liquid), and then turn off the steam.

The organic liquid can be separated from the distillate using a separatory funnel or by extraction [OP-15] with ether or another suitable solvent. Extraction is necessary if the volume of the organic liquid is small compared to that of the water. If the aqueous layer is cloudy, you can saturate it with sodium chloride or other salt to salt out [OP-15c] the organic liquid.

Take Care! Do not burn yourself with the live steam.

Summary

1 Assemble apparatus for external steam distillation.
2 Add organic mixture and water (if necessary) to boiling flask.
3 Turn on condenser water.
4 Purge steam line, connect to steam trap, turn on steam.
5 Distill rapidly until distillate is clear; drain trap periodically.
6 Open steam-trap valve, turn off steam.
7 Separate organic liquid from distillate.
8 Disassemble and clean apparatus.

 ## Internal Steam Distillation

An organic liquid can be separated by internal steam distillation using essentially the same procedure as for simple distillation [OP-27], except that additional water may need to be added during the distillation. If water is to be added during a standard scale steam distillation, the apparatus illustrated in Figure C15 should be used; otherwise, an ordinary simple distillation apparatus is adequate. If the organic distillate is quite volatile, a thermometer can be used to indicate when the end of the distillation is near. For example, with a toluene–water mixture, the temperature will rise rather rapidly from 85°C to about 100°C when the toluene is nearly gone. With less volatile materials, the temperature may be close to 100°C throughout the distillation, so a thermometer will be of little use.

General Directions for Internal Steam Distillation

See OP-27 for more detailed directions for conducting a distillation.

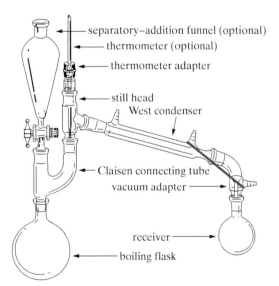

Figure C15 Apparatus for standard scale internal steam distillation

Standard Scale

Equipment and Supplies

- heat source
- ring stand, rings, clamps
- condenser tubing
- round-bottom flask
- boiling chips or a stir bar
- still head (connecting adapter)
- thermometer (optional)
- thermometer adapter or stopper
- West condenser
- vacuum adapter
- receiver
- Claisen adapter (optional)
- separatory–addition funnel (optional)

If it will be necessary to add more water during the distillation, assemble the apparatus shown in Figure C15; otherwise; assemble the apparatus pictured in Figure E7 of OP-27. Add the mixture to be steam-distilled, boiling chips or a stir bar, and enough water to fill the boiling flask about one-third to one-half full (unless enough water is already present). Turn on the condenser water and the stirrer (if you have one) and heat the flask with an appropriate heat source [OP-7a] to maintain a rapid rate of distillation. If necessary, add water to replace that lost during the distillation. Discontinue heating when the fresh distillate contains no more of the organic component *and* the distillation temperature is about 100°C. The distillate should no longer be cloudy or contain droplets of organic liquid at this point. Separate the organic liquid from the distillate as described for external steam distillation.

See the Summary on the next page.

 Microscale

Equipment and Supplies

- heat source (aluminum block or sand bath)
- round-bottom flask (or conical vial)
- Hickman still
- water-cooled condenser
- stir bar (optional)
- condenser tubing
- ring stand, clamp
- thermometer (optional)
- $5\frac{3}{4}$-inch Pasteur pipet
- 9-inch Pasteur pipet (optional)
- collecting container

The Operations

If it will be necessary to add more water during the distillation, measure out the approximate amount of water that will be needed. Assemble the apparatus pictured in Figure E11B of OP-27 by attaching a Hickman still to the boiling flask (or vial) and a water-cooled condenser to the top of the still. Add the mixture to be steam-distilled, a stir bar, and enough water to fill the boiling flask about one-half full (unless enough water is already present). In some cases, the stir bar may cause excessive frothing and should be omitted. Turn on the stirrer, if you are using one, and heat the flask with an appropriate heat source to maintain a rapid rate of distillation without allowing any boilover into the Hickman still. As the well of the Hickman still fills with liquid, use a short Pasteur pipet to transfer the distillate to an appropriate collecting container. As necessary, use a long Pasteur pipet to add water through the condenser to replace that lost during distillation. Discontinue heating when the fresh distillate appears to contain no more of the organic component *or* after a designated volume of liquid has been collected. When distillation is complete, the distillate should no longer be cloudy or contain droplets of organic liquid. If droplets of the organic component have collected on the inner walls of the Hickman still, use a Pasteur pipet to rinse the walls into the well with some of the distillate or an appropriate solvent, and transfer the contents of the well to the collecting container. Separate the organic liquid from the distillate by microscale extraction with a suitable solvent.

Summary

1 Assemble apparatus for internal steam distillation.
2 Add organic mixture and water to boiling flask.
3 Turn on condenser water and stirrer (if used).
4 Distill until distillate is clear, adding water as necessary.
5 Separate organic liquid from distillate.
6 Disassemble and clean apparatus.

OPERATION 18   # Column Chromatography

If you touch the tip of a felt-tip pen to a piece of absorbent paper, such as a coffee filter, and then slowly drip isopropyl rubbing alcohol onto the spot with a medicine dropper, the spot will spread and separate into rings of different color—the dyes of which the ink is composed. This is a simple example of *chromatography*, the separation of a mixture by distributing its components between two phases. The *stationary phase* (the coffee filter in this example) remains fixed in place, while the *mobile phase* (the rubbing alcohol) flows through it, carrying components of the mixture along with it. The stationary phase acts as a "brake" on most components of a mixture, holding them back so that they move along more slowly than the mobile phase itself. Because of differences in such factors as the solubility of the components in the mobile phase and the strength of their interactions with the stationary phase, some components move faster than others, and the components therefore become separated from one another.

Different types of chromatography can be classified according to the physical states of the mobile and stationary phases. In *liquid–solid* chromatography, which is used in most applications of column chromatography [OP-18] and thin-layer chromatography [OP-19], a liquid mobile phase filters down or creeps up through the solid phase, which may be cellulose, silica gel, alumina, or some other *adsorbent*. The adsorbent is a solid that holds onto molecules of different substances by surface attraction. In *liquid–liquid chromatography*, which is used in high-performance liquid chromatography [OP-35], the mobile phase is usually an organic solvent and the stationary phase can be a high-boiling liquid that is adsorbed by or chemically bonded to a solid *support*. In *gas–liquid chromatography*—the most common type of gas chromatography [OP-34]—the mobile phase is a gas, such as helium, that passes through a hollow or packed column containing a high-boiling liquid on a solid support. Gas chromatagraphy (GC) and high-performance liquid chromatography (HPLC) are instrumental methods that are used primarily for analyzing mixtures, so they will be discussed in the "Instrumental Analysis" section of the Operations.

a. Liquid–Solid Column Chromatography

Principles and Applications

The usual stationary phase for liquid–solid column chromatography is a finely divided solid adsorbent, which is packed into a glass tube called the *column*. The mixture to be separated (the *sample*) is placed on top of the column and *eluted*—washed down the column—by the mobile phase, which is a liquid solvent or solvent mixture. Different components of the sample are attracted to the surface of the adsorbent more or less strongly, depending on their polarity and other structural features. The more strongly a component is adsorbed, the more slowly it will move down the column, all other factors being equal. So as the mobile phase (called the *eluent*) filters down through the adsorbent, the components of the sample spread out to form separate bands of solute, some passing down the column rapidly and others lagging behind.

For example, consider a separation of carvone and limonene on a silica gel adsorbent using hexane as the eluent. At any given time, a molecule of one component will either be adsorbed on the silica gel stationary phase or dissolved in the mobile phase. While it is adsorbed, the molecule will stay put; while dissolved, it will move down the column with the eluent. Molecules with polar functional groups are attracted to polar adsorbents, such as silica gel, and are relatively insoluble in nonpolar solvents, such as hexane. So a molecule of carvone, with its polar carbonyl group, tends to spend more time adsorbed on the silica than dissolved in the hexane. It will therefore pass down the column very slowly with this solvent. On the other hand, a nonpolar molecule of limonene is quite soluble in hexane and only weakly attracted to silica gel, so it will spend less time sitting still and more time moving than will a carvone molecule. As a result, limonene molecules pass down the column rapidly and are soon separated from the slow-moving carvone molecules.

The separation attained by column chromatography depends on a number of factors, including the nature of the components in the mixture, the

Carvone and limonene are major constituents of spearmint oil.

limonene   carvone

The Operations

quantity and kind of adsorbent used, and the polarity of the mobile phase. The lists that follow show how strongly different functional groups are attracted to polar adsorbents and how strongly different adsorbents attract polar molecules. Table 4 shows how different eluents compare in their ability to elute different components.

Approximate strength of adsorption of different functional groups on polar adsorbents

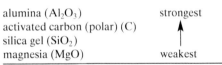

COOH	strongest
OH	
NH$_2$	
SH	
CHO	
C=O	
COOR	
OR	
C=C	
Cl, Br, I	weakest

Common chromatography adsorbents in approximate order of adsorbent strength

alumina (Al$_2$O$_3$)	strongest
activated carbon (polar) (C)	
silica gel (SiO$_2$)	
magnesia (MgO)	weakest

Note: Adsorbent strength varies with grade, particle size, and other factors.

Experimental Considerations

Adsorbents. A number of different adsorbents are used for column chromatography, but alumina and silica gel are the most popular. Adsorbents are available in a wide variety of activity grades and particle size ranges; alumina can be obtained in acidic, basic, or neutral forms as well. The *activity* of an adsorbent is a measure of its attraction for solute molecules, the most active grade of a given adsorbent being one from which all water has been removed. The most active grade may not be the best for a given application, since too active an adsorbent may catalyze a reaction or cause bands to move down the column too slowly. Less active grades of alumina, for example, are prepared by adding different amounts of water to the most active grade (see Table C3). Since all polar adsorbents are deactivated by water, it is important to keep their containers tightly closed and to minimize their exposure to atmospheric moisture. Some samples should not be separated on certain kinds of adsorbents. For example, basic alumina would be a poor choice to separate a mixture containing aldehydes or ketones, which might undergo aldol reactions on the column. Silica gel, which is less active than alumina, is a good all-purpose adsorbent that can be used with most kinds of functional groups.

The amount of adsorbent required for a given application depends on the sample size and the difficulty of the separation. If the components of a mixture differ greatly in polarity, a long column of adsorbent should not be necessary, since the separation will be easy. The more difficult the separation, the

Table C3 Alumina activity grades (Brockmann scale)

Grade	Mass % water
I	0
II	3
III	6
IV	10
V	15

more adsorbent will be needed. About 20–50 g of adsorbent per gram of sample is recommended for most separations, but easy separations may require less adsorbent and difficult separations may require more.

Eluents. In a column chromatography separation, the eluent acts primarily as a solvent to differentially remove molecules of solute from the surface of the adsorbent. In some cases, polar solvent molecules will also *displace* solute molecules from the adsorbent by becoming adsorbed themselves. If the solvent is too strongly adsorbed, the components of a mixture will spend most of their time in the mobile phase and will not separate efficiently. For this reason, it is usually best to start with a solvent of low polarity, and then (if necessary) increase the polarity gradually to elute the more strongly adsorbed components. Table C4 lists a series of common chromatographic solvents in order of increasing eluting power from alumina and silica gel. Such a listing is called an *eluotropic series*.

Table C4 Eluotropic series for alumina and silica gel

Alumina	Silica gel
pentane	cyclohexane
petroleum ether	petroleum ether
hexane	pentane
cyclohexane	trichloromethane
ethyl ether	ethyl ether
trichloromethane	ethyl acetate
dichloromethane	ethanol
ethyl acetate	water
2-propanol	acetone
ethanol	acetic acid
methanol	methanol
acetic acid	

Elution Techniques. Many chromatographic separations cannot be performed efficiently with a single solvent, so several solvents or solvent mixtures are used in sequence, starting with the weaker eluents—those near the top of the eluotropic series for the adsorbent being used. Such eluents will wash down only the most weakly adsorbed components, while strongly adsorbed solutes remain near the top of the column. The remaining solute bands can then be washed off the column by more powerful eluents.

In practice, it is best to change eluents gradually by using solvent mixtures of varying composition, rather than to change directly from one solvent to another. In *stepwise elution*, the strength of the eluting solvent is changed in stages by adding varying amounts of a stronger eluent to a weaker one. The proportion of the stronger eluent is increased more or less exponentially. For example, 5% dichloromethane in hexane may be followed by 15% and 50% mixtures of these solvents. According to one rule of thumb, the eluent composition should be changed after about three column volumes of the previous eluent have passed through. For example, if the packed volume of the adsorbent is 15 mL, the eluent composition should be changed with every 45 mL or so of eluent.

The Operations

Columns. There are many different kinds of chromatography columns, from a simple glass tube with a constriction at one end to an elaborate column with a porous plate to support the packing and a detachable base. A buret, preferably one with a Teflon stopcock, is adequate for standard scale and some microscale separations, but the lack of a detachable base makes it difficult to remove the adsorbent afterward. If a column does not have a stopcock, the tip can be closed with a piece of flexible tubing equipped with a screw clamp. Unless the tubing is resistant to the eluents (polyethylene and Teflon will not contaminate most solvents), it should be removed before elution begins.

In selecting a column for a standard scale chromatographic separation, first consider the amount of adsorbent needed for a given amount of sample, and then choose a column that will completely contain the adsorbent with about 10–15 cm to spare. Ordinarily, the height of the column packing should be at least 10 times its diameter. If the column contains a porous plate to support the packing, no additional support is necessary; otherwise, the column packing should be supported on a layer of glass wool and clean sand.

A $5\frac{3}{4}$-inch Pasteur pipet packed with a suitable adsorbent makes an adequate chromatography column for simple microscale separations. (Cutting off most of the pipet's capillary tip reduces the amount of solvent needed to fill the column, but this can reduce the flow rate and makes very little difference in the total solvent volume required, so do this only at your instructor's request.) This microscale column provides the best separation when used with no more than 100 mg of sample, but it can be used to remove small amounts of impurities from larger quantities of sample.

Figures C16 and C18 illustrate packed chromatography columns for standard scale and microscale use.

Flow Rate. The rate of eluent flow through the column should be slow enough so that the solute can attain equilibrium, but not so slow that the solute bands will broaden appreciably by diffusion. For most purposes, a flow rate of between 5 and 50 drops per minute should be suitable. Microscale columns have lower flow rates than do standard scale columns, and difficult separations require the slowest rates. The flow rate can be reduced by partly closing the stopcock or pinch clamp on the column (if it has either) or by reducing the *solvent head*—the depth of the eluent layer above the adsorbent. The flow rate can be increased by opening the stopcock or pinch clamp fully and maintaining a high solvent head.

For a microscale column, the flow rate can be increased using a pipet pump with a quick-release lever. This method can decrease the separation efficiency, however, and removing the pump during elution without proper pressure release may damage the column, so it should be used only when absolutely necessary. With its plunger fully extended, attach the pipet pump firmly to the top of the column and rotate the thumbwheel until a suitable flow rate is achieved; then periodically rotate it just enough to keep the flow rate relatively constant. When more eluent must be added or if the plunger is down as far as it will go, hold the quick-release lever down as you carefully remove the pipet pump. Add the eluent and pull out the plunger; then replace the pipet pump on top of the column.

Packing the Column. To achieve good separation with a chromatographic column, it must be packed properly. The packing must be uniform, without air bubbles or channels, and its surface must be even and horizontal. Standard scale columns using alumina can be packed by pouring the dry adsorbent through a layer of solvent; microscale columns are often packed without solvent. Columns using silica gel are usually packed with a slurry containing the adsorbent suspended in a solvent. The following general directions give detailed instructions for packing standard scale and microscale columns. The directions for standard scale chromatography can also be used for microscale separations using a microburet and about 5–20 g of adsorbent.

General Directions for Column Chromatography

Standard Scale

Equipment and Supplies

> chromatography column
> buret funnel (or small powder funnel)
> column-packing solvent
> glass wool
> tapper
> clean sand
> adsorbent
> collectors (flasks, test tubes, vials, etc.)
> Pasteur pipet with bulb
> eluent(s)
> separatory–addition funnel (optional)

Obtain an appropriate column and clamp it securely to a ring stand so that it is as vertical as possible. Be sure that the stopcock or screw clamp at the outlet of the column is closed. Construct a "tapper" by (for example) inserting one end of a pencil into a small one-hole rubber stopper. Measure out the amount of adsorbent you will need to prepare the column and keep it in a tightly closed container. Number and weigh the collectors you will be using to collect the eluent fractions. Then pack the column with adsorbent by one of the following methods (omit the glass wool and sand support if it has a porous plate). Method **1** is generally used for silica gel, and method **2** for alumina.

1 *Slurry Packing the Column.* Fill the column about half full with the least powerful eluting solvent to be used in the separation or a solvent recommended in the experiment directions. Use a long glass rod to push a plug of glass wool to the bottom of the column, and tamp the glass wool down gently to form a level surface and press out any air bubbles. Using a *dry* funnel, slowly pour in enough clean sand to form a 1-cm layer at the bottom of the column. As the sand filters down through the solvent, tap the column gently and continuously with the tapper so that the sand layer is uniform and level. The column should be tapped near the middle, where it is clamped, to avoid displacing it from the vertical.

    Mix the measured amount of silica gel (or another suitable adsorbent) thoroughly with enough of the column-packing solvent to make a fairly thick, but pourable, slurry. Pour a little of this slurry into the column, with tapping, through the funnel, so that the adsorbent gently filters down to

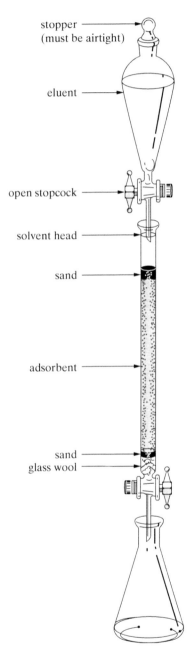

Figure C16 Packed column with continuous-feed reservoir

form a layer about 2 cm thick at the bottom. Then open the column outlet so that the solvent drains slowly into a flask as you add the rest of the slurry, tapping constantly to help settle and pack the adsorbent. If the slurry becomes too thick to pour, add more solvent to it. There should be enough solvent in the column so that the solvent level is well above the adsorbent level at all times; if necessary, add more solvent. When all of the adsorbent has been added, close the outlet. The surface of the adsorbent should be as even and horizontal as possible, so continue tapping until it has settled. Gently stirring the top of the solvent layer as the adsorbent is settling can also help form a level surface. Use a Pasteur pipet containing the solvent to rinse down any adsorbent that adheres to the sides of the column. Add enough clean sand to form a protective layer about 0.5 cm thick on top of the adsorbent; the sand surface should also be level. Open the outlet until the solvent surface drops to within 1–2 cm of the sand surface, then close the outlet and stopper the column tightly. Keep the adsorbent covered with solvent at all times; allowing it to dry out creates channels that lead to uneven bands and poor separation.

2 *Packing the Column with Dry Adsorbent.* Read **1** for more detailed directions about packing a column, disregarding only those directions that apply to making a slurry. Fill the column about two-thirds full with the column-packing solvent and add glass wool and a layer of sand as described in **1**. With the stopcock closed, pour enough alumina (or another suitable adsorbent) through a dry funnel, with tapping, to form a 2-cm layer at the bottom of the column. Then open the column outlet and add the rest of the dry alumina as the solvent drains, tapping constantly so that the alumina settles uniformly. Finish preparing the column as described in **1**. Keep the adsorbent covered with solvent at all times.

Separating the Sample. If the sample is a solid, dissolve it in a minimum amount of a suitable nonpolar solvent; use liquid samples without dilution. Open the column outlet until the solvent surface comes down *just* to the top of the sand layer, and then close it. Use a Pasteur pipet to apply the sample around the circumference of the sand so that it spreads evenly over the surface. Open the outlet until the sample's surface comes down to the top of the sand layer, and then close it. Pipet a small amount of the initial eluent around the inside of the column to rinse down any adherent sample. Open the outlet again until the eluent's surface comes down to the top of the sand layer, and then close it.

Clamp a solvent reservoir, such as a separatory–addition funnel, over the column and measure the initial eluent into it. (Alternatively, add the eluents through an ordinary funnel, or use a continuous-feed reservoir as shown in Figure C16, moistening the stopper with solvent to provide an airtight seal.) Add enough eluent to nearly fill the column. Place a tared collector at the column outlet, open the outlet, and continue adding eluent to keep the liquid level near the top of the column throughout the elution. If you need to change eluents during the elution, let the previous eluent drain to the top of the sand layer before adding the next one.

If the components are colored or can be observed on the column by some visualization method (such as irradiation with ultraviolet light), change collectors each time a new band of solute begins to come off the column *and* when it has about disappeared from the column. If two or more bands overlap, collect the overlapping regions in separate collectors to avoid contaminating the purer fractions. Unless directed otherwise, evaporate [OP-16] the solvent from any fractions that contain the desired component(s).

If the components are not visible and the procedure does not specify the fraction volumes, collect equal-volume fractions (about 25 mL each) in tared collectors. Evaporate the solvent from each fraction, weigh the collectors and their contents, and plot the mass of each residue versus the fraction number to obtain an elution curve, such as the one illustrated in Figure C17. From the elution curve, you should be able to identify separate components and decide which fractions can be combined before evaporation.

To remove the contents of the column, let it dry completely, then invert it over a beaker and tap it as needed to dislodge the adsorbent. If necessary, attach the column outlet to an air line, hold its other end over the beaker, and *slowly* open the air valve to blow out the glass-wool plug and any remaining adsorbent. Dispose of any unused or recovered solvents as directed by your instructor.

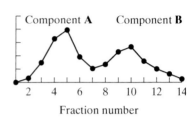

Figure C17 Elution curve

Summary

1 Pack column using appropriate adsorbent, solvent, packing method.
2 Drain column to top of sand layer, add sample, drain, rinse, drain again.
3 Add eluent, put collector in place, open column outlet.
4 Elute sample, keeping eluent level nearly constant.
5 To change eluents, drain current eluent to top of sand, add next eluent.
   IF components are visible, GO TO 6.
   IF components are not visible, GO TO 7.
6 Change collectors when new band starts or ends and where bands overlap.
   GO TO 8.
7 Change collectors after a predetermined volume has been collected.
8 Stop elution after last fraction has been collected.
9 Evaporate and weigh appropriate fractions.
10 Disassemble and clean apparatus, dispose of solvents as directed.

 ### Microscale

Equipment and Supplies

   2 $5\frac{3}{4}$-inch Pasteur pipets, one with rubber bulb
   column-packing solvent
   plastic weighing dish
   cotton
   pencil
   clean sand
   adsorbent
   collectors (vials, test tubes, etc.)
   eluent(s)

Obtain a clean, dry $5\frac{3}{4}$-inch Pasteur pipet and use a wooden applicator stick or glass stirring rod to push a small plug of cotton to the point at which the pipet narrows. Be careful not to tamp it down so tightly as to restrict the solvent flow. Clamp the pipet vertically to a ring stand. If desired, add about

The Operations

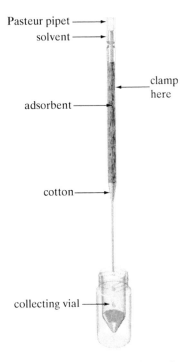

Pasteur pipet

solvent

clamp here

adsorbent

cotton

collecting vial

Figure C18 Apparatus for microscale column chromatography

50 mg of fine sand while gently tapping the column with the eraser end of a pencil to form a layer on top of the cotton (this is not essential, but it keeps fine alumina particles from passing through the cotton). The top of the sand layer should be even and horizontal. Measure the approximate amount of adsorbent you will need (usually 1.5–2.0 g) and keep it in a tightly closed container. Number and weigh the collectors you will be using to collect the eluent fractions. Then pack the column by one of the methods that follow. Method **2** gives a more evenly packed column when alumina is used as the adsorbent; it is not satisfactory for silica gel. If you use method **2**, you should be prepared to add your sample immediately after filling the column.

1 *Packing the Column with No Solvent.* Put the adsorbent in a small, square plastic weighing dish. (Alternatively, you can use a microscoop made by cutting a 1-mL automatic pipet tip in half.) Bend the dish to form a spout (see OP-6) and add the adsorbent *slowly* to the top of the column, while continuously tapping the column near its middle with the eraser end of a pencil, until the specified amount of adsorbent has been added *or* the adsorbent level is about 1 cm below the upper constriction in the column. The surface of the adsorbent should be as even and horizontal as possible; if necessary, tap gently near the surface to make it so. If desired, you can sprinkle a thin, even layer of clean sand on top to protect the adsorbent layer.

2 *Packing the Column Using a Solvent.* This method requires constant attention, because the adsorbent layer must be completely covered with solvent at all times. Put the adsorbent in a square plastic weighing dish. Put a collector under the column (containing its cotton plug) and use a

Pasteur pipet to fill it about half full with the least polar eluent to be used in the chromatography (or another suitable solvent). Immediately bend the dish to form a spout (see OP-6) and add the adsorbent *slowly* to the top of the column as the solvent drains, while continuously tapping the column near its middle with the eraser end of a pencil. If the solvent is draining too fast, stop the flow temporarily by holding your fingertip on top of the column, and allow the adsorbent to settle before adding the next portion of adsorbent. Continue adding adsorbent until the specified amount has been added *or* until the adsorbent level is about 1 cm below the upper constriction in the column. The surface of the adsorbent should be as even and horizontal as possible; if necessary, tap gently near the surface to make it so. Be ready to add your sample *immediately* when the solvent surface drops to the top of the adsorbent layer. (If you are not ready, stopper the column with a size 000 cork to stop the solvent flow.)

Separating the Sample.   Once it is moistened with solvent, the column of adsorbent must not be allowed to dry out until the separation is complete. If the sample is a solid, dissolve it in a minimum amount of a nonpolar solvent; use liquid samples without dilution. Be sure that there is a suitable collector under the column. If the column was packed without solvent, use a Pasteur pipet to add enough of the initial eluent to moisten all of the adsorbent and cover the adsorbent (or sand) layer to a depth of about 1 cm. When the solvent surface *just* drops to the top of the adsorbent (or sand) layer, add the sample with a Pasteur pipet. Quickly rinse this pipet with a very small amount of the initial eluent and use it to rinse the sides of the column. When the liquid surface has fallen to the top of the adsorbent (or sand) layer, use a Pasteur pipet to add enough of the initial eluent to nearly fill the column. Be careful not to disturb the surface of the adsorbent as you add it. Continue adding eluent as necessary to keep the solvent level near the top of the column throughout the elution. If you need to change eluents, allow the previous eluent to drain to the level of the adsorbent (or sand) before adding the next one. Collect the fractions as described previously for standard scale column chromatography. Stop the elution when a designated volume of eluent has been added or when the desired sample bands have been collected. Unless directed otherwise, evaporate [OP-16] the solvent from any fractions that contain the desired component(s).

To remove the contents of the column, let it dry completely, then attach a rubber hose from an air line to the column at its narrow end (be careful you don't break the tip!). Hold the open end over a beaker and *slowly* open the air valve until the air blows out the adsorbent. To remove the cotton plug, which should now be near the wide end of the column, twirl the end of an applicator stick in the cotton until it catches the fibers, and then pull it out. Dispose of any unused or recovered solvents as directed by your instructor.

Summary

1 Prepare microscale chromatography column.
2 Pack column with adsorbent, put collector in place.
  IF column was packed using a solvent, GO TO 4
3 Cover adsorbent with eluent.

The Operations

4 Drain column to top of adsorbent, add sample, rinse, drain again.
5 Add eluent to elute sample, keeping eluent level nearly constant.
6 To change eluents, drain current eluent to top of adsorbent, add next eluent.
   IF components are visible, GO TO 7.
   IF components are not visible, GO TO 8.
7 Change collectors when new band starts or ends and where bands overlap.
   GO TO 9.
8 Change collectors after a predetermined volume has been collected.
9 Stop elution after last fraction has been collected.
10 Evaporate and weigh appropriate fractions.
11 Disassemble and clean apparatus, dispose of solvents as directed.

b. Flash Chromatography

Flash chromatography is a variation of liquid–solid column chromatography that uses a single elution solvent and takes less time than the standard method. Pressurized nitrogen, air, or another gas is applied to the top of the column to force eluent through the adsorbent, which is usually a finely divided silica gel with a particle size of ~40–63 μm. Since only one eluent is used, it must be selected carefully to ensure good separation. Separation is poor if the sample size is too large; the procedure described next works best with 0.25 g of sample or less, although it may be suitable for 1 g or so of an easily separated sample.

This flash chromatography apparatus is described in J. Chem. Educ. **1992**, *69, 939.*

Commercial flash chromatography systems may require expensive columns, pumps, and flow controllers, so they are rarely available for use in undergraduate laboratories. An inexpensive flash chromatography system can be constructed using the homemade flow controller shown in Figure C19. The flow controller is assembled by inserting the bottom of a small plastic T-tube into a one-hole rubber stopper that fits into the top the column, attaching two lengths of $\frac{3}{8}$-inch i.d. (inner diameter) Tygon tubing to the straight ends of the T, and securing them with copper wires. One tube is attached to the gas inlet on a Bunsen burner base (the barrel can be removed), and the other to a source of clean, dry, compressed air.

To carry out a standard scale separation using this flow controller, pack a 50-mL buret (or other suitable column) to a depth of 15 cm or so with the

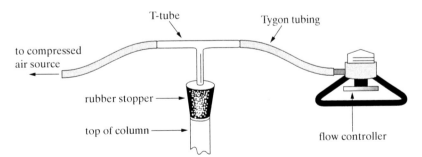

Figure C19 Flow controller for flash chromatography

appropriate adsorbent, using the eluent as the column-packing solvent (see the Directions for packing a column). Drain the solvent to the top of the adsorbent, and then introduce the sample onto the top of the adsorbent. Close the column outlet and add 25 mL or more of eluent to the column, taking care not to disturb the adsorbent surface. Insert the stopper of the flow controller into the top of the column with a firm twist to keep it from popping out (it should stay in place at the desired pressure). Open the needle valve on the burner base; then open the column outlet with a collector in place. Carefully turn on the air valve to pressurize the system, and adjust the needle valve so that the eluent level decreases at a rate of ~5 cm per minute. Collect and evaporate the fractions by the usual procedure.

c. Reversed-phase Column Chromatography

Adsorbents are polar solids that attract polar compounds more strongly than nonpolar ones, so nonpolar solutes are eluted from adsorbent-packed columns more rapidly than polar ones. Another kind of stationary phase can be prepared by coating particles of silica gel with a high-boiling nonpolar liquid. With such a stationary phase, components of the sample are partitioned between the liquid mobile phase and the liquid layer of the stationary phase, where to *partition* a solute means to distribute it between two phases. If the mobile phase is more polar than the stationary phase, the usual order of elution will be reversed; that is, polar compounds will be eluted before nonpolar ones. This general method is called *reversed-phase chromatography*. The mobile phases for reversed-phase column chromatography are usually polar solvents or mixtures of such solvents as water, methanol, and acetonitrile. Stationary phases can be prepared by coating a specially treated (silanized) silica gel with a nonpolar liquid phase, such as a hydrocarbon or silicone. Bonded liquid phases, such as the ones described for HPLC [OP-35], can also be used.

To prepare a column using coated silica gel, the liquid mobile and stationary phases are shaken together in a separatory funnel to saturate each phase with the other and the layers are separated. The stationary phase is then stirred with the silica gel and the coated support is made into a slurry with the saturated mobile phase. The column is slurry packed, usually with stirring to make it more uniform and to remove air bubbles. A separation is carried out by eluting with the saturated mobile phase, essentially as previously described for normal-phase column chromatography.

Thin-Layer Chromatography

OPERATION **19**

Principles and Applications

Like column chromatography, thin-layer chromatography (TLC) utilizes a solid adsorbent as the stationary phase and a liquid solvent as the mobile phase, but the mobile phase creeps *up* the adsorbent layer by capillary action rather than filtering down through it by gravity. A solid support, or *backing*,

The Operations

is coated with a thin layer of the adsorbent to make a *thin-layer plate* or *TLC plate*. The sample (or several samples) is dissolved in a suitable solvent and applied near the lower edge of the plate as one or more small spots. The plate may also be spotted with a selection of standard solutions for comparison. The plate is then *developed* by immersing its lower edge in a suitable mobile phase, the *developing solvent*. This solvent moves up the adsorbent layer by capillary action, carrying with it the components of each spot. In the process, the components are separated as described in OP-18 for column chromatography.

Although TLC is not useful for separating large amounts of a mixture, it is much faster than column chromatography and it can be carried out with very small sample volumes, so that little is wasted. TLC provides better separation than the related technique of paper chromatography [OP-20], and it can be applied to a wider range of organic compounds. Although TLC is categorized under separation operations in this book, it can also be used for qualitative and quantitative analysis of organic compounds.

During an organic synthesis, TLC may be used to monitor the course of the reaction and determine the purity of its product. For example, an experimenter can determine the optimum reaction time for a synthesis by obtaining thin-layer chromatograms of the reaction mixture at regular intervals and comparing the relative amounts of product, reactants, and by-products on successive chromatograms. If a mixture is to be separated by column chromatography, TLC can be used to determine the best solvent for the separation, as described under "Choosing a Developing Solvent." The fractions eluted from a chromatography column can also be analyzed by TLC to determine which component is in each fraction; then the fractions containing the same component can be combined and evaporated. Finally, if a product is purified by recrystallization or another method, TLC analysis can quickly show whether the purified product still contains appreciable amounts of impurities.

Experimental Considerations

Adsorbents.   The most commonly used adsorbents for TLC are silica gel, alumina, and cellulose. The adsorbent is more finely divided than that used in column chromatography, and it is provided with a *binder*, such as polyacrylic acid, to make it stick to the backing. It may also contain a *fluorescent indicator*, which makes most spots visible under ultraviolet light.

TLC Plates.   Small do-it-yourself TLC plates can be prepared by dipping a glass microscope slide into a slurry of the adsorbent and binder in a suitable solvent, and allowing the solvent to evaporate. Such plates may give inconsistent results because of variations in the thickness of the adsorbent layer. More uniform TLC plates measuring 20×20 cm or larger are manufactured commercially with a wide variety of adsorbents, backings, and layer thicknesses. For example, a typical TLC plate suitable for use in undergraduate laboratories has a flexible plastic backing coated with a 200-μm-thick layer of silica gel mixed with a binder, and possibly a fluorescent indicator as well. TLC plates with metal and glass backings are also available. The adsorbent layer of a TLC plate is easily damaged, so it is important to avoid unnecessary contact with its coated surface and to protect the plate from foreign materials. A TLC adsorbent will pick up moisture when exposed to the atmosphere, making it less active; the adsorbent can be *activated* by heating TLC plates in a 110°C oven for an hour or so.

Spotting. A TLC plate is prepared for development by spotting it with solutions of the sample(s) to be analyzed, and often with standard solutions as well. The sample is dissolved in a suitable solvent to make an approximately 1% solution. If possible, the solvent should be quite nonpolar and have a boiling point of 50–100°C. Column chromatography fractions and other solutions can often be used as is, if the solute is present at a concentration in the 0.2–2.0% range.

If you touch the surface of the adsorbent, your fingerprints may hinder development, obscure developed spots, or be mistaken for spots upon visualization, so it is best to wear thin disposable gloves while spotting a TLC plate. Position the spots accurately, because incorrectly placed spots may run into one another or onto the edge of the adsorbent layer. This can be done with a transparent plastic ruler supported just above the surface of the plate so that it does not touch the adsorbent. Mark the starting line with a pencil on both edges, about 1.5 cm from the bottom of the plate (or 1.0 cm for a microscope-slide plate), and position the spots along the starting line at least 1.5 cm from each edge of the plate and 1.0 cm from each other. Thus, a 10 × 10 cm TLC plate can accommodate up to eight spots, as shown in Figure C20.

Large, diffuse spots spread out too much for accurate results, so each spot should be as small and concentrated as possible. The spots are best applied with a microliter syringe or a capillary micropipet. Capillary micropipets can be obtained commercially, but suitable micropipets can also be prepared by heating an open-ended melting-point capillary in the middle over a small flame and drawing it out to form a fine capillary about 4–5 cm long. The tube is allowed to cool and is then scored and snapped apart in the middle to form two micropipets (see Figure C21). To spot a plate with a micropipet, dip the narrow tip into the solution, and gently touch the tip to the surface of the TLC plate, at the proper location, for only an instant. Do not dig a hole in the adsorbent surface; this will obstruct solvent flow and distort the chromatogram. Make several successive applications at each location, letting the solvent dry each time, delivering about 1–5 μL of solution to form a spot 1–3 mm in diameter. It may be worthwhile to try one, two, and three applications at three separate locations on the TLC plate to determine which quantity gives the best results. Too much solution can result in "tailing" (a zone of diffuse solute following the spot), "bearding" (a zone of diffuse solute preceding the spot), and overlapping of components. Too little solution will make it difficult to detect some of the components. Capillary micropipets can be reused a few times, but a different micropipet should be used for each different solution to avoid cross-contamination.

When using a microliter syringe for spotting, deliver about 1 μL of solution with each application and make two to three applications for each spot. Rinse the syringe with a suitable solvent and remove excess solvent by pumping the plunger gently a few times before filling it with a different solution.

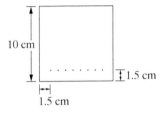

Figure C20 Spotted 10 × 10 cm TLC plate

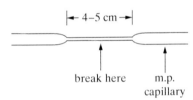

Figure C21 Drawing a capillary micropipet

You can practice your spotting technique on a used or damaged TLC plate.

The Operations

Choosing a Developing Solvent.

Solvents that are suitable eluents for column chromatography are equally suitable as TLC developing solvents; the eluotropic series of Table C4 may help you choose a solvent for a particular application. A quick way to find a suitable solvent is to mark a TLC plate with as many dots as you have solvents to test (you can use a grid pattern with the dots 1.5–2.0 cm apart), and then apply enough solvent directly to each dot to form a circle of solvent 1–2 cm in diameter. Mark the circumference of each circle before the solvent dries. A solvent whose chromatogram (after visualization) shows well-separated rings, with the outermost ring about 50–75% of the distance from the center to the solvent front, should be satisfactory. It is preferable to use the least polar solvent that gives good separation. Hexane, toluene, dichloromethane, and methanol or ethanol (alone or in binary combinations) are suitable for most separations. If no single solvent is suitable, choose two mutually miscible solvents whose outermost rings bracket the 50–75% range (one with too little solute migration, the other with too much), and test them in varying proportions.

Development.

TLC plates are developed by placing them in a *developing chamber* containing the developing solvent. A paper wick can be used to help saturate the air in the developing chamber with solvent vapors, which increases reproducibility and the rate of development. The developing chamber can be a jar with a screw-cap lid, a beaker covered with plastic film or aluminum foil, or a commercial developing tank with a lid. It should utilize the smallest available container that will accommodate the TLC plate, since a larger container takes longer to fill with solvent vapors. Development should be carried out in a place away from direct sunlight or drafts to prevent temperature gradients. It may take 20 minutes or more to develop a 10×10 cm TLC plate; a microscope slide plate can often be developed in 5–10 minutes. The solvent should not be allowed to reach the top edge of the plate, since the spots will spread by diffusion once the solvent has stopped advancing. When the *solvent front* (the boundary between the wet and dry parts of the adsorbent) is within 5 mm or so of the top of the plate, remove the TLC plate from the developing chamber and mark the solvent front with a pencil before the plate has had time to dry. Outline any colored spots with a pencil and let the plate dry, preferably under a hood.

Visualization.

If the spots are colored, they can be observed immediately; otherwise, they must be *visualized* (made visible) by some method. The simplest way to visualize many spots is to observe the TLC plate under ultraviolet light. Fluorescent compounds produce bright spots, and if the adsorbent contains a fluorescent indicator, compounds that quench fluorescence will show up as dark spots on a light background. Mark the center of each spot immediately with a pencil, because the spots will disappear when the ultraviolet light is removed. If a spot is irregular, its center of concentration, the midpoint of its most densely shaded region, is marked instead. It is also a good idea to outline each spot with your pencil.

Another general visualization procedure is to place the dry plate in a closed chamber, such as a wide-mouthed jar with a screw-cap lid, add a few crystals of iodine, and gently heat the chamber on a steam bath so that the iodine vapors sublime onto the adsorbent. Most organic compounds, except saturated hydrocarbons and halides, form brown spots with iodine vapor. Un-

See J. Chem. Educ. **1985**, *62, 156 for an alternative method of visualizing TLC plates with iodine.*

saturated compounds may show up as light spots against the dark background. The iodine color fades in time, so mark the spots shortly after visualization.

Spots can also be made visible by applying a visualizing reagent to the TLC plate. The visualizing reagent can be applied by spraying it onto the plate, dipping the plate into the reagent, or wiping the plate with a cotton ball that has been saturated with the reagent. A solution of phosphomolybdic acid in ethanol can be used to visualize most organic compounds; the spots appear after the plate is heated with a heat gun or in an oven. Other visualizing reagents are used for specific classes of compounds, such as ninhydrin reagent for amino acids and 2,4-dinitrophenylhydrazine reagent for aldehydes and ketones. All spraying should be done under a hood in a "spray box," which can be made from a large cardboard box with the top and one side removed. A thin spray is applied to the TLC plate from about 2 feet away, using an aerosol can or spraying bottle containing the visualizing reagent. Large plates are sprayed by crisscrossing them with horizontal and vertical passes.

See J. Chem. Educ. **1996**, *73, 358 for a description of the cotton-ball procedure.*

Analysis. The ratio of the distance a component travels up a TLC plate to the distance the solvent travels is called its R_f *value.*

$$R_f = \frac{\text{distance traveled by spot}}{\text{distance traveled by solvent}}$$

The R_f (ratio to front) value of a spot is determined by measuring the distance from the starting line to the center of the spot and dividing that value by the distance from the starting line to the the solvent front, both distances being measured along a line extending from the starting point of the spot to its final location. If the spot is irregular, its center of concentration—that is, the midpoint of its most densely shaded region—is used instead. The R_f value of a substance with a given mobile and stationary phase depends on the polarity of its functional groups and other structural features, so it is a physical property of the substance that can be used in its identification. R_f values for some compounds have been reported in the literature, using specified mobile and stationary phases. Reported R_f values can seldom be used to establish the identity of a substance, however, since they depend on a number of factors that are difficult to standardize, such as the sample size, the thickness and activity of the adsorbent, the purity of the solvent, and the temperature of the developing chamber. The only way to be reasonably sure that a TLC unknown is identical to a known compound is to spot a solution of the known compound on the same TLC plate as the unknown. Even then, the identity of the unknown may have to be confirmed by an independent method. An unknown substance or mixture is often analyzed on the same plate with a series of standard solutions, each containing a substance that may be identical to the unknown, or to one of its components if it is a mixture.

Directions for Preparing Microscope-Slide TLC Plates

Several students should work together so they can use the same slurry. Clean as many microscope slides as you need TLC plates using detergent and water, and then rinse them with distilled water and 50% aqueous methanol. After a slide has been cleaned, do not touch the surface that will be coated; hold the slide by the edges or at the top. *Under the hood,* measure 100 mL of dichloromethane into a 4-oz (125-mL) screw-cap jar, add 35 g of Silica Gel G

Take Care! Avoid contact with dichloromethane and do not breathe its vapors.

The Operations

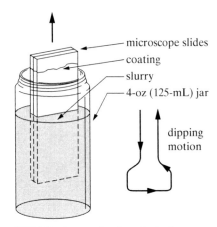

Figure C22 Dipping a pair of stacked microscope slides

with vigorous stirring or swirling, and shake the capped jar vigorously for about a minute to form a smooth slurry. Stack two clean microscope slides back to back, holding them together at the top. Without allowing the slurry to settle (shake it again, if necessary), dip the stacked slides into the slurry for about 2 seconds, using a smooth, unhurried, paddlelike motion (see Figure C22) to coat them uniformly with the adsorbent. Immerse the slides deeply enough so that only the top 1 cm or so remains uncoated. Touch the bottom of the stacked slides to the jar to drain off the excess slurry, and let them air-dry a minute or so to evaporate the solvent; then separate them and wipe off the excess adsorbent from the edges with a tissue paper. Repeat with more slides, as needed; if the slurry becomes too thick, dilute it with dichloromethane. Activate the coated slides by heating them in a 110°C oven for 15 minutes. Slides with streaks, lumps, or thin spots in the coating should be wiped clean and redipped. If the coating is too fragile, try adding some methanol (up to one-third by volume) to the slurry. Coated slides can be stored in a microscope-slide box inside a desiccator.

General Directions for Thin-Layer Chromatography

 Standard Scale and Microscale

Equipment and Supplies

TLC plate(s)
developing chamber
paper wick
developing solvent
capillary micropipets or microliter syringe
pencil and ruler
standard solution(s)
visualizer (sprayer, iodine chamber, UV lamp, etc.)

Obtain a beaker, screw-cap jar, or another container large enough to hold the TLC plate. A 4-oz screw-cap jar is suitable for a microscope-slide TLC plate,

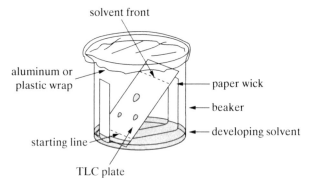

Figure C23 Development of a TLC plate

a 400-mL beaker will hold a 6.7 × 10 cm plate, and a 1-L beaker will hold a 10 × 10 cm plate. If necessary, prepare and insert a paper wick made from filter paper or chromatography paper. The wick can be prepared by cutting a rectangular strip of paper 3–5 cm wide and long enough to extend in a "U" down one side of the developing chamber, along the bottom, and up the opposite side. Pour in enough developing solvent to form a liquid layer about 5 mm deep on the bottom of the developing chamber. Cover the chamber with a screw cap, a square of plastic food wrap, or another suitable closure. Tip the chamber, slosh the solvent around to soak the wick with developing solvent, and then put it in a place where it can sit undisturbed away from drafts and direct sunlight. Let the developing chamber stand for 30 minutes or more to saturate the atmosphere inside the chamber with solvent vapors.

The wick may not be necessary if the developing chamber is allowed to stand for an hour or more after the solid has been added.

Mark the starting line on a TLC plate and spot it with (1) the solution to be analyzed and (2) any standard solutions required, making spots 1–3 mm in diameter. Except on a microscope-slide TLC plate, which can accommodate up to three evenly spaced spots, the spots should be at least 1.0 cm apart and the outermost spots should be 1.5 cm from the edges of the plate. When the spots are dry, place the TLC plate in the chamber, with its spotted end down, so that it leans *across* the wick (perpendicular to it) with its top against the glass wall of the chamber. No part of a plastic- or aluminum-backed TLC plate should touch the wick, because solvent can diffuse onto the adsorbent at that point. Cover the developing chamber without delay, and do not move it during development.

Observe the development frequently, and when the solvent front is within about 5 mm of the top of the plate, remove the plate from the developing chamber. Before the solvent evaporates, use a pencil to trace a line along the solvent front and mark the centers (or centers of concentration) of any visible spots. Let the plate dry thoroughly, and visualize the spots (if necessary) by one of the methods described previously, marking the center (or center of concentration) of each spot with a pencil. You should also outline each spot with your pencil. Keeping your ruler parallel to the edges of the plate along the line of development, measure the distance in millimeters from the starting line to the solvent front and from the starting line to the center of each spot. Calculate the R_f value for each spot. If requested, make a permanent record of the chromatogram by photocopying or photographing it.

The distance from the starting line to the solvent front may vary, so measure that distance for each spot along an imaginary vertical line that goes through the spot.

The Operations

Summary

1 Put wick and developing solvent in developing chamber, cover, and let stand.
2 Obtain or prepare TLC plate.
3 Spot TLC plate with solutions of the unknown(s) and any standards.
4 Place TLC plate in developing chamber, cover, and observe.
5 Remove TLC plate when solvent front nears top of plate.
6 Mark solvent front and visible spots, let plate dry.
7 Visualize and mark spots, as needed.
8 Measure R_f values.
9 Clean up, dispose of solvent as directed.

OPERATION **20**   # Paper Chromatography

Principles and Applications

Paper chromatography is similar to thin-layer chromatography [OP-19] in practice, but quite different in principle. Although paper consists mainly of cellulose, the stationary phase is not cellulose itself but the water that is adsorbed by it. Chromatography paper can adsorb up to 22% water, and the developing solvents usually contain enough water to keep it saturated. Development is carried out by passing a comparatively nonpolar mobile phase through the cellulose fibers, partitioning the solutes between the bound water and the mobile phase. Paper chromatography thus operates by a liquid–liquid partitioning process rather than by adsorption on the surface of a solid.

Since only polar compounds are appreciably soluble in water, paper chromatography is most frequently used to separate polar substances such as amino acids and carbohydrates. Manufactured chromatography paper is quite uniform, and the activity of cellulose doesn't vary as much as the activity of most TLC adsorbents, so R_f values obtained by paper chromatography may be more reproducible than those from thin-layer chromatography. However, the resolution of spots is often poorer and the development times are usually much longer. Nevertheless, paper chromatography is a useful analytical technique that can accomplish a variety of separations.

Experimental Considerations

Since many of the experimental aspects of paper chromatography are similar or identical to those for thin-layer chromatography, you should read the appropriate parts of OP-19 for additional information about experimental techniques.

Paper.   Various grades of chromatography paper, such as Whatman #1 Chr, are manufactured in rectangular sheets, strips, and other convenient shapes. For good results, the chromatography paper must be kept clean. The bench top or other surface on which the paper is handled should be covered with a sheet of butcher paper or some other liner. The chromatography paper should be held only by the edges or along the top; alternatively, an extra strip of paper can be left on one or both ends of the chromatography paper, used for handling it, and then cut off just before development. The paper should

Paper Chromatography

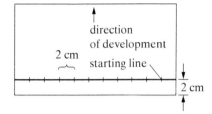

Figure C24 11 × 22 cm chromatography paper marked for spotting

be cut so that its grain is parallel to the direction of development. For most purposes, the paper should be 10–15 cm high (in the direction of development) and wide enough to accommodate the desired number of spots.

Spotting. As for thin-layer chromatography, the substance(s) to be analyzed should be dissolved in a suitable solvent, usually at a concentration of about 1% (mass/volume). The starting line should be marked in pencil about 2 cm above the bottom edge, and the positions of the spots can also be marked lightly with pencil. The spots tend to spread out more with paper chromatography than with TLC, so they should be applied farther apart— about 1.5–2.0 cm from each other and 2.0 cm from the edges of the paper, as shown in Figure C24. Spotting can be performed by the same techniques as for TLC using a capillary micropipet or syringe (see OP-19), but a round wooden toothpick is adequate for most purposes. During the spotting, nothing should touch the underside of the paper at the point of application. Each spot can be made with up to 10 μL of solution and should be 2–5 mm in diameter. Keep in mind that too little solution is usually better than too much. The solution can be applied in steps, drying the spot after each application. You should practice your spotting technique on a piece of filter paper before attempting to spot the chromatogram.

Developing Solvents. Nearly all paper chromatography developing solvents contain water, which is needed to maintain the composition of the aqueous stationary phase on the cellulose. As a rule, they also contain an organic solvent and (if necessary) one or more additional components to increase the solubility of the water in the organic solvent or provide an acidic or basic medium. A developing solvent for paper chromatography may be prepared by saturating the organic solvent(s) with water in a separatory funnel, separating the two phases, and using the organic phase for development. Alternatively, a monophase (single-phase) mixture with essentially the same composition as the organic phase of the saturated mixture can be used. Some typical monophase solvent mixtures are listed in Table C5. Most solvent mixtures should be made up fresh each time they are used and not kept for more than a day or two.

Table C5 Some monophase solvent mixtures for paper chromatography

Solvents	Composition
2-propanol/ammonia/water	9:1:2
1-butanol/acetic acid/water	12:3:5
phenol/water	500 g phenol, 125 mL water
ethyl acetate/1-propanol/water	14:2:4

Note: All solvent ratios are by volume.

solvent front

12

B

10

6

A

$$A \quad R_f = \frac{6}{12} = 0.50$$

$$B \quad R_f = \frac{10}{12} = 0.83$$

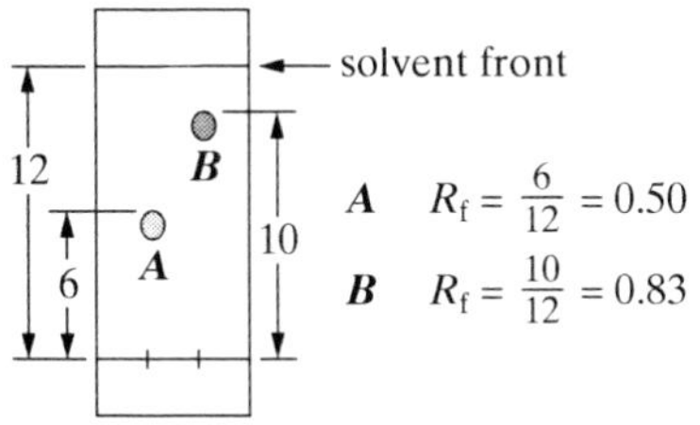

$$R_f = \frac{\text{Distance to leading edge of spot}}{\text{Distance to solvent front}}$$

Figure C25 Measuring R_f values on a paper chromatogram

Development.   Narrow paper strips accommodating two or more spots can be developed in test tubes, bottles, cylinders, or Erlenmeyer flasks. A wider sheet can be rolled into a cylinder and developed in a beaker. A typical paper chromatogram is developed in much the same way as for TLC, but more time is required to saturate the developing chamber with solvent vapors.

Visualization.   Visualization of spots by ultraviolet light is quite useful in paper chromatography, since paper fluoresces dimly in a dark room and many organic compounds will quench its fluorescence. Paper chromatograms can also be visualized by spraying them or by dipping them into a solution of a suitable visualizing reagent.

Analysis.   A substance responsible for a spot on a developed chromatogram is characterized by its R_f value, which is determined as illustrated in Figure C25. Spot migration distances are customarily measured from the starting line to the *front* of each spot, rather than to its center as for TLC. It is usually necessary to run one or more standards along with an unknown to identify the unknown. Whenever possible, the solvent and concentration should be the same for the standard as for the unknown.

General Directions for Paper Chromatography

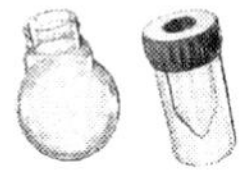

Standard Scale and Microscale

Equipment and Supplies

   developing chamber
   developing solvent
   chromatography paper
   pencil and ruler
   capillary micropipets (or toothpicks, etc.)
   solutions to be spotted
   visualizing reagent and equipment

The following procedure can be used when up to 13 spots are to be applied. For fewer spots, a strip of chromatography paper can be spotted, folded in the middle or hung from a wire embedded in a cork for support, and developed in a test tube, a jar, or another appropriate container.

   Add enough developing solvent to a 600-mL beaker (or another suitable developing chamber) to provide a liquid layer about 1 cm deep. Cover the chamber tightly with plastic food wrap (or cap it), slosh the solvent around in it for about 30 seconds, and then put it in a place in which it can sit undisturbed away from drafts and direct sunlight. Allow sufficient time (usually an hour or more) for the solvent to saturate the developing chamber. While the developing chamber is equilibrating, obtain a sheet of chromatography paper and cut it to form an 11 × 22 cm rectangle (or another appropriate size). Without touching the surface of the paper, use a pencil to draw a starting line 2 cm from one long edge (the bottom edge) and lightly mark the positions for spots with a pencil, spacing them about 2 cm from each side and 1.5–2.0 cm apart. Spot the paper with all solutions to be chromatographed; then roll it into a cylinder and staple the ends together, leaving a small gap between them (see Figure C26). Uncover the developing chamber, place the

(cover omitted for clarity)

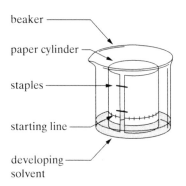

beaker

paper cylinder

staples

starting line

developing solvent

Figure C26 Developing a paper chromatogram

paper cylinder inside (spotted end down), and cover it without delay. The paper must not touch the sides of the chamber, and the chamber should not be moved during development. Development may take an hour or more, depending on the developing solvent and the distance traveled.

When the solvent front is a centimeter or less from the top of the paper, remove the cylinder and separate its edges; then accurately draw a line along the entire solvent front with a pencil. If any spots are visible at this time, outline them with a pencil (carefully, to avoid tearing the wet paper), as they may fade in time. Again roll the paper into a cylinder, and stand it on edge to air dry. When it is completely dry, visualize the spots by an appropriate method, if necessary. Keeping your ruler parallel to the edges of the paper along the line of development, measure the distance in millimeters from the starting line to the solvent front and from the starting line to the leading edge of each spot. Calculate the R_f value of each spot.

Summary

1 Add developing solvent to developing chamber, cover, and let stand.
2 Obtain chromatography paper and cut it to size.
3 Spot chromatography paper with solutions.
4 Place paper in developing chamber, cover, and observe.
5 Remove paper chromatogram when solvent front nears top of paper.
6 Mark solvent front and visible spots, let chromatogram dry.
7 Visualize and mark spots, as needed.
8 Measure R_f values.
9 Clean up, dispose of solvent as directed.

The Operations

D. Washing and Drying Operations

Washing Liquids

In practice, the process of washing liquids is identical to liquid–liquid extraction [OP-15], but its purpose is different. *Extraction* separates a desired substance (such as the product of a reaction) from an impure mixture; *washing* removes impurities from a desired substance. The liquid being washed may be a neat liquid (one without solvent) or a solvent containing the desired substance. In either case, that substance must not dissolve appreciably in the wash liquid or it will be extracted along with the impurities.

The *wash liquid* is usually water or an aqueous solution, although organic solvents, such as ethyl ether, can be used to remove low-polarity impurities from aqueous solutions containing polar solutes. Both water and saturated aqueous sodium chloride remove water-soluble impurities, such as salts and polar organic compounds, from organic liquids. Saturated sodium chloride is frequently used for the last washing before a liquid is dried [OP-22], because it removes excess water from the organic liquid by the salting-out effect [OP-15c]. It is preferred to water in some other cases, because it helps prevent the formation of emulsions at the interface between the liquids.

Some aqueous wash liquids contain chemically reactive solutes that convert water-insoluble impurities to water-soluble salts, which then dissolve in the wash solvent. Aqueous solutions of bases such as sodium hydroxide, sodium carbonate, and sodium bicarbonate remove acidic impurities; aqueous solutions of acids such as hydrochloric acid and sodium bisulfate remove alkaline impurities; and aqueous sodium bisulfite removes certain aldehyde and ketone impurities by forming soluble bisulfite addition compounds.

Reactions in some chemically reactive washing solutions

$NaHCO_3 + HA$ (acidic impurity) $\longrightarrow Na^+A^-$ (soluble salt) $+ H_2O + CO_2$

$HCl + B$ (basic impurity) $\longrightarrow BH^+ Cl^-$ (soluble salt)

$NaHSO_3 + RCHO$ (aldehyde impurity) $\longrightarrow$
$$RCH(OH)SO_3^- Na^+ \text{ (soluble salt)}$$

When a chemically reactive wash liquid is used, it is usually advisable to perform a preliminary washing with water or aqueous NaCl to remove most of the water-soluble impurities. This may prevent a potentially violent reaction between the reactive wash liquid and the impurities. Sometimes a follow-up washing with water or aqueous NaCl is used to remove traces of the chemically reactive solute from the product.

The effectiveness of washing with a given total volume of wash liquid increases if it is carried out in several steps. Unless otherwise indicated, a liquid should be washed in two or three stages using equal volumes of wash liquid for each stage, and the total volume of wash liquid should be roughly equal to the volume of the liquid being washed. For example, if you are washing 6 mL of a liquid, you can use two 3-mL or three 2-mL portions of the wash liquid. When several different wash liquids are used in succession, one or two washings with

Rule of Thumb: *Total volume of wash liquid ≈ volume of liquid being washed.*

each wash liquid may be sufficient, but the total volume of all of the wash liquids should usually equal or exceed the volume of the liquid being washed.

The procedure for washing liquids is essentially the same as that for liquid–liquid extraction [OP-15], except that the wash liquid is discarded and the liquid being washed is saved. As for extraction, it is important to save *both* layers until you are absolutely certain you are working with the right layer. Refer to the general directions in OP-15 for experimental details and summaries.

General Directions for Washing Liquids

 Standard Scale

Combine the wash liquid and the liquid being washed in a separatory funnel. If the wash liquid contains sodium carbonate, sodium bicarbonate, or another reactive solute that generates a gas, use a glass stirring rod to stir it vigorously with the liquid being washed until gas evolution subsides. Otherwise, a pressure buildup might cause the stopper to pop out and your product to spray all over the lab. Then stopper the separatory funnel and shake it, very gently at first, with frequent venting. When you no longer hear a "whoosh" of escaping vapors upon venting, shake the separatory funnel more vigorously for 1–2 minutes, and then set it on a support until the layers separate sharply.

If the liquid being washed is *less* dense than the wash liquid (for example, if it is an ether solution), drain the lower layer (the wash liquid) after each washing and save it for later disposal; then add the next portion of wash liquid to the liquid being washed, which remains in the separatory funnel. If the liquid being washed is *more* dense than the wash liquid (for example, if it is a dichloromethane solution), drain the lower layer into a flask after each washing and then pour the wash liquid out of the top of the separatory funnel, saving it for later disposal. Return the lower layer to the separatory funnel and repeat the washing as needed.

 Microscale

Combine the wash liquid and the liquid being washed in a conical vial, conical centrifuge tube, or other appropriate container. If the wash liquid contains sodium carbonate, sodium bicarbonate, or another reactive solute that generates a gas, use a thin stirring rod to stir it vigorously with the liquid being washed, until gas evolution subsides. Then cap the washing container securely, shake it gently 5–10 times, and unscrew the cap slightly to allow gases to escape. Shake it more vigorously about 100 times, venting occasionally if you are using a gas-generating wash liquid, then loosen the cap and let it stand until the layers separate sharply.

If the liquid being washed is *less* dense than the wash liquid (for example, if it is an ether solution), remove the lower layer (the wash liquid) with a Pasteur pipet after each washing and set it aside for later disposal. Add the next portion of wash liquid to the liquid being washed, which remains in the washing container, and repeat the operation as needed. After the last washing, try to remove all of the wash solvent from the liquid being washed.

If the liquid being washed is *more* dense than the wash liquid (for example, if it is a dichloromethane solution), transfer the lower layer to a vial or another container after each washing, and then transfer the wash liquid to a different container for later disposal. Return the lower layer to the washing container and repeat the washing as needed. After the last washing, try to exclude any of the wash solvent when you remove the lower layer.

| OPERATION **22** | # Drying Liquids |

When an organic substance (or a solution containing it) is extracted from an aqueous reaction mixture, washed with an aqueous wash liquid, steam-distilled from a natural product, or comes into contact with water in some other way, the substance or its solution will retain traces of water that must be removed before such operations as evaporation and distillation are carried out. Organic liquids and solutions are usually dried in bulk by allowing them to stand in contact with a *drying agent*, which is then removed by decanting or filtration. They may also be dried by flowing through a *drying column*, such as a Pasteur pipet packed with a suitable drying agent.

Drying Agents

Most drying agents are anhydrous (water-free) inorganic salts that form hydrates by combining chemically with water. For example, a mole of anhydrous magnesium sulfate can combine with up to seven moles of water to form hydrates of varying composition.

$$MgSO_4 + nH_2O \rightleftharpoons MgSO_4 \cdot nH_2O \qquad (n = 1\text{--}7)$$

The effectiveness and general applicability of a drying agent depends on the following characteristics:

- Speed—how fast drying takes place
- Capacity—the amount of water absorbed per unit of mass
- Intensity—the degree of dryness attained
- Chemical inertness—unreactivity with substances being dried
- Ease of removal

Ideally, a drying agent should be very fast and have both a high capacity and a high intensity. It should not react with (or dissolve in) a substance being dried, and it should be easy to remove when drying is complete. Table D1 summarizes the properties of some common drying agents. As you can see in the table, there is no ideal drying agent, but magnesium sulfate is perhaps the best all-around drying agent. Because anhydrous magnesium sulfate may consist of a fine powder with a large surface area, it can adsorb much of your product, so it should be washed with fresh solvent to recover the adsorbed product. Other drying agents have advantages for specific applications. For example, sodium sulfate is often used to predry very wet solutions, because it has a high capacity and is easy to remove. Final drying of a predried solution can be accomplished with a high-intensity drying agent, such as calcium sulfate.

The choice of a drying agent depends, in part, on the properties of the liquid being dried and the degree of drying required. Solvents such as ethyl

Table D1 Properties of commonly used drying agents

Drying agent	Speed	Capacity	Intensity	Comments
magnesium sulfate	fast	medium	medium	good general drying agent, suitable for nearly all organic liquids
calcium sulfate (Drierite)	very fast	low	high	fast and efficient, but low capacity
sodium sulfate	slow	high	low	good for predrying; loses water above 32.4°C
calcium chloride	slow to fast	low to medium	medium	removes traces of water quickly, larger amounts slowly; reacts with many organic compounds
silica gel	medium	medium	high	good general drying agent, more expensive than most
potassium carbonate	fast	low	medium	cannot be used to dry acidic compounds
potassium hydroxide	fast	very high	high	used to dry amines, reacts with many other compounds; caustic

ether and ethyl acetate retain appreciable quantities of water, so they are often washed with saturated sodium chloride (see OP-21) to salt out some of the water before further drying. They should then be dried by a drying agent with a relatively high capacity, such as magnesium sulfate. Less polar solvents, such as hexane, petroleum ether, and dichloromethane, retain little water and can be dried with calcium sulfate (Drierite) or calcium chloride. Calcium chloride reacts with many organic compounds that contain oxygen or nitrogen, including alcohols, aldehydes, ketones, carboxylic acids, phenols, amines, amides, and some esters, so it should not be used to dry such compounds or their solutions. Sodium sulfate is often used when thorough drying is not necessary, especially for microscale work, because it doesn't absorb much of the liquid being dried and is easy to remove. If a dichloromethane solution will later be evaporated, it may be sufficient to filter the solution through a cotton plug or a layer of sodium sulfate to remove water droplets (if there are any), since any remaining water should be removed as an azeotrope during evaporation.

Carrier Solvents

Very small quantities of neat liquids should be dissolved in a *carrier solvent*, such as ethyl ether or dichloromethane, before drying; otherwise, you may lose much of your product by adsorption on the drying agent. After drying, the solvent is removed by evaporation [OP-16].

Drying Liquids in Bulk

The *quantity* of drying agent needed for bulk drying depends on the capacity and particle size of the drying agent and on the amount of water present. Usually about 1 g of drying agent should be used per 25 mL of liquid, or 40 mg per milliliter. More may be needed if the drying agent has a low capacity or large particle size or if the liquid has a high water content. It is best to start with a small amount of drying agent and then add more if necessary, since using too much results in excessive losses by adsorption of liquid on the drying agent. For microscale work, it may be satisfactory to start with

Rule of Thumb: Use about 1 g of drying agent per 25 mL of liquid (40 mg/mL).

The Operations

the amount of drying agent that will fit in the V-shaped groove of a Hayman-style microspatula, and then add more if most of the drying agent clumps up or shows other evidence of hydration, as described next. The appearance of the drying agent when the drying time is up often suggests whether more drying agent is needed. As they become hydrated, magnesium sulfate clumps together in large crystals, calcium chloride displays a glassy surface appearance, and blue indicating Drierite changes to pink. If much of a drying agent has changed as described after the initial drying period, more drying agent should be used or (preferably) the spent drying agent should be removed and replaced with fresh drying agent.

Spent drying agent contains hydrates that reduce drying efficiency.

The *time* required for bulk drying depends on the speed of the drying agent and the amount of water present. Most drying agents attain at least 80 percent of their ultimate drying capacity within 15 minutes, so longer drying times are seldom necessary. Five minutes is usually sufficient for magnesium sulfate or Drierite, while 15 minutes is recommended for calcium chloride and sodium sulfate. When more complete drying is required, it is better to replace the spent drying agent or use a more efficient drying agent than to extend the drying time.

A drying agent should be removed as completely as possible when the drying period is over. For standard scale work, most drying agents are removed by gravity filtration through a coarse, fluted filter paper. A coarse-grained drying agent, such as granular calcium chloride or Drierite, can sometimes be removed by carefully decanting the liquid, but granular calcium chloride often contains fine powder that requires filtration. For microscale work, the liquid being dried can be separated from the drying agent with a filter-tip pipet [OP-6] or by passing the liquid through a glass-wool plug in a filtering pipet [OP-12].

When a solution (an ether extract, for example) is being dried, the spent drying agent should be washed with a small amount of the pure solvent to recover adsorbed solute that would otherwise be discarded with the drying agent. When a neat liquid is being dried, the drying agent can be washed with dichloromethane or ethyl ether and the solvent evaporated to recover the adsorbed liquid.

Drying Columns

Drying columns can be used for both standard scale and microscale work, but because the quantity of drying agent required is quite large, they are seldom practical for standard scale drying in undergraduate laboratories.

Relatively small quantities of liquids can be dried in a microscale drying column constructed by supporting some drying agent on a glass-wool plug inside a Pasteur pipet. When thorough drying is not necessary, granular anhydrous sodium sulfate can be used. This form of sodium sulfate comes in relatively large grains, allowing liquids to flow through easily, and a sodium sulfate column can absorb relatively large amounts of water without plugging up. The powdered form of anhydrous magnesium sulfate is not suitable for a drying column because liquids won't flow through it, but a granular form of the drying agent can be used for that purpose. Although magnesium sulfate is a more effective drying agent than sodium sulfate, a magnesium sulfate column is more likely to plug up if the liquid being dried is quite wet. Thus, it is important to make sure that the liquid does not contain any visible water droplets, such as those resulting from imperfect separation during an extraction.

General Directions for Bulk Drying

 Standard Scale and Microscale

Equipment and Supplies

> Erlenmeyer flask, conical vial, or other drying container
> drying agent
> funnel and fluted filter paper (SS), filter-tip pipet (μS), or filtering pipet (μS)

If you are drying a small amount of neat liquid, it is advisable to dissolve the liquid in a carrier solvent, such as diethyl ether or dichloromethane, and evaporate the solvent after drying. If the liquid to be dried contains water droplets or a separate aqueous layer, remove the water using a Pasteur pipet or separatory funnel. Alternatively, pass the wet liquid through a filtering pipet [OP-12] containing a cotton plug, using a rubber bulb to force the last droplets through.

Select an Erlenmeyer flask, conical vial, or other suitable container that will hold the liquid with plenty of room to spare, and add the liquid. Measure the estimated quantity of a suitable drying agent (protect it from atmospheric moisture until you are ready to use it), being sure to cap its original container tightly. Add the drying agent to the liquid, stopper or cap the container, and swirl or shake the container gently for a few seconds. Then let it dry for 5–15 minutes, using the longer drying time with sodium sulfate and other slow drying agents. Swirl, stir, or shake the mixture frequently during the drying period. If you are using a conical vial, you can stir the mixture by twirling the pointed end of a flat-bladed spatula in it. If a second (aqueous) phase forms during drying, remove it with a Pasteur pipet and add more drying agent.

When the drying period is over, examine the drying agent carefully. If most of it is spent, add more drying agent (or remove it and replace it with fresh drying agent), and continue drying for 5 minutes or more. When drying appears to be complete, separate the dry liquid from the drying agent by one of the following methods. For standard scale work, filter it by gravity [OP-12] through fluted filter paper. (With a coarse-grained drying agent, you may be able to decant the liquid into another container, leaving the solid behind.) For microscale work, withdraw the liquid with a dry filter-tip pipet and transfer it to another container, or filter it by gravity through a filtering pipet containing glass wool. If you are drying a solution, rinse the drying agent with a small volume of the pure solvent and combine the rinse liquid with the dried liquid. If you are drying a neat liquid, you can rinse the drying agent with a suitable solvent, combine it with the dried liquid, and evaporate the solvent.

Summary

1 Select drying agent and measure estimated quantity needed.
2 Add drying agent to liquid in drying container
3 Stopper container and mix contents, set aside.
4 Shake, stir, or swirl intermittently until drying time is up.
   IF drying agent is spent or aqueous phase separates, GO TO 5.
   IF not, GO TO 6.

The Operations

5 Remove aqueous phase or spent drying agent if necessary; add fresh drying agent. GO TO 3.
6 Separate liquid from drying agent.
  IF liquid being dried is a neat liquid, GO TO 6.
  IF liquid being dried is a solution, GO TO 7.
7 (Optional) Wash drying agent with appropriate solvent, combine solvent with dried liquid, evaporate solvent. GO TO 9.
8 Wash drying agent with fresh solvent, combine with dried solution.
9 Clean up, dispose of spent drying agent as directed.

General Directions for Using a Drying Column

 Microscale

Equipment and Supplies

2 5¾-inch Pasteur pipets
latex rubber bulb
cotton or glass wool
applicator stick or stirring rod
drying agent
collecting container

If you are drying a neat liquid, dissolve it in approximately 2 mL of a carrier solvent, such as diethyl ether or dichloromethane. (Evaporate the solvent after drying.) If the liquid to be dried contains water droplets or a separate aqueous layer, use a filter-tip pipet [OP-6] to transfer the organic liquid to a dry container, leaving the water behind, or pass the wet liquid through a filtering pipet [OP-12] containing a cotton plug. Obtain a 5¾-inch Pasteur pipet and use an applicator stick or glass stirring rod to gently tamp a small ball of clean cotton or glass wool into the column until it lodges where the pipet narrows. Add enough anhydrous sodium sulfate or *granular* anhydrous magnesium sulfate (usually about 1 g) through the top of the Pasteur pipet to provide a 2–3-cm layer of the drying agent. Clamp this drying column vertically to a ring stand, place a suitable collecting container under the outlet, and transfer the liquid being dried to the column with a Pasteur pipet (preferably filter tipped). If the liquid flow stops or becomes very slow, attach a latex rubber bulb to the top of the column and squeeze it just enough to force the liquid *slowly* through the column. If that doesn't work, obtain a pipet pump, pull out its plunger, attach it to the top of the column, and rotate the thumbwheel enough to force the liquid slowly through the column. When all of the liquid has passed through the drying agent, add about 0.5 mL of fresh solvent (the solvent present in the liquid being dried) to the top of the drying column and let it drain into the container holding the dried liquid. Use a latex rubber bulb to gently expel any liquid remaining on the column into the container.

When it is dry, remove the drying agent by inverting the column in a beaker and tapping it gently, and remove the plug with a wooden applicator stick. If that doesn't work, attach a rubber hose from an air line to the column at its narrow end (be careful you don't break the tip), hold the open end over a beaker, and *slowly* open the air valve until the air blows out the drying agent.

Summary

1 Select drying agent and measure quantity needed.
2 Prepare drying column containing drying agent.
3 Clamp drying column to ring stand over collecting container.
4 Add liquid to column with Pasteur pipet, drain into collecting container.
5 Rinse drying agent with fresh solvent, combine with dried liquid.
6 Clean up, dispose of spent drying agent as directed.

Drying Solids

OPERATION **23**

Solids that have been separated from a reaction mixture or isolated from other sources usually retain traces of water or other solvents used in the separation. Solvents can be removed by a number of drying methods, depending on the nature of the solvent, the amount of material to be dried, and both the melting point and thermal stability of the solid compound.

Experimental Considerations

Solids that have been collected by vacuum filtration [OP-13] are usually air-dried on the filter by leaving the vacuum on for a few minutes after filtration is complete. Unless the solvent is very volatile, further drying is then required. Comparatively volatile solvents can be removed by simply spreading the solid on a watch glass or evaporating dish (covered to keep out airborne particles) and placing the container in a location with good air circulation, such as a hood, for a sufficient period of time. Clamping an inverted funnel above the watch glass or evaporating dish and passing a gentle stream of dry air or nitrogen over it will accelerate the drying rate. A very wet solid can be partially dried by transferring it to a filter paper on a clean surface and blotting it with another filter paper to remove excess water. The solid is then rubbed against the filter paper with the blade of a flat-bladed spatula until it is finely divided and friable, using fresh filter paper if necessary. It should then be dried completely by one of the methods described next.

    Many wet solids can be spread out in a shallow ovenproof container and dried in a laboratory oven set at 110°C or another suitable temperature. The expected melting point of the solid should be at least 20°C above the oven temperature, and the solid should not be heat sensitive or sublime readily at the oven temperature. It is not unusual for a student to open an oven door and discover that the product he or she worked many hours to prepare has just turned into a charred or molten mass, or disappeared entirely. Aluminum weighing dishes and other commercially available containers made of heavy aluminum foil are usually suitable for oven-drying because the aluminum conducts heat well, cools quickly, and is not likely to burn your fingers. Aluminum reacts with some acidic and basic compounds, which should be dried in Pyrex or porcelain containers such as watch glasses or evaporating dishes. A *vacuum oven* combines the use of heat with low air pressure for very fast, efficient drying. A simple vacuum oven can be constructed by clamping

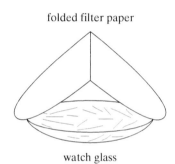

folded filter paper

watch glass

Figure D1 Covered watch glass for drying solids

Take Care! Don't blow the crystals away.

If you are not sure whether your product can be oven-dried safely, consult your instructor.

The Operations

a sidearm test tube horizontally and connecting it to a vacuum source (see *J. Chem. Educ.* **1988**, *65*, 460). The sample, in an open vial, is inserted in the sidearm test tube, which is stoppered and heated with a heat lamp while the vacuum is turned on.

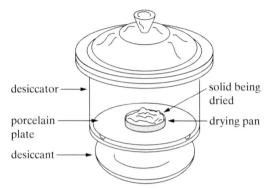

Figure D2 Commercial desiccator

A similar desiccator with a polyethylene storage rack is available commercially.

When time permits, the safest way to dry a solid is to leave it in a *desiccator* overnight or longer. A desiccator consists of a tightly sealed container partly filled with a *desiccant* (drying agent) that absorbs water vapor, creating a moisture-free environment in which the solid should dry thoroughly. Desiccators such as the one shown in Figure D2 are available commercially. A simple homemade desiccator for drying small amounts of solid is illustrated in Figure D3. This desiccator consists of an 8-oz (~250-mL) wide-mouthed jar with a screw cap, containing a 1-cm layer of solid desiccant at the bottom. Its size is well suited to microscale work, since several samples in small vials can be dried at the same time, but it is also useful for standard scale work. The wet solid, in an appropriate container, is set inside the desiccator, which is capped and allowed to stand undisturbed until drying is complete. If there is any danger of the container tipping over, a wire screen can be cut to fit on top of the desiccant layer and provide a more stable surface. Except when a product is being added or removed, the desiccator must be kept tightly closed at all times to keep the dessicant active.

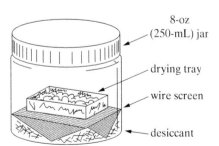

Figure D3 Homemade desiccator

Anhydrous calcium chloride is a good (if rather slow working) desiccant because it is inexpensive and has a high water capacity. Drierite (anhydrous calcium sulfate) is faster and more efficient than calcium chloride, but has a much lower capacity. A combination of calcium chloride with a small amount of indicating (blue) Drierite works better than either desiccant separately. The blue Drierite removes traces of moisture that calcium chloride cannot, and it turns pink when the desiccant is spent and needs to be replaced. Unless your instructor indicates otherwise, spent desiccant should be placed in a designated container for reactivation. Drierite can be reactivated by heating it in a 225°C oven overnight; calcium chloride should be heated overnight at 250–350°C.

General Directions for Drying Solids

Drying in an Oven

Obtain a wide, shallow, ovenproof container, such as a watch glass or aluminum weighing dish. Weigh it, and label it to prevent mixups. Spread the solid on the bottom of the container in a thin, uniform layer and place it in the oven, preferably where it is well separated from other containers. After 30 minutes or so, remove the container (wear gloves when handling a glass container) and let it cool to room temperature. Weigh it, let it stand for 5 minutes or more, and weigh it again. If the mass has decreased by 0.5% or more, place it back in the oven until successive weighings made at 5-minute intervals differ by no more than 0.5%.

Drying in a Desiccator

If the sample will remain in the desiccator until the next lab period, you can dry it in a tared, labeled storage vial with the cap removed. (At the beginning of the next lab period, you should cap the vial and weigh it.) If the sample will be in the desiccator only overnight or for a day or two, spread it out in a wide, low container, such as a polystyrene or aluminum weighing dish or a drying tray made by folding a square of heavy aluminum foil. Set the container inside a desiccator containing fresh desiccant, taking care to place it securely so that it won't tip over. With a homemade desiccator, vials can be pushed down into the desiccant layer, and low containers set on a rack made of wire screen or another material (see Figure D3). Label the container if the desiccator will be used by other students or if you are drying several samples at the same time. Cap or cover the desiccator securely and let it stand overnight or longer (preferably longer). Remove and weigh the container, then reweigh it after 30 minutes or so. If the mass decreases by 0.5% or more, dry the solid further, using fresh desiccant if necessary.

Drying and Trapping Gases

OPERATION 24

Gases such as air and nitrogen should be dry for applications such as evaporating solvents and providing an inert atmosphere for a nonaqueous reaction mixture. Many reactions, such as Grignard reactions, must be carried out in a dry atmosphere to prevent decomposition or side reactions brought about by contact with atmospheric moisture. Other reactions generate toxic gases that must be *trapped* to keep them out of the laboratory. Gases can be dried and moisture can be excluded from reaction mixtures using desiccants like the ones described in OP-23 for drying solids. Toxic gases can often be trapped using water, activated charcoal, or reactive solutions that convert acidic and basic gases to soluble salts.

The Operations

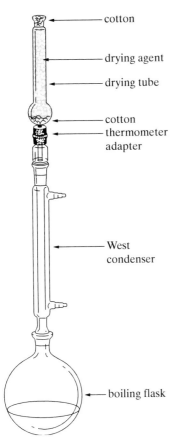

Figure D4 Standard scale apparatus for heating under reflux in a dry atmosphere

Take Care! Never stopper the drying tube, as this will result in a closed system that might explode or fly apart when heated.

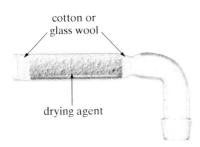

Figure D5 Microscale drying tube

a. Drying Gases

Many gases, such as nitrogen, are available in cylinders and can be purchased in a form that is dry enough for most applications. Other gases, especially compressed air obtained from a laboratory air line, should be dried before use. Air from an air line can be dried by passing it slowly through a large drying tube or a U-tube filled with a suitable desiccant. Plugs of cotton should be placed at both ends of the tube to support the desiccant and remove particles or other impurities from the air line. Indicating silica gel and granular alumina are very efficient desiccants; indicating Drierite and calcium chloride are satisfactory for many purposes.

b. Excluding Moisture from Reaction Mixtures

A *drying tube* containing a suitable desiccant (drying agent) is used when it is necessary to exclude moisture from an experimental setup during an operation such as refluxing or distillation. Calcium chloride, calcium sulfate (Drierite), granular alumina, and silica gel can be used for this purpose. Calcium chloride is the least efficient of these, but it is adequate in many cases. When a very dry atmosphere is required, the apparatus should be swept out by passing dry nitrogen or another dry gas through it using a gas delivery tube. Unless your instructor directs otherwise, put used desiccant in a designated container (*not* the container you got it from) when you are done. If you leave calcium chloride in a drying tube exposed to the atmosphere, its granules will eventually clump together in a solid mass that can be removed only by immersing the drying tube in water overnight or longer, until the solid dissolves.

To prepare a standard scale drying tube, use a glass rod, applicator stick, or long stiff wire to push a small plug of dry cotton (or glass wool) into the drying tube until it covers the narrow opening, and tamp it down gently to hold it in place. Add calcium chloride or another drying agent through the top of the drying tube until it is filled to within a few centimeters of the top; then insert another plug of cotton in the top to prevent spills. Push the narrow end of the drying tube into a thermometer adapter and insert the adapter in the top of a reflux condenser (or any other part of an apparatus that is open to the atmosphere) as shown in Figure D4. If the apparatus contains a vacuum adapter, the drying tube can be attached to its sidearm using a short length of rubber tubing.

To prepare a microscale drying tube (Figure D5), use an applicator stick or glass rod to push a plug of cotton or glass wool through its long end nearly to the bend. Holding the drying tube with its long arm upright (open end up), use a plastic weighing dish to add enough calcium chloride (~1.5 g)

or other drying agent to form a layer 3–4 cm deep; then insert another plug of cotton or glass wool to keep the desiccant in place. Insert the drying tube in the top of a reflux condenser or any other part of an apparatus that is open to the atmosphere.

c. Trapping Gases

The best way to keep toxic gases out of the laboratory air is to conduct all reactions under an efficient fume hood. If that is not possible or if the hood is not adequate, a gas trap containing a suitable gas-absorbing liquid or solid should be used. Water alone will dissolve some gases effectively, but dilute aqueous aqueous sodium hydroxide is generally used for acidic gases, such as HBr or SO_2. It converts them to salts that dissolve in the water.

$$HBr + NaOH \longrightarrow NaBr + H_2O$$
$$SO_2 + NaOH \longrightarrow NaHSO_3$$

Similarly, dilute aqueous HCl can be used to trap ammonia and other alkaline gases. Activated charcoal, in the form known as pelletized Norit, is quite effective for removing small quantities of gases during microscale reactions. It removes neutral gases as well as acidic and basic ones, so it can also be used to keep strong or offensive odors out of the lab. Glass wool moistened with water can remove some odors, but it is most effective for the odors of water-soluble organic compounds.

You can construct a simple gas trap for standard scale work by clamping an inverted narrow-stemmed funnel over a beaker containing a suitable gas-absorbing liquid and then lowering the funnel so that its rim just touches the surface of the liquid, as shown in Figure D6. Connect the gas trap to the reaction apparatus at any point that is open to the atmosphere (usually the top of a reflux condenser) using a short length of fire-polished glass tubing inserted into a thermometer adapter or rubber stopper.

For small amounts of gases, a straight glass tube inserted into a large test tube containing the gas-absorbing liquid may be adequate. Clamp the outlet of the glass tube about a millimeter *above* the surface of the liquid to keep it from backing up into the reaction apparatus when gas evolution ceases or heating is discontinued (see Figure D7). Connect it to the reaction apparatus as shown in Figure D6.

For microscale work, it is most convenient to use a Norit gas trap, which consists of a layer of pelletized Norit in a microscale drying tube (see Figure D5). To construct the gas trap, push a plug of cotton or glass wool

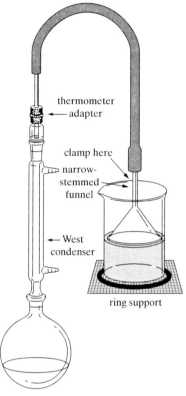

Figure D6 Apparatus for trapping gases during reflux

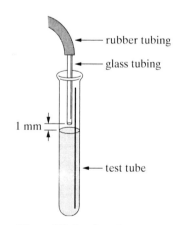

Figure D7 Small-scale gas trap

The Operations

nearly to the bend in a microscale drying tube; then hold it with the long arm upright (open end up) and use a plastic weighing dish to add enough pelletized Norit (~0.5 g) to form a layer 3–4 cm deep. Insert another plug of cotton or glass wool to keep the Norit in place. Insert the drying tube in any part of the reaction apparatus that is exposed to the atmosphere, usually the top of a reflux condenser. If the reaction is to be conducted in a dry atmosphere, you can add a layer of calcium chloride on top of the Norit layer before inserting the second cotton plug.

A gas trap consisting of a plug of moistened glass wool in a microscale drying tube can effectively trap some water-soluble gases, but care must be taken to keep water from dripping into the reaction apparatus. Such a trap is prepared by filling most of the long arm of the drying tube with glass wool and using a Pasteur pipet to drop water onto it until it is moist but not dripping wet.

E. Purification Operations

Recrystallization

The simplest and most widely used operation for purifying organic solids is *recrystallization*. Recrystallization is so named because it involves dissolving a solid that (in most cases) had originally crystallized from a reaction mixture or other solution and then causing it to *again* crystallize from solution. In a typical recrystallization procedure, the crude solid is dissolved by heating it in a suitable *recrystallization solvent*. The hot solution is then filtered by gravity and the filtrate is allowed to cool to room temperature or below, whereupon crystals appear in the saturated solution and are collected by vacuum filtration. The crystals are ordinarily much purer than the crude solid because most of the impurities either fail to dissolve in the hot solution, from which they are separated by gravity filtration or transfer, or remain dissolved in the cold solution, from which they are separated by vacuum filtration or centrifugation.

Recrystallization is based on the fact that the solubility of a solid in a given solvent increases with the temperature of the solvent. Consider the recrystallization from boiling water of a 5.00-g sample of salicylic acid contaminated by 0.25 g of acetanilide. The solubility of salicylic acid in water at 100°C is 7.5 g per 100 mL, so the amount of water required to just dissolve 5.00 g of salicylic acid at the boiling point of water is 67 mL.

$$5.00 \text{ g} \times \frac{100 \text{ mL}}{7.5 \text{ g}} = 67 \text{ mL of water}$$

All of the acetanilide impurity will also dissolve in the boiling water. If the solution is cooled to 20°C, at which temperature the solubility of salicylic acid is only 0.20 g per 100 mL, about 0.13 g of salicylic acid will remain dissolved.

$$67 \text{ mL} \times \frac{0.20 \text{ g}}{100 \text{ mL}} = 0.13 \text{ g of salicylic acid}$$

The dissolved salicylic acid will end up in the filtrate during the vacuum filtration; the remaining 4.87 g will crystallize from solution (if sufficient time is allowed) and be collected on the filter. The solubility of acetanilide in water is 0.50 g per 100 mL at 20°C, so up to 0.35 g of acetanilide can dissolve in 67 mL of water at 20°C.

$$67 \text{ mL} \times \frac{0.50 \text{ g}}{100 \text{ mL}} = 0.35 \text{ g of acetanilide}$$

This means that all 0.25 g of acetanilide in the crude product should remain in solution and end up in the filtrate. Therefore, under ideal conditions, the recrystallization should yield a 97% recovery of salicylic acid uncontaminated by acetanilide.

$$\frac{4.87 \text{ g}}{5.00 \text{ g}} \times 100 = 97\% \text{ recovery}$$

The Operations

The recovery could be increased by cooling the mixture in an ice/water bath to further lower the solubility of salicylic acid, but even then, some of the salicylic acid would remain in solution. You can never recover all of your product after a recrystallization, but by allowing plenty of time for the product to crystallize and making careful transfers, you should be able to minimize your losses.

This is a simplified description of a rather complex process; a number of factors may bring about results different from those calculated.

- Crystals of the desired solid may adsorb impurities on their surfaces or trap them within their crystal lattice.
- The solubility of one solute in a saturated solution of another solute may not be the same as its solubility in the pure solvent.
- Using only enough recrystallization solvent to dissolve a solid can result in premature crystallization, so additional solvent may be added to prevent this.

a. Recrystallization from a Single Solvent

Experimental Considerations

For most experiments in this book that require recrystallization of a solid, a suitable recrystallization solvent is specified in the directions. If the solvent is not specified, see section **c**, "Choosing a Recrystallization Solvent."

In its simplest form, the recrystallization of a solid is carried out by dissolving the impure solid in the hot (usually boiling) recrystallization solvent and letting the resulting solution cool to room temperature or below to allow crystallization to occur. In practice, additional steps, such as filtering or decolorizing the hot solution, may be required. Sometimes it is desirable to collect a second or third crop of crystals by concentrating (see OP-16) the *mother liquor* (the liquid from which the crystals are filtered) from the first crop. These crystals will contain more impurities than the first crop and may require recrystallization from fresh solvent. A melting-point determination [OP-30] or TLC analysis [OP-19] can be used to determine whether a recrystallized solid is sufficiently pure.

Recrystallization of a gram or more of solid is usually carried out in an Erlenmeyer flask, which—depending on the boiling point of the solvent—can be heated over a steam bath or on a hot plate. If necessary, the hot solution is filtered by gravity through fluted filter paper to remove insoluble impurities. After crystallization is complete, the product is collected by vacuum filtration on a Buchner funnel.

Recrystallization of about 0.1 g to 1 g of solid can be carried out using test tubes or small (10–25-mL) Erlenmeyer flasks. A sand bath or an aluminum block [OP-7a] is generally used for heating. If necessary, the hot solution is filtered using a preheated filter-tip pipet or filtering pipet, and the crystals are collected by vacuum filtration on a Hirsch funnel.

For quantities smaller than about 0.1 g, a specialized crystallization tube called a Craig tube can be used. A Craig tube looks much like a small test tube except that it widens at the top, where it has a ground-glass inner surface that accommodates a glass or Teflon plug (see Figure E3). The impure solid is dissolved in the recrystallization solvent and allowed to crystallize in the Craig tube. Then the Craig tube and its plug are inverted in a centrifuge tube and spun in a centrifuge, forcing liquid past the plug into the centrifuge tube and leaving the solid behind on the plug. This procedure reduces the number of transfers needed for recrystallization and therefore reduces product losses. Craig tubes are fragile, expensive, and can easily roll off a bench top and break. (Most microscale recrystallizations in this book can be performed using small test tubes rather than Craig tubes.)

Dissolving the Impure Solid. The impure solid is ordinarily dissolved by heating it with a sufficient amount of recrystallization solvent at the boiling point of the solvent. Unless you know the solubility of the solid substance in the solvent, you will have to determine the necessary amount of solvent by trial and error: adding a measured amount of the hot recrystallization solvent, boiling the mixture for a minute or so to see if it dissolves, adding more solvent if it doesn't, and continuing to add and boil fresh portions of hot solvent until it eventually goes into solution. Since the solid is most soluble at the boiling point of the solvent, it is important to bring the mixture back to the boiling point after each solvent addition and to boil it for a minute or so before making the next addition. Most solids dissolve fairly rapidly in a boiling solvent, but a few, such as 2-phenylindole, do not. Such solids can usually be dissolved by heating them under reflux (to prevent solvent loss) for 5–10 minutes after each addition of fresh solvent.

Filtering the Hot Solution. Some impurities in a substance being crystallized may be insoluble in the boiling solvent and should be removed after the desired substance has dissolved. Don't mistake such impurities for the substance being purified and add too much solvent in an attempt to dissolve them, because excess solvent will reduce the yield of crystals and may even prevent the substance from crystallizing at all. If, after most of the solid has dissolved, addition of another portion of hot solvent does not appreciably reduce the amount of solid in the flask, that solid is probably an impurity—particularly if it is different in appearance from the remainder of the solid.

Excess solvent can be removed by evaporation [OP-16] if necessary.

For most standard scale recrystallizations, you can remove undissolved impurities by filtering the hot solution through coarse fluted filter paper by the procedure for gravity filtration [OP-12], using a preheated funnel and flask. To help prevent premature crystallization during the filtration, you should use at least 10% more recrystallization solvent than the minimum amount needed to dissolve the crude solid. A convenient way of preheating the apparatus is to set the funnel on an Erlenmeyer flask containing the hot recrystallization solvent so that it is heated by boiling solvent vapors; this flask is then used as the collecting flask after unused solvent has been poured out. You can also heat the funnel in an oven or inverted inside a large beaker set on a steam bath. Carry out the filtration as quickly as possible to reduce the likelihood of premature crystallization. If a few crystals form on the filter paper or in the funnel stem during filtration, dissolve them by pouring a small amount of hot recrystallization solvent over them. If a relatively large quantity of solid crystallizes in the filter or funnel stem, scrape it into the filtrate and redissolve it by adding about 10% more recrystallization solvent and heating the mixture to boiling. Then refilter the hot solution and dissolve any precipitate or cloudiness that forms in the collecting flask by heating it before you set it aside to cool.

If the particles of the solid impurity are relatively large and settle to the bottom of the recrystallization container, you may be able to remove them

The Operations

by decanting (pouring) the liquid into another container without disturbing the solid. This is not possible with finely divided solids, however.

In microscale work, filtering the hot solution is complicated by the fact that small quantities of liquid and small-scale filters cool more rapidly than larger ones, making premature crystallization much more likely. For that reason, you should dilute the hot solution with additional recrystalization solvent—about 25–50% more than was needed to dissolve the solid—before filtering. For relatively small amounts of solution, you can use a shortened filter-tip pipet—one with all but 5 mm of the capillary tip cut off (see OP-6). Preheat the filter-tip pipet by drawing in and expelling several portions of the boiling recrystallization solvent (*not* the solution you are filtering). Without delay, transfer the hot solution, while it is just below its boiling point, to another container such as a test tube or Craig tube. To remove the excess solvent, continuously twirl the rounded end of a microspatula in the tube as you boil the resulting solution (see Figure C13B). Stop boiling when solid begins to form on the spatula just above the liquid level, indicating that the solution is near the saturation point. Then set the solution aside to cool and crystallize as described later.

Filtration of larger amounts of hot solution can be accomplished with a shortened filtering pipet (see OP-12). Clamp the preheated filtering pipet over the crystallization container (test tube, Craig tube, etc.). Add 25–50% more recrystallization solvent than was needed to dissolve the solid, heat the solution to boiling, and then use a preheated Pasteur pipet to transfer the recrystallization solution to the filtering pipet. If necessary, you can increase the filtration rate through a filtering pipet by applying gentle pressure with a rubber bulb or pipet pump. Boil off the excess solvent, as described previously, before cooling.

If premature crystallization occurs in either kind of filtering apparatus, you may be able to redissolve the crystals in the solvent by blowing hot air from a heat gun over the pipet while its outlet is over the crystallization container, adding a little more solvent if necessary. Otherwise, return the contents of the pipet to the hot recrystallization mixture, add more recrystallization solvent, and try again. If necessary, use a freshly prepared and preheated filtering device to complete the filtration.

Removing Colored Impurities. If a crude sample of a compound known to be white or colorless yields a recrystallization solution with a pronounced color, activated carbon (Norit) can often be used to remove the colored impurity. Pelletized Norit, which consists of small cylindrical pieces of activated carbon, is usually preferable to finely powdered Norit. Although it is somewhat more efficient than the pelletized form, powdered Norit obscures the color and is more difficult to filter.

To use pelletized Norit, let the boiling recrystallization solution cool down for a minute or so, then stir in a *small* amount of the Norit. Unless otherwise directed, start with about 20 mg of Norit for microscale work and 0.1 g or so for standard scale work. Stir or swirl the mixture for a few minutes, keeping it hot enough to prevent your product from crystallizing, but not boiling it. Then let it settle and observe the color of the solution. If much color remains, you can add more pelletized Norit and repeat the process. Avoid adding too much, because any excess Norit can adsorb your product

Take Care! Never add Norit to a solution at or near the boiling point—it may boil up violently.

as well as impurities, and some color may remain no matter how much you use. Then heat the solution just to boiling and separate it from the Norit by one of the methods described in the section "Filtering the Hot Solution." Note that even pelletized Norit contains some fine particles that can plug up a filter-tip pipet, so for microscale work, a filtering pipet may be preferable.

Powdered Norit can be used in much the same way as pelletized Norit, except that less is needed and you will not be able to see whether the decolorization was successful until the solution is filtered. If Norit particles pass through the filter during gravity filtration of the hot solution, they can be removed (with some product loss) by vacuum filtration through a bed of a filtering aid, such as Celite. To prepare such a bed, mix the filtering aid with enough low-boiling solvent (such as ethyl ether or dichloromethane) to form a thin slurry, then pour it onto the filter paper in a Buchner or Hirsch funnel, with the vacuum turned on, until it forms a layer about 3 mm thick. When the Celite bed is dry, remove the solvent from the filter flask. Quickly filter the hot solution through the Celite under vacuum and wash the Celite with a small amount of hot recrystallization solvent. Turn off the vacuum without delay to prevent evaporation of the filtrate. Redissolve any solid that forms in the filtrate by heating it and, as necessary, adding more hot solvent. Then let it cool and crystallize as described later.

Inducing Crystallization. If no crystals form after a hot recrystallization solution is cooled to room temperature, the solution may be supersaturated. If so, crystallization can often be induced by one or more of the following methods:

- Dip the end of a glass stirring rod into the liquid and remove it until the solvent evaporates, leaving a coating of the solid. Then reinsert the glass rod in the liquid and stir gently.
- Rub the tip of the glass rod against the side of the recrystallization container, just above the liquid surface, for a minute to two. Use an up-and-down motion with the rod tip just touching the liquid on the downstroke. If you are using a Craig tube, rub gently so as not to scratch or break the tube.
- Cool the solution in an ice/water bath, then continue rubbing as described previously for several minutes.
- If they are available, drop a few *seed crystals* (crystals of the pure compound) into the solution with cooling and stirring.

A glass rod that has not been fire-polished works best, but it will also scratch the glass, so don't use one without your instructor's permission.

If crystals still do not form, you may have used too much recrystallization solvent. In that case try one or both of the following measures, in order:

- Concentrate the solution by evaporation [OP-16] until it becomes cloudy or crystals appear, heat it until the cloudiness or crystals disappear (add a little more recrystallization solvent if necessary), and then let it cool. If necessary, use any of the previous methods to induce crystallization.
- Heat the solution back to boiling and add another solvent that is miscible with the first and in which the compound should be less soluble (for example, try adding water to an ethanol solution). Add just enough of the second solvent to induce cloudiness or crystals at the boiling point. Then add enough of the original solvent to cause the cloudiness or crystals to disappear from the boiling solvent and let it cool.

As a last resort, remove all of the solvent by evaporation and try a different recrystallization solvent—but see your instructor for advice first.

The Operations

Cooling the Hot Solution. The size and purity of the crystals formed depends on the rate of cooling; rapid cooling yields small crystals and slow cooling yields large ones. The medium-sized crystals obtained from moderately slow cooling are usually the best, because larger crystals tend to *occlude* (trap) impurities, while smaller ones adsorb more impurities on their surfaces and take longer to filter and dry. You can reduce the rate of cooling by setting the recrystallization container on a surface that is a poor heat conductor and inserting it inside or covering it with another container. For standard scale work, the flask can be set on the bench top and its mouth covered with a watch glass. For slower cooling, a large beaker can be inverted over the flask and some paper towels or other insulating material placed under it. For microscale work, a test tube can be supported in a small Erlenmeyer flask and a beaker inverted over the apparatus. A Craig tube, with its plug inserted, can be supported in a 25-mL Erlenmeyer flask, which is set inside a 100-mL beaker; if desired, a larger beaker can be inverted over this assembly.

You can increase the yield of crystals somewhat by cooling the mixture in an ice/water bath once a good crop of crystals is present, but their purity may decrease slightly as a result. Cooling the mixture before well-formed crystals are present may result in small, impure crystals that take longer to filter and dry.

Dealing with Oils and Colloidal Suspensions. When the solid being recrystallized is quite impure or has a low melting point, it may separate as an *oil* (a second liquid phase) on cooling. Oils are undesirable because, even if they solidify on cooling, the solid retains most of the original impurities.

Using a lower-boiling solvent usually results in a lower percent recovery.

If the solid to be purified has a melting point below the boiling point of the expected recrystallization solvent, it may be possible to prevent oiling by substituting a lower-boiling solvent with similar properties. For example, methanol (b.p. 65°C) might be substituted for ethanol (b.p. 78°C) or acetone (b.p. 57°C) for 2-butanone (b.p. 80°C). Oiling may also be prevented by using more recrystallization solvent, adding seed crystals, or both. Seed crystals can sometimes be obtained by dissolving a small amount of the oil in an equal volume of a volatile solvent in a small open test tube and letting the solvent evaporate slowly. If oiling occurs, try the following methods, in order:

1 Heat the solution until the oil dissolves completely, adding more solvent if necessary; then cool it slowly while rubbing the sides of the container (see "Inducing Crystallization").
2 Add an amount of pure recrystallization solvent equal to about 25% of the total solvent volume and repeat the process described in Step **1**.
3 Follow the procedure in Step **1**, but add a seed crystal or two at the approximate temperature where oiling occurred previously.
4 Try to crystallize the oil by either (a) cooling the solution in an ice–salt bath, rubbing the oil with a stirring rod and adding seed crystals if necessary, or (b) removing all of the oil with a Pasteur pipet, dissolving it in an equal volume of a volatile solvent, and letting the solvent evaporate slowly in an open test tube. Then collect the solid by vacuum filtration and recrystallize it from the same solvent or a more suitable one. If necessary, use one or more of the previous methods to prevent further oiling.

A *colloid* is a suspension of very small particles dispersed in a liquid or other phase. Colloids generally have a cloudy appearance and cannot be filtered through ordinary filter paper, because the particles go through the paper. If a solid separates from a cooled solution as a colloidal suspension, the colloid can often be coagulated to form normal crystals by extended heating in a hot water bath or (if the solvent is polar) by adding an electrolyte such as sodium sulfate. Colloid formation can sometimes be prevented by treating a recrystallization solution with Norit, as described previously, or by cooling the solution very slowly.

General Directions for Single-Solvent Recrystallization

Safety Notes

Unless you are informed otherwise, consider all recrystallization solvents (except water) to be flammable and harmful by ingestion, inhalation, and contact. Avoid contact with and inhalation of such solvents and keep them away from flames and hot surfaces.

 Standard Scale

Use this method when you have approximately 1 g or more of crude solid.

Equipment and Supplies

> 2 Erlenmeyer flasks
> recrystallization solvent
> graduated cylinder
> heat source
> boiling sticks or boiling chips
> flat-bottomed stirring rod
> small watch glass
> Buchner funnel with filter paper
> filter flask
> cold washing solvent
> watch glass or beaker (to cover crystallization flask)
> powder funnel (optional)
> fluted filter paper (optional)
> Norit (optional)

If you know the approximate solubility of the solid in the recrystallization solvent, estimate the volume of solvent you will need to recrystallize it and measure out that amount plus 10–20% extra. Otherwise, start with about 10 mL per gram of solid and use more if needed. Measure the solvent into an Erlenmeyer flask—the *solvent flask*. Add a boiling stick or a few boiling chips, insert a powder funnel in the flask mouth, and heat the solvent to boiling with an appropriate heat source [OP-7] (see Figure E1). A steam bath is often preferred for organic solvents that boil below 100°C; a hot plate can be used for water and higher-boiling organic solvents. Place the solid to be purified in a second Erlenmeyer flask—*the boiling flask*—and add about one-quarter of the liquid in the solvent flask to the boiling flask (use three-quarters of the liquid if you have accurately estimated the total amount needed). Heat the mixture *at the boiling point* with constant swirling or stirring, breaking up any large particles with a spatula or flat-bottomed stirring rod,

The Operations

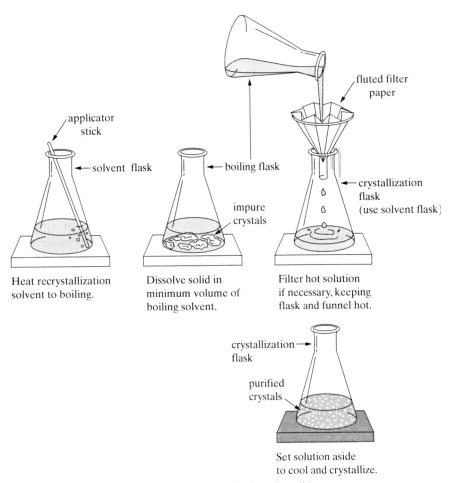

Figure E1 Steps in the standard scale recrystallization of a solid

until it appears that no more solid will go into solution. If undissolved solid remains, add more portions of hot solvent, about 10% of the total each time, heating the solution *at the boiling point* with swirling or stirring after each addition. Continue this process until (1) the solid is completely dissolved *or* (2) no more solid dissolves when a fresh portion of solvent is added and it appears that only solid impurities remain.

If the solution has an intense color but the pure product should not be colored, decolorize it as directed in the section "Removing Colored Impurities." If the boiling solution contains no solid impurities, use the boiling flask as a crystallization flask and skip to the next paragraph. If it does contain solid impurities (including Norit for decolorizing), add about one-tenth as much recrystallization solvent as you used so far and heat the mixture back to boiling. Put a preheated powder funnel on the neck of the emptied solvent flask (with a bent wire or paper clip between them) and set this flask (which is now the *crystallization flask*) on the heat source. Insert a coarse fluted filter paper and rapidly filter the hot solution while it is still near the boiling point, keeping any unfiltered solution hot throughout the filtration. If any

See the section "Filtering the Hot Solution" for additional information.

solid crystallizes on the filter paper or inside the funnel, redissolve it as described in the section "Filtering the Hot Solution."

Set the crystallization flask on the bench top, cover it with a watch glass or inverted beaker, and let the solution cool slowly to room temperature. If no crystals form by the time the solution reaches room temperature, see "Inducing Crystallization." If an oil separates or the solution becomes cloudy but no solid precipitates, see "Dealing with Oils and Colloidal Suspensions." Once crystals have begun to form, allow at least 15 minutes (sometimes much longer) for complete crystallization. If desired, cool the flask further in an ice bath for 5 minutes or more to improve the yield.

Collect the crystals by vacuum filtration [OP-13] on a Buchner funnel of appropriate size. Transfer any crystals remaining in the crystallization flask to the funnel with a small amount of ice-cold recrystallization solvent (or another appropriate solvent) and use more of the cold solvent to wash the solid on the filter (see OP-13). Air-dry the crystals by leaving the vacuum on for a few minutes after the last washing, then dry [OP-23] them further as necessary.

Summary

1 Measure recrystallization solvent into solvent flask, heat to boiling.
2 Add some hot solvent to solid in boiling flask, boil with stirring.
3 Add more hot solvent in portions (as necessary) until solid dissolves.
   IF solution contains colored impurities, GO TO 4.
   IF solution contains undissolved impurities, add more solvent, GO TO 5.
   IF not, GO TO 6.
4 Cool below boiling point, stir in Norit, heat to boiling.
5 Filter hot solution by gravity.
6 Cover flask and set aside to cool until crystallization is complete.
7 Collect crystals by vacuum filtration, wash and air-dry on filter.
8 Clean up, dispose of solvent as directed.

 ## Microscale (Test-Tube Method)

Use this method when you have approximately 0.1 g to 1 g of crude solid.

Equipment and Supplies

   2 test tubes, 13 × 100 mm or 15 × 125 mm
   recrystallization solvent
   calibrated Pasteur pipet (preferably filter-tipped)
   flat-bladed microspatula
   Hirsch funnel with filter paper
   small filter flask
   cold washing solvent
   small Erlenmeyer flask (to hold test tube)
   beaker (to cover flask and test tube)
   filter-tip pipet or filtering pipet (optional)
   pelletized Norit (optional)

If you know the approximate solubility of the solid in the recrystallization solvent, estimate the volume of solvent you will need to recrystallize it and

The Operations

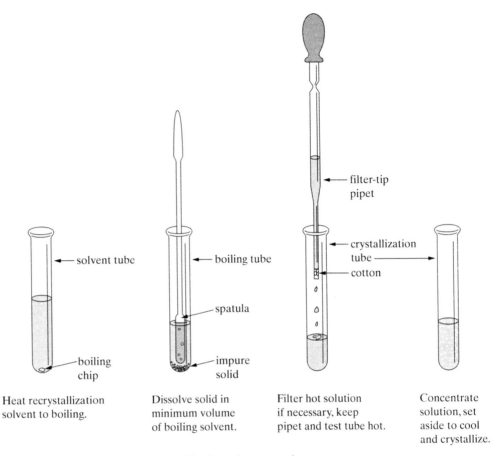

Figure E2 Steps in microscale recrystallization using a test tube

If you will need less than ~2 mL of recrystallization solvent, it is not necessary to preheat the solvent.

measure out that amount plus 20–50% extra (use the higher amount if you think you will need to filter the hot solution). Otherwise, start with about 1 mL per 0.1 g of solid and use more if needed. Measure the recrystallization solvent into a small test tube (the *solvent tube*), add a boiling chip or applicator stick, and heat it to boiling (see Figure E2) using a heating block or sand bath. Place the solid to be purified in an identical test tube (the *boiling tube*) and clamp this test tube *above* the heat source (not in it, as the solid may melt) so that you can control the heating rate quickly by raising or lowering it. Use a calibrated Pasteur pipet to transfer about one-quarter of the liquid in the solvent tube to the boiling tube (use three-quarters of the liquid if you have accurately estimated the total amount needed). Lower the boiling tube and heat the mixture *at the boiling point* while continually stirring it by twirling the rounded end of a flat-bladed microspatula in the test tube, until it appears that no more solid will go into solution. If undissolved solid remains, add more portions of hot solvent—about 10% of the total each time— heating the solution *at the boiling point* with swirling or stirring after each addition. Continue this process until (1) the solid is completely dissolved *or* (2) no more solid dissolves when a fresh portion of solvent is added and it appears that only solid impurities remain.

If the solution has an intense color but the pure product should not be colored, see the section "Removing Colored Impurities." If the boiling solution contains no solid impurities, use the boiling tube as a crystallization tube and skip to the next paragraph. If it does contain solid impurities (including Norit for decolorizing), add 25–50% as much recrystallization solvent as you used so far and heat the mixture back to boiling. Use a preheated filter-tip pipet to transfer the hot solution to a *crystallization tube* (use the emptied solvent tube), leaving the impurities behind. (Alternatively, you can filter the solution into the crystallization tube through a preheated filtering pipet.) If crystals begin to form in the pipet, redissolve them as described in the section "Filtering the Hot Solution." Concentrate the filtered solution by boiling it while stirring with a flat-bladed microspatula, until traces of solid begin to form on the microspatula just above the solvent level.

See the section "Filtering the Hot Solution" for additional information.

Set the crystallization tube in a small Erlenmeyer flask, cover it with an inverted beaker, and let the solution cool slowly to room temperature. If no crystals form by the time the solution reaches room temperature, see "Inducing Crystallization." If an oil separates or the solution becomes cloudy, but no solid precipitates, see "Dealing with Oils and Colloidal Suspensions." Once crystals have begun to form, allow at least 10 minutes (sometimes much longer) for complete crystallization. If desired, cool the test tube further in an ice bath for 5 minutes or more to improve the yield.

Collect the product by vacuum filtration [OP-13] on a Hirsch funnel. Transfer any crystals remaining in the crystallization flask to the funnel with a small amount of ice-cold recrystallization solvent (or another appropriate solvent) and use more cold solvent to wash the solid on the filter (see OP-13). Air-dry the crystals by leaving the vacuum on for a few minutes after the last washing, then dry [OP-23] them further as necessary.

Summary

1 Measure recrystallization solvent into solvent tube, heat to boiling.
2 Add some hot solvent to solid in boiling tube; boil with stirring.
3 Add more hot solvent in portions (as necessary) until solid dissolves.
   IF solution contains colored impurities, GO TO 4.
   IF solution contains undissolved impurities, add more solvent, GO TO 5.
   IF not, GO TO 6.
4 Cool below boiling point, stir in pelletized Norit, heat to boiling.
5 Filter and concentrate hot solution.
6 Cover hot solution and set aside to cool until crystallization is complete.
7 Collect crystals by vacuum filtration; wash and air-dry on filter.
8 Clean up, dispose of solvent as directed.

 ## Microscale (Craig-Tube Method)

You can use this method when you have approximately 0.1 g or less of crude solid or know that the recrystallization will require no more than 2 mL of recrystallization solvent.

Equipment and Supplies

Craig tube with plug
recrystallization solvent

The Operations

calibrated Pasteur pipet (preferably filter tipped)
flat-bladed microspatula
25-mL Erlenmeyer flask (to hold Craig tube)
100-mL beaker
copper wire
centrifuge tube (plastic preferred)
centrifuge
13 × 100 mm test tube (optional)
filter-tip pipet (optional)
pelletized Norit (optional)

The experimental procedure or your instructor may indicate whether the hot solution will need to be filtered.

If it may be necessary to filter the hot solution because of the likelihood of insoluble or colored impurities, put the impure solid in a 13 × 100 mm test tube and dissolve it in the boiling recrystallization solvent (adding 50% more solvent than is needed to dissolve it), as described in the previous directions. If necessary, decolorize the solution with pelletized Norit as described in "Removing Colored Impurities." Then transfer the hot solution to a Craig tube using a preheated filter-tip pipet. Concentrate the solution by boiling it while stirring with a flat-bladed microspatula until traces of solid begin to form on the microspatula just above the solvent level. Skip the next paragraph and go on to the following one.

If it will not be necessary to filter the hot solution, place the impure solid in a Craig tube and add just enough room-temperature recrystallization solvent

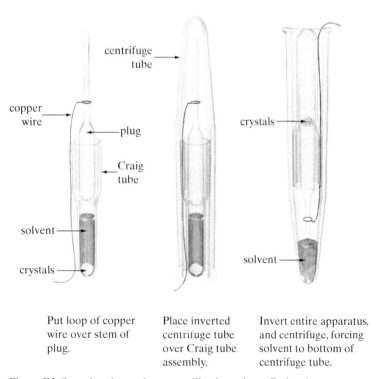

Put loop of copper wire over stem of plug.

Place inverted centrifuge tube over Craig tube assembly.

Invert entire apparatus, and centrifuge, forcing solvent to bottom of centrifuge tube.

Figure E3 Steps in microscale recrystallization using a Craig tube to cover it. Heat the mixture *at the boiling point* with a heating block or sand bath while continually stirring it by twirling the rounded end of a flat-bladed microspatula in the Craig tube, until it appears that no more solid will go into solution. If undissolved solid remains, add more solvent drop by drop with stirring, keeping the solution at the boiling point, until the solid is completely dissolved.

Insert the plug into the Craig tube, support it in a 25-mL Erlenmeyer flask, and set the flask inside a 100-mL beaker. If desired, cover the apparatus with a large inverted beaker. Let the solution cool slowly to room temperature. If no crystals form by the time the solution reaches room temperature, see "Inducing Crystallization." If an oil separates or the solution becomes cloudy but no solid precipitates, see "Dealing with Oils and Colloidal Suspensions." Once crystals have begun to form, allow at least 10 minutes (sometimes much longer) for complete crystallization. If desired, cool the Craig tube further in an ice bath for 5 minutes or more to improve the yield.

Obtain a length of thin copper wire that is about as long as the combined length of the assembled Craig tube and its plug. Make a loop in the copper wire that is large enough to fit over the narrow stem of the plug and bend it so that it is at right angles to the straight part of the wire (see Figure E3). Holding the Craig tube vertically, slip the loop over the plug stem and slide it down as far as it will go, with the straight part of the wire parallel to the Craig tube. Hold the wire against the bottom of the Craig tube between your thumb and forefinger, then invert a conical centrifuge tube over the Craig tube assembly until the narrow end of the plug is nested in (or nearly touching) the V-shaped end of the tube. Pressing the wire firmly against the bottom of the Craig tube to keep the plug in place, take the centrifuge tube in your other other hand and carefully invert the entire apparatus so that the centrifuge tube is upright. Bend the wire over the lip of the centrifuge tube and down the outside so that it does not stick out. Place the centrifuge tube in a centrifuge [OP-14] opposite another tube containing enough water to balance it *or* a centrifuge tube containing another student's Craig tube assembly. If the wire scrapes against any part of the centrifuge, cut it shorter, but not so short that you will not be able to grasp it to pull the Craig tube out. Run the centrifuge for 3 minutes or more. When the centrifuge has stopped turning, remove the centrifuge tubes and use the copper wire to lift the Craig tube assembly out of its centrifuge tube. All of the solvent should be in the bottom of the centrifuge tube, and most of the solid should be packed near the ground joint where the plug fits into the Craig tube. If there is still solvent in the Craig tube, replace the assembly in the centrifuge tube and centrifuge it again. Use a microspatula to transfer the solid to another container for further drying, if necessary.

Don't add solvent to the level where the Craig tube widens; if it takes that much solvent to dissolve the solid, transfer the hot solution to a test tube for recrystallization as described in the previous directions.

Summary

1 IF filtering the hot solution will be necessary, dissolve solid in excess hot recrystallization solvent in test tube.
IF filtering the hot solution should not be necessary, dissolve solid in boiling recrystallization solvent in Craig tube, GO TO 3.
2 Transfer hot solution to Craig tube with filter-tip pipet and boil to concentrate.
3 Insert plug, cover hot solution, cool until crystallization is complete.
4 Collect crystals by centrifugation.
5 Clean up, dispose of solvent as directed.

The Operations

b. Recrystallization from Mixed Solvents

Solids that cannot be recrystallized readily from any single recrystallization solvent can usually be purified by recrystallization from a mixture of two compatible solvents, such as those listed here.

Some compatible solvent pairs

ethanol–water
methanol–water
acetic acid–water
acetone–water
ethyl ether–methanol
ethanol–acetone
ethanol–petroleum ether
ethyl acetate–cyclohexane
chloroform–petroleum ether

The solvents must be miscible in one another, and the compound should be quite soluble in one solvent and relatively insoluble in the other. If the composition of a suitable solvent mixture is known beforehand (such as 40% ethanol in water, for example), the recrystallization can be carried out with the premixed solvent in the same manner as for a single-solvent recrystallization. But a mixed-solvent recrystallization is usually performed by heating the compound in the solvent in which it is most soluble (which we will call solvent A) until it dissolves, then adding enough of the second solvent (solvent B) to bring the solution to the saturation point.

If the compound is *very* soluble in solvent A, the total volume of solvent may be quite small compared with that of the crystals, which may then separate as a dense slurry. In such a case, you should use more of solvent A than is needed to just dissolve the compound, and add correspondingly more of solvent B to bring about saturation. Be careful to avoid adding so much of solvent A that *no* amount of solvent B will result in saturation. If that occurs, you will have to concentrate the solution (see OP-16) or remove all of the solvent and start over.

 ## General Directions for Mixed-Solvent Recrystallization

Most of the steps in a mixed-solvent recrystallization are the same as for single-solvent recrystallization; refer to the previous "General Directions" for experimental details.

Place the crude solid in a boiling flask or tube and add solvent A (previously heated to boiling) in portions, while boiling and stirring, until the solid dissolves or only undissolved impurities remain. If necessary, the solution can be decolorized with Norit at this point. If the hot solution contains undissolved impurities, add enough solvent A to prevent premature crystallization, heat it to boiling, and filter it. For microscale work, concentrate the solution after filtration. Add solvent B in small portions, with stirring, keeping the mixture boiling after each addition. When a persistent cloudiness appears or a precipitate starts to form, keep the solution boiling as you add just enough hot solvent A drop by drop to clear it up or dissolve the precipitate.

Set the mixture aside to cool to room temperature, allow sufficient time for crystallization, and cool it further in ice if desired. When crystallization is complete, collect the product by vacuum filtration (or centrifugation if you are using a Craig tube). After vacuum filtration, wash the product on the filter with cold solvent B or another suitable solvent.

c. Choosing a Recrystallization Solvent

A solvent suitable for recrystallization of a given solid should meet the following criteria, or as many of them as is practical:

- Its boiling point should be in the 60–100°C range.
- Its freezing point should be well below room temperature.
- It must not react with the solid.
- It should not be excessively hazardous to work with.
- It should dissolve between 5 g and 25 g of the solid per 100 mL at the boiling point, and less than 2 g per 100 mL at room temperature, with at least a 5:1 ratio between the two values.

Solubility information from *The Merck Index* or other reference books help you choose a suitable solvent. For example, a solvent in which the compound is designated as *sparingly soluble* or *insoluble* when cold and *very soluble* or *soluble* when hot may be suitable for recrystallization. If solubility data are not available, a solvent may have to be chosen by trial and error from a selection such as that in Table E1.

Ordinarily the recrystallization solvent should be either somewhat more or somewhat less polar than the solid, since a solvent of very similar polarity will

Table E1 Properties of common recrystallization solvents

Solvent	b.p.	f.p.	Comments
water	100	0	solvent of choice for polar compounds; crystals dry slowly
methanol	64	−94	good solvent for relatively polar compounds; easy to remove
95% ethanol	78	−116	excellent general solvent; often preferred over methanol because of higher boiling point
2-butanone	80	−86	good general solvent; acetone is similar, but its boiling point is lower
ethyl acetate	77	−84	good general solvent
toluene	111	−95	good solvent for aromatic compounds; high boiling point makes it difficult to remove
petroleum ether (high-boiling)	~60–90	low	a mixture of hydrocarbons; good solvent for less polar compounds;
hexane	69	−94	good solvent for less polar compounds; easy to remove
cyclohexane	81	6.5	good solvent for less polar compounds; freezes in some cold baths

Note: b.p. and f.p. (freezing point) are in °C. Solvents are listed in approximate order of decreasing polarity.

The Operations

dissolve too much of it. Once some possible solvents are identified, test them as described next. You can test several solvents at the same time and choose the best one.

General Directions for Testing Recrystallization Solvents

J. Chem. Educ. **1989**, *66*, 88 *describes another microscale method for determining recrystallization solvents.*

 ### Standard Scale and Microscale

For microscale work, use the quantities in parentheses. Drops should be added from a medicine dropper, not from a Pasteur pipet.

Weigh about 0.1 g (μS, 10 mg) of the finely divided solid into a test tube or Craig tube and add 1 mL (μS, 3 drops) of the solvent. Stir the mixture by twirling the round end of a flat-bladed microspatula in it, and carefully observe what happens. If the solid dissolves in the cold solvent, the solvent is unsuitable. If the solid does not dissolve, heat the mixture to boiling, with stirring. If it dissolves after heating, try to induce crystallization as described next. If it does not dissolve completely, add more solvent in 0.5-mL (μS, 1 drop) portions, gently boiling and stirring after each addition, until it dissolves *or* until the total volume of added solvent is about 3 mL (μS, 10 drops). If the solid *does not* dissolve in that amount of hot solvent, the solvent is probably not suitable (unless it is water). If it *does* dissolve at any point, record the volume of boiling solvent required to dissolve it. Let the solution cool while scratching the side of the tube with a glass rod to see if crystallization occurs. If crystals separate, examine them for apparent yield and evidence of purity (absence of extraneous color, good crystal structure).

If no single solvent is satisfactory, choose one solvent in which the compound is quite soluble and another in which it is comparatively insoluble (the two solvents must be miscible). Dissolve the specified amount of solid in the first solvent with stirring and boiling, recording the amount of solvent required. Add the second hot solvent drop by drop with boiling and stirring until saturation occurs. Then cool the mixture and try to induce crystallization.

Once a suitable solvent or solvent pair has been identified, use the volume of solvent you recorded to estimate the volume of solvent needed to dissolve all of the sample to be purified.

OPERATION **26**   Sublimation

Principles and Applications

Sublimation is a phase change in which a solid passes directly into the vapor phase without going through an intermediate liquid phase. Many solids that have appreciable vapor pressures below their melting points can be purified by (1) heating the solid to sublime it (convert it to a vapor), (2) condensing the vapor on a cold surface, and (3) scraping off the condensed solid. This method works best if impurities in the crude solid do not sublime appreciably. Sublimation is not as selective as recrystallization or chromatography, but it has some advantages in that no solvent is required and losses in transfer can be kept low.

Experimental Considerations

Sublimation is usually carried out by heating the *sublimand* (the solid before it has sublimed) with an oil bath, steam bath, or other uniform heat source, and collecting the *sublimate* (the solid after it has sublimed and condensed) on a cool surface. For best results, the sublimand should be dry and finely divided, and the distance between the sublimand and the condenser should be minimized. A simple but effective sublimator consists of two nested beakers with a space of about 1–2 cm between them at the bottom. In some cases, it may be necessary to place separators made of folded-over strips of filter paper or paper toweling between the beakers to get the right spacing. Good beaker combinations are 100 mL/150 mL (for microscale work), 250 mL/400 mL, and 400 mL/600 mL. The sublimand is spread out on the bottom of the outer beaker, and the condensing (inner) beaker is partially filled with crushed ice or ice water. As the outer beaker is heated, crystals of sublimate collect on the bottom of the condensing beaker. Figure E4 illustrates a sublimator operating on the same principle, except that an Erlenmeyer flask is used as a condenser and the temperature is controlled by flowing water.

Solids that do not sublime rapidly at atmospheric pressure may do so under vacuum. Figure E5A illustrates a vaccuum sublimator that can be assembled by fitting a 15 × 125 mm test tube snugly inside an 18 × 150 mm sidearm test tube, using a rubber O–ring from a microscale lab kit to act as a vacuum seal. A 15-mm i.d. ring of Tygon tubing (or several layers of masking tape) is placed around the lip of the inner tube to keep it from slipping inside the sidearm test tube (see *J. Chem. Educ.* **1991**, *68*, A63). A commercial vacuum sublimator such as the one in Figure E5B is more efficient because the condenser has a flat, wide bottom that is close to the sublimate. The microscale vacuum sublimation apparatus pictured in Figure E5C can be constructed using a special sublimation tube and adapter.

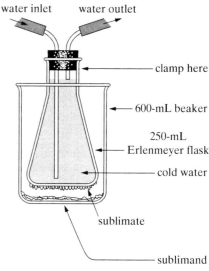

Figure E4 Sublimation apparatus

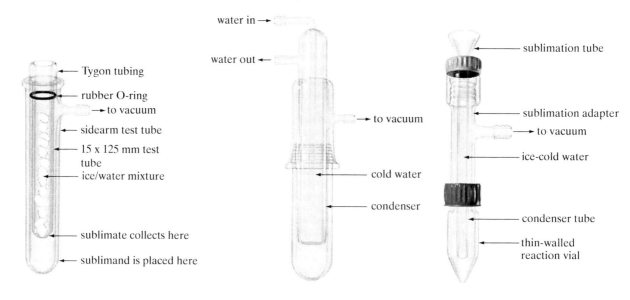

A Simple vacuum sublimator

B Commercial vacuum sublimator

C Microscale vacuum sublimator

Figure E5 Apparatus for vacuum sublimation

The Operations

The best heat source for sublimation is an oil bath, because it provides uniform heating and reduces the likelihood of decomposition. Depending on the temperature required and the nature of the sublimation apparatus, other heat sources such as a hot water baths, steam baths, hot plates (for nested beakers), heating blocks, and sand baths can also be used successfully. With your instructor's permission, you can use a microburner flame, but great care must be taken to avoid charring the sublimate. With some of these heat sources, crystals tend to collect on the sides of the sublimation container as well as the condenser; wrapping the base of the sublimation container with aluminum foil or other insulation will help prevent this.

An ordinary lab burner with its barrel removed can function as a microburner.

 General Directions for Sublimation

Equipment and Supplies

> sublimation apparatus
> heat source
> cooling fluid
> flat-bladed spatula

Assemble one of the sublimation setups described or one suggested by your instructor. Powder the dry sublimand finely and spread it in a thin, even layer over the bottom of the sublimation container. If you are using a vacuum sublimator, attach the apparatus to a trap and vacuum source, then turn on the vacuum. Turn on the cooling water *or* partly fill the condensing tube or beaker with crushed ice or ice water. Heat the sublimation container with an appropriate heat source until sublimate begins to collect on the condenser, then adjust the temperature to attain a suitable rate of sublimation without melting or charring the sublimand. As needed, add small pieces of ice to the condenser to replace melted ice. When the condenser is well covered with sublimate (but before sublimate crystals begin to drop into the sublimand), stop the sublimation, remove the sublimate as described in the next paragraph, and then resume sublimation. If the sublimand hardens or becomes encrusted with impurities, stop the sublimation, grind the sublimand to a fine powder, and then resume sublimation.

When all of the compound has sublimed or only a nonvolatile residue remains, remove the apparatus from the heat source, break the vacuum if you are using a vacuum sublimator, and let the apparatus cool. Carefully remove the condenser (avoid dislodging any sublimate) and scrape the crystals into a suitable tared container using a flat-bladed spatula.

Summary

1 Assemble sublimation apparatus, add sublimand.
2 Turn on vacuum if necessary; add cooling mixture or turn on cooling water.
3 Heat until sublimation begins, adjust heating to maintain good sublimation rate.
4 When sublimation is complete, stop heating, break vacuum if necessary, let cool.
5 Scrape sublimate into tared container.
6 Clean sublimation apparatus.

Simple Distillation

a. Distillation of Liquids

A pure liquid in a container open to the atmosphere boils when its vapor pressure equals the external pressure, which is usually about 1 atmosphere (760 torr, 101.3 kPa). The vapor contains the same molecules as the liquid, so its composition is identical to that of the pure liquid. A mixture of two (or more) liquids with different vapor pressures will boil when the total vapor pressure over the mixture equals the external pressure, but the composition of the vapor will be different from that of the liquid itself, being richer in the more volatile component (the one with the higher vapor pressure). If this vapor is condensed into a separate receiving vessel, the condensed liquid will have the same composition as the vapor; that is, it will be enriched in the more volatile component.

The process of vaporizing a liquid mixture in one vessel and condensing the vapors into another is called *distillation*. The liquid mixture being distilled, the *distilland*, can be heated in a boiling flask—sometimes called the *pot*—using an apparatus such as the one shown in Figure E7. The vapors are condensed on a cool surface, such as the inside of a water-cooled condenser, and the resulting liquid, the *distillate*, is collected in a suitable *receiver*. If the components of the distilland have sufficiently different vapor pressures, most of the more volatile component will end up in the receiver and most of the less volatile component(s) will remain behind in the pot.

The distilland is usually a solution of two or more miscible liquids, but it may also be a liquid–solid solution. The distillation of immiscible liquids is discussed in OP-17.

The purity of the distillate increases with the number of vaporization–condensation cycles it experiences—the number of times it is vaporized and condensed--on its way to the receiver. *Simple distillation* involves only a single vaporization–condensation cycle. It is most useful for purifying a liquid that contains either nonvolatile impurities or small amounts of higher- or lower-boiling impurities. *Fractional distillation* allows for several vaporization–condensation cycles in a single operation. It can be used to separate liquids with comparable volatilities and to purify liquids containing relatively large amounts of volatile impurities. *Vacuum distillation* is carried out under reduced pressure, which reduces the temperature of the distillation. It is used to purify high-boiling liquids and liquids that decompose when distilled at atmospheric pressure.

Principles and Applications

To understand how distillation works, consider a mixture of two ideal liquids with ideal vapors, which obey both Raoult's law (Equation **1**) and Dalton's law (Equation **2**).

$$\text{Raoult's law:} \quad P_A = X_A \cdot P_A^\circ \tag{1}$$

$$\text{Dalton's law:} \quad P_A = Y_A \cdot P \tag{2}$$

In these expressions, P_A is the partial pressure of component A over the mixture, P_A° is the equilibrium vapor pressure of pure A at the same temperature, X_A is the mole fraction of A in the liquid, and Y_A is the mole fraction of A in the vapor. Unfortunately, there are no real liquids that obey these laws

Presumably, entane and orctane exist only in J. R. R. Tolkien's Middle-Earth, where they are used for fuel by Ents and Orcs, respectively.

P is the total presssure over the mixture, assumed here to be 1 atm (760 torr).

perfectly, so we shall consider the behavior of two imaginary hydrocarbons, *entane* (b.p. = 50°C) and *orctane* (b.p. = 100°C), that obey them both. If a mixture of entane and orctane is heated at normal atmospheric pressure, it will begin to boil at a temperature that is determined by the composition of the liquid mixture, producing vapor of a different composition. For example, an equimolar mixture of entane and orctane will start to boil at a temperature just above 66°C, and the vapor will contain more than four moles of entane for every mole of orctane. The liquid and vapor composition of an entane–orctane mixture at any temperature can be calculated using Equations **3** and **4**, which are derived from Dalton's law and Raoult's law.

$$X_A = \frac{P - P_B^\circ}{P_A^\circ - P_B^\circ} \tag{3}$$

$$Y_A = \frac{P_A^\circ}{P} X_A \tag{4}$$

For example, at 70°C the vapor pressure of orctane is 315 torr and that of entane is 1030 torr (see Table E2), so the mole fraction of entane in a distilland that boils at 70°C will be (from Equation **3**),

$$X_{entane} = \frac{760 - 315}{1370 - 315} = 0.422$$

Its mole fraction in the vapor will be (from Equation **4**),

$$Y_{entane} = \frac{1370}{760} \times 0.422 = 0.761$$

showing that the vapor (and thus the distillate) is considerably richer in entane than is the liquid. The vapor pressures and approximate liquid–vapor compositions for entane and orctane at this and other temperatures are given in Table E2.

Table E2 Equilibrium vapor pressures and mole fractions of entane and orctane at different temperatures

T, °C	Entane P°, torr	X	Y	Orctane P°, torr	X	Y
50°	760	1.00	1.00	160	0.00	0.00
60°	1030	0.67	0.90	227	0.33	0.10
70°	1370	0.42	0.76	315	0.58	0.24
80°	1790	0.24	0.57	430	0.76	0.43
90°	2300	0.11	0.32	576	0.89	0.68
100°	2930	0.00	0.00	760	1.00	1.00

Note: P° = equilibrium vapor pressure of the pure liquid; X = mole fraction in liquid mixture; Y = mole fraction in vapor.

The key to an understanding of distillation is this: *The vapor over any mixture of volatile liquids contains more of the lower-boiling component than does the liquid mixture itself.* So at any time during a distillation, the liquid condensing into the receiver contains more of the lower-boiling component than does the liquid in the pot. As more of the lower-boiling component distills away, the pot liquid becomes richer in the higher boiling liquid, so by

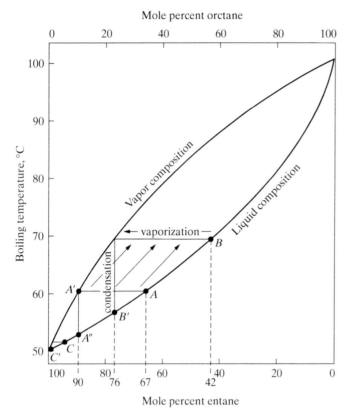

Figure E6 Temperature–composition diagram for entane–orctane mixtures

the end of the distillation, most of the lower-boiling liquid is in the receiver and most of the higher-boiling liquid is in the pot.

The purification process is diagrammed in Figure E6, in which the liquid and vapor compositions are plotted against the boiling temperature of an entane–orctane mixture. Suppose we distill a mixture containing 2 moles of entane for every mole of orctane (67 mol % entane). From the graph (and Table E2), you can see that such a mixture will boil at 60°C (point A) and that its vapor will contain 90 mol % entane (point A'). Thus, the distillate that is condensed from this vapor (point A") will be much richer in entane than was the original mixture in the pot. As the distillation continues, however, the more volatile component will boil away faster and the pot will contain progressively less entane. Thus, the vapor will also contain less entane and the boiling temperature will rise. When the mole percent of entane has fallen to 42 (point B), the boiling temperature will have risen to 70°C and the distillate will contain only 76 mol % entane (point B'). Only when nearly all of the entane has been distilled will the distillate be richer in the less volatile component; at 90°C, for example, more than two-thirds of the distillate will be orctane.

This example shows that the purification effected by simple distillation of a mixture of volatile liquids may be very imperfect. In the example, the distillate never contains more than 90 mol % entane, and it may be considerably less pure than that, depending on the temperature range over which it is

The Operations

collected. If we start with a mixture containing only 5 mol % orctane (point C′), however, considerably better purification can be accomplished. The initial distillate will be 99 mol % entane (point C′) at 51°C, and if the distillation is continued until the temperature rises to 55°C, the final distillate will be 95 mol % entane. The average composition of the distillate will lie somewhere between these values, so most of the orctane will remain in the boiling flask along with some undistilled entane, and the distillate will be relatively pure entane.

Thus, simple distillation can be used to purify a liquid containing *small* amounts of volatile impurities if (1) the impurities have boiling points appreciably higher or lower than that of the liquid, and (2) the distillate is collected over a narrow range (usually 4–6°C), starting at a temperature that is within a few degrees of the liquid's normal boiling point.

Experimental Considerations

Apparatus. The size of the components should be consistent with the volume of the distilland; otherwise, excessive losses will occur. For example, suppose you recovered 20 mL of crude isopentyl acetate and decided to distill it from a 250-mL boiling flask. At the end of the distillation, the flask would be filled with 250 mL of undistilled vapor at the distillation temperature of 142°C (415 K). An ideal-gas law calculation shows that this is about 7.3 mmol of vapor.

$$n = \frac{PV}{RT} = \frac{(1.00 \text{ atm})(0.25 \text{ L})}{(0.0821 \text{ L atm mol}^{-1} \text{ K}^{-1})(415 \text{ K})} = 0.0073 \text{ mol}$$

The vapor would condense to about 1.1 mL of the liquid ester, which would not be recovered. By comparison, a 50-mL boiling flask will retain only one-fifth as much vapor and adsorb about one-third as much liquid on its inner surface. Therefore, using the smaller flask will cut your losses considerably.

Additional liquid losses occur in the still head, condenser, and any other parts of the apparatus that can trap vapors or adsorb liquid.

Figure E7 illustrates a typical setup for standard scale simple distillation. The boiling flask should be about one-third to one-half full of the distilland

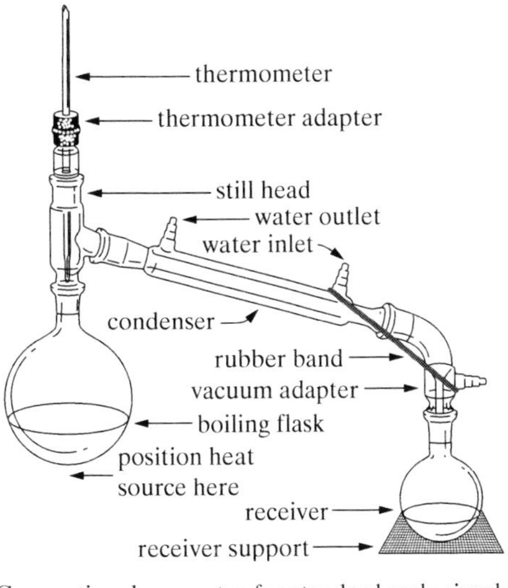

Figure E7 Conventional apparatus for standard scale simple distillation

and should contain several boiling chips or a magnetic stir bar to prevent bumping [OP-7b]. A thermometer is used to monitor the temperature of the distillate vapors during a distillation, both to ensure that the right substance is being collected and to get an estimate of its boiling point. The thermometer is inserted into the *still head* (a connecting adapter) through a stopper or thermometer adapter. It should be well centered in the still head (not closer to one wall than another) with the entire bulb below a line extending from the bottom of the sidearm. In other words, the *top* of the bulb should be aligned with the *bottom* of the sidearm, as illustrated in Figure E8. In this way, the entire bulb will become moistened by condensing vapors of the distillate. The placement of the thermometer is extremely important, since otherwise the observed distillation temperature will be inaccurate (usually too low) and the distillate will be collected over the wrong temperature range.

The condenser should have a straight inner section of comparatively small diameter. A condenser used for heating under reflux can also be used for distillation, but do not use a jacketed distillation column for that purpose; its larger inner diameter results in less efficient condensation. The vacuum adapter (and sometimes the still head as well) should be secured to the condenser by a joint clip or a rubber band. If the distillate is quite volatile or hazardous, the receiver should be a ground-joint flask that fits snugly on the vacuum adapter. If not, an open container can be used. If a ground-joint receiver is used, the vacuum adapter sidearm must not be plugged up—otherwise, heating the system will build up pressure that could result in an explosion and severe injury from flying glass.

If you distill a comparatively small quantity of a liquid ($\sim$1–10 mL) in a conventional distillation apparatus, losses due to trapping of vapors and adsorption of liquid in the apparatus can comprise a large fraction of your product mass. You can reduce such losses by using the smallest available boiling flask from a standard scale lab kit and assembling the compact distillation apparatus shown in Figure E9, where the distillate is condensed by a cold bath surrounding the receiver rather than a West condenser. The vacuum adapter should be secured by a wire or joint clip, because a rubber band exposed to the heat of the vapors may break. If a bulky heat source is used, it may be necessary to twist the vacuum adapter and receiver at an angle to the still head to allow room for the heat source.

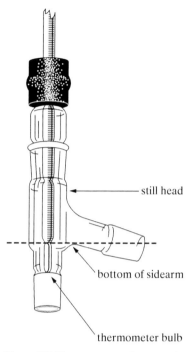

still head

bottom of sidearm

thermometer bulb

Figure E8 Thermometer placement in still head

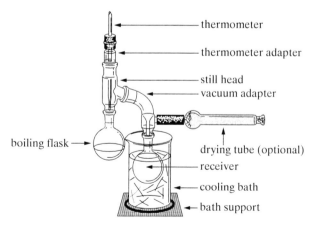

thermometer

thermometer adapter

still head

vacuum adapter

drying tube (optional)

boiling flask

receiver

cooling bath

bath support

Figure E9 Compact distillation apparatus

Both flasks must be clamped or otherwise supported.

The Operations

In order for the cooling bath to work properly, the ground-glass joint between the receiver (which cannot be an open container) and vacuum adapter must be tight, so the receiving flask should be clamped in place or secured by a joint clip. The type of coolant needed depends on the boiling point of the distillate. The following coolants should be suitable for the distillate boiling point ranges indicated:

$<50°C$ ice–salt
$50–100°C$ ice/water
$101–150°C$ cold tap water
$>150°C$ no coolant if receiver is well insulated from heat source

When an ice/water or ice–salt bath is used, the vacuum adapter sidearm should be connected to a drying tube [OP-24b], so that moisture will not condense inside the receiver.

With the two following qualifications, distillation with the compact apparatus is carried out as described in "General Directions" for standard scale simple distillation: (1) if vapors begin to come out of the vacuum adapter outlet, use a colder bath or add ice (or salt) to the one you are already using; (2) if you need to change receivers, stop the distillation and remove the heat source first.

In a distillation apparatus such as the one in Figure E7, the vapor has a long way to travel between pot and receiver. This increases the likelihood that distillate will be lost by sticking to the glass surfaces it encounters along the way or by being diverted into dead ends, such as the top of the still head. For microscale distillation, the path between the pot and the receiver should be as short as is practicable. The *Hickman still* (or *Hickman head*) illustrated in Figure E10 is the most commonly used short-path receiver for microscale distillation. Vapors from the pot (usually a conical vial or small round-bottom

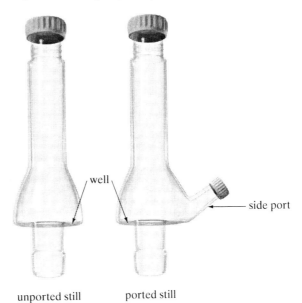

unported still   ported still

Figure E10 Hickman stills

flask) rise through the neck of the still and collect in a *well* (also called a *reservoir*), which functions as the receiver. The well resembles a hollow doughnut sliced in half and has a capacity of 1–2 mL. Vapors of high-boiling liquids condense on the upper walls of the Hickman still, from which the condensed liquid drains into the well. For lower-boiling liquids, a condenser must be attached to the top of the still (see Figure E11) to keep the vapors from escaping. The following rough guidelines tell you what kind of condenser you should use for a given distillate boiling point *if* the distillation is conducted slowly:

$<100°C$ water-cooled condenser
$100–150°C$ air condenser
$>150°C$ no external condenser

Of course you can *always* use a water-cooled condenser, just to be on the safe side. If, during a distillation, you smell any escaping distillate or see distillate droplets collecting near the top of the condenser (or the top of the still, with no external condenser), either slow the distillation rate, attach a more efficient condenser, or both.

Two types of Hickman still are illustrated in Figure E10. The ported still has a capped *side port*, allowing distillate to be withdrawn from the well with a Pasteur pipet and transferred to a tared screw-cap vial or another collecting vessel. To remove distillate from a ported still during the course of a distillation, carefully remove the port cap, remove the liquid without delay, and quickly recap the port. It is important to avoid leaving the port uncapped for long, because distillate vapors will escape through it.

With an unported still, the distillate is collected by inserting a 9-inch Pasteur pipet through the top of the still. To remove distillate from an unported still during a distillation, you may need to remove the condenser and thermometer, if you are using them, and replace them immediately after you withdraw the liquid. Before you remove a condenser, raise the apparatus above the heat source so that the liquid in the pot stops boiling. If the Pasteur pipet doesn't reach all of the distillate, try attaching a short length of fine plastic tubing (of the type used for gas collection) to its capillary tip or bending the tip in a microburner flame. (With plastic tubing attached to your pipet, you may be able to withdraw liquid without removing the condenser.)

The thermometer is inserted through the top of the condenser (if there is one) and the Hickman still and held in place with a small clamp, as shown in Figure E11. It should *never* be inserted through a thermometer adapter (unless the adapter's cap is removed), because that makes the distillation apparatus a closed system, which could shatter when heated and cause severe injury due to flying glass. The thermometer should be placed so that the *top* of its bulb is even with the *bottom* of the well, or slightly below it, as illustrated in Figure E12. The bulb should not touch the sides of the well.

Take Care! Never heat a closed system!

Heating. Almost any of the heat sources described in OP-7a can be used for simple distillation. Heating mantles and oil baths are preferred for standard scale distillation, because they provide reasonably constant, even heating over a wide temperature range. Such a heat source should be positioned so that it can be easily lowered and removed at the end of the distillation. For microscale simple distillation, the heat source is usually an aluminum block or a sand bath.

The Operations

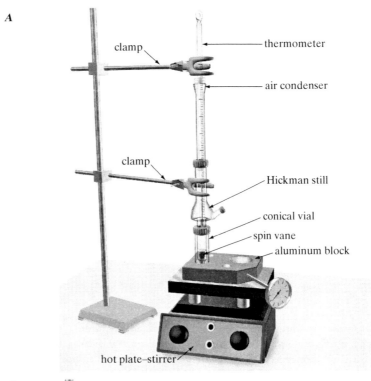

A

clamp — thermometer

air condenser

clamp

Hickman still

conical vial

spin vane

aluminum block

hot plate–stirrer

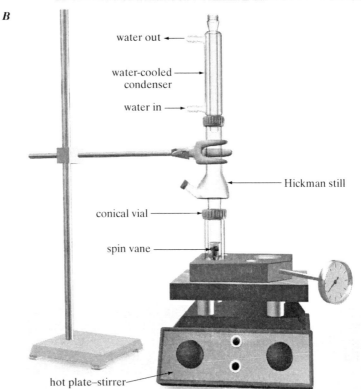

B

water out

water-cooled condenser

water in

Hickman still

conical vial

spin vane

hot plate–stirrer

Figure E11 A. Microscale distillation apparatus with air condenser and internal thermometer **B.** Microscale distillation apparatus with water-cooled condenser (internal thermometer not shown)

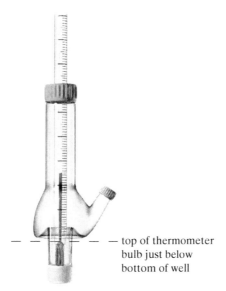

— top of thermometer
bulb just below
bottom of well

Figure E12 Thermometer placement in Hickman still

The heating rate should be adjusted to maintain gentle boiling in the pot and a suitable distilling rate. In most standard scale distillations, a distilling rate of 1–3 drops per second (about 3–10 mL of distillate per minute) is recommended. It's hard to count drops if you are using a Hickman still, but a distillation rate sufficient to fill its well in 5–15 minutes or more should be suitable. Distilling at higher rates will decrease the purity of the product and, in microscale work, may make it difficult to record the boiling temperature accurately. If you are distilling a liquid over a wide boiling range, it may be necessary to increase the heating rate gradually to maintain the same distilling rate.

The temperature at the heat source should be kept relatively constant throughout a simple distillation. If you are using an aluminum block or a sand bath as a heat source, you can monitor its temperature with an external thermometer. If the temperature of the heat source is well above the expected boiling point of the distilland, you may need to reduce the heating rate. An excessive temperature, in addition to reducing distillation efficiency, may cause mechanical carryover or decomposition of the distilland. A temperature decrease during distillation can cause the still-head temperature to fluctuate and distillation to slow down or stop altogether. Keep in mind that the temperature an external thermometer records will always be higher than the still-head temperature, so it is no substitute for an internal thermometer, which records the actual vapor temperature of the distillate.

Boiling Range.   An approximate boiling range for a distillation may be specified in the experimental procedure. Because the major impurity in that case is the more volatile isopentyl alcohol, the isopentyl acetate should distill below its normal boiling point of 142°C. (Using 143° as the end of the range allows for experimental error.) If the boiling range for a distillation is not given, you should collect the *main fraction* (the distilled liquid containing the desired component) over a relatively narrow boiling range, usually 4–6°C, that brackets the boiling point of the desired component. A liquid fraction that distills below the expected boiling range for the main fraction is called a *forerun*. It should be collected in a different container than the main fraction and disposed of as directed.

General Directions for Simple Distillation

 Standard Scale

Equipment and Supplies

heat source
supports for heat source and receiver
clamps, ring stands
round-bottom flask
boiling chips *or* stir bar and magnetic stirrer
connecting adapter (still head)
thermometer adapter
thermometer
condenser
condenser tubing
vacuum adapter
receiver(s)
joint clip(s) or rubber band

Assemble [OP-2] the apparatus pictured in Figure E7, using a clean, dry round-bottom flask of appropriate size and taking great care to position the thermometer correctly in the still head (Figure E8). If the liquid being distilled is quite volatile or hazardous, use a round-bottom flask as the receiver; otherwise you can use an open container (usually tared), such as an Erlenmeyer flask, graduated cylinder, or large vial. Remove the thermometer assembly and add the distilland to the boiling flask through a stemmed funnel, then drop in a few boiling chips or a stir bar. Replace the thermometer assembly and turn on the condenser water to provide a slow but steady stream of cooling water. Note that the condenser water should flow *in* the lower end of the condenser and *out* the upper end.

Start the stirrer (if you are using one) and turn on the heat source, adjusting the heating rate so that the liquid boils gently and the reflux ring of condensing vapors rises slowly into the still head. Shortly after the reflux ring reaches the thermometer bulb, the temperature reading should rise rapidly and vapors should begin passing through the sidearm into the condenser, coalescing into droplets that run into the receiving flask. As the first few droplets come over, the thermometer reading should rise to an equilibrium value and stabilize at that value. At this time, the entire thermometer bulb should be bathed in condensing liquid, which drips off the end of the bulb into the pot. Record the temperature at which the thermometer reading stabilizes; if it is lower than expected, recheck the thermometer placement. Distill the liquid at a rate of about 1–3 drops per second (or 1 drop per second or less using the compact apparatus shown in Figure E9), monitoring the temperature frequently throughout the distillation.

If the initial thermometer reading is below the expected boiling range, carry out the distillation until the lower end of the range is reached, collecting the forerun in the receiver, then replace the receiver by another one. Try to make the switch quickly enough so that no distillate is lost. (Stop the distillation before changing receivers if you are using the apparatus shown in Figure E9.) If the initial thermometer reading is within the expected boiling range, there is no need to change receivers. Continue distilling until the upper end of the expected boiling range is reached or until only a small volume of liquid remains in the boiling flask. Turn off and remove the heat source before the boiling flask is completely dry; heating a dry flask might cause tar formation or even an explosion. Disassemble and clean the apparatus as soon as possible after the distillation is completed.

Summary

1 Assemble distillation apparatus.
2 Add distilland and boiling chips or stir bar.
3 Turn on condenser water and stirrer (if used).
4 Start heating; adjust heat so that vapors rise slowly into still head.
5 Record temperature after distillation begins and thermometer reading stabilizes.
   IF initial temperature is below expected boiling range, GO TO 6.
   IF initial temperature is within expected boiling range, GO TO 7.
6 Collect forerun, change receivers at low end of boiling range.
7 Distill until temperature reaches high end of boiling range or until pot is nearly dry.
8 Turn off and remove heat source.
9 Disassemble and clean apparatus, dispose of forerun (if any) and residue in pot.

Microscale (Hickman-Still Method)

Equipment and Supplies

   heat source
   microclamps
   conical vial or round-bottom flask
   boiling chip *or* stirring device and magnetic stirrer
   Hickman still
   thermometer(s)
   thermometer adapter (optional)
   condenser (omit for high-boiling liquids)
   collecting container(s)

Transfer the distilland to a clean, dry conical vial or round-bottom flask of appropriate size (the pot) and add a boiling chip, stir bar, or spin vane. Use the smallest container for which the liquid volume will be roughly half or less of the container's capacity; for example, use a 3-mL conical vial if the liquid volume is 1.5 mL or less. Assemble [OP-2] one of the distillation setups pictured in Figure E11 and clamp it securely to a ring stand, with the pot

The Operations

positioned correctly in the heat source (a sand bath or heating block). Depending on the boiling point of the liquid to be distilled, you can use a water-cooled condenser, an air condenser, or no condenser (see the "Apparatus" section). Insert the thermometer through the condenser (if any) and into the Hickman still so that its bulb is positioned correctly in the neck of the still (see Figure E12) and clamp it in place. If desired, place a thermometer in the heat source to monitor its temperature as well. If you are using a water condenser, turn on the condenser water to provide a slow but steady stream of cooling water. Note that the condenser water should flow *in* the lower end of the condenser and *out* the upper end.

Start the stirrer (if you are using one) and adjust the heat control so that the liquid boils *gently* and condensing vapors rise *slowly* into the neck of the Hickman still. If vapors begin rising rapidly into the still shortly after boiling begins, raise the apparatus just above the heat source to reduce the heating rate; then carefully reposition the apparatus and readjust the heating rate for slow distillation (be careful not to bump the thermometer when you move the apparatus). Shortly after the vapors reach the thermometer bulb, the temperature reading should rise rapidly and liquid droplets should begin to appear on the sides of the still and drain into the well. During this time, the thermometer reading should rise to an equilibrium value and stabilize at that value, and the entire thermometer bulb should be bathed in the condensing liquid that drips off the end of the bulb into the pot. Record the temperature when the reading stabilizes and continue to monitor it during the distillation.

If the initial thermometer reading is below the expected boiling range, carry out the distillation until the lower end of the range is reached, then transfer any liquid in the well to a small beaker or another container (this forerun, if any, will be discarded later). The distillate should collect in the well slowly, taking 5–15 minutes (or even more) to fill the well completely, if there is enough liquid to fill it. If it distills more rapidly than this, especially if the temperature reading never stabilizes or stabilizes at the wrong temperature, return the to the pot and redistill it slowly. If the well becomes filled (or nearly so) with distillate, use a Pasteur pipet to transfer it to a collecting container, such as a tared screw-cap vial. (If you don't collect the distillate when the well is full, the excess will simply overflow and drip down into the pot.) Continue distilling and transferring the distillate as needed until the upper end of the expected boiling range is reached *or* until only a small volume of liquid remains in the pot. Turn off the heat source and raise the apparatus away from the heat source before the pot is completely dry. Let the apparatus cool down, then transfer any remaining distillate to the collecting container. You should be able to recover more distillate by tilting the Hickman still so that the liquid flows to one side of the well as you collect it. Gently tapping the sides of the still or cooling it with air or cold water may cause more distillate to collect in the well. You can also rinse the still with a volatile solvent in which the distillate is soluble, and then evaporate [OP-16] the solvent. Disassemble and clean the apparatus as soon as possible after the distillation is completed.

Summary

1 Add distilland and boiling chips or stirring device to pot.
2 Assemble distillation apparatus.
3 Turn on condenser water (if used) and stirrer.
4 Start heating; adjust heat so that vapors rise slowly into Hickman still.

5 Record temperature after distillation begins and thermometer reading stabilizes.
   IF initial temperature is below expected boiling range, GO TO 6.
   IF initial temperature is within expected boiling range, GO TO 7.
6 Remove forerun when temperature reaches low end of boiling range.
7 Distill until temperature reaches high end of boiling range or until pot is nearly dry, transferring distillate to collector when well is full.
8 Stop heating and let apparatus cool.
9 Transfer any remaining distillate to collector.
10 Disassemble and clean apparatus, dispose of forerun (if any) and residue in pot.

b. Distillation of Solids

Low-melting solids can be distilled using the apparatus pictured in Figure E9 or with a special apparatus designed for that purpose. Unless the solid has a boiling point below 150°, a cooling bath should not be necessary. Use a vacuum adapter with the drip tip (outlet tube) removed, if any are available; otherwise, have a heat gun or heat lamp handy to melt any solid that forms in the outlet tube. It is very important to keep this tube free from solid, because heating a closed system could build up pressure and cause the apparatus to shatter or fly apart. When distillation is complete, melt the solid by heating the receiving flask, then transfer it to a tared vial or other container. The last traces of solid can be transferred with a small amount of ethyl ether or another volatile solvent, which is then evaporated under a hood.

A "cool" burner flame can be used if no flammable liquids are in the vicinity.

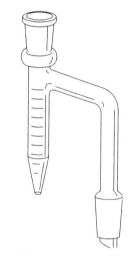

Figure E13 Dean–Stark trap

A homemade Dean–Stark trap can be constructed as described in J. Chem. Educ. **1963**, *40*, 349.

c. Water Separation

During some reactions that yield water as a by-product, it may be necessary to remove the water to prevent the decomposition of a water-sensitive product or to increase the yield. This is sometimes done by codistilling the water with an organic solvent such as toluene, which forms an azeotrope with water. The codistillation can be accomplished with an ordinary simple distillation apparatus, but for standard scale work, it is more convenient to use a *water separator*, such as the Dean–Stark trap shown in Figure E13.

A Dean–Stark trap is inserted in the reaction flask, filled to the level of the sidearm with the reaction solvent (which must be less dense than water and immiscible with it), and fitted with a reflux condenser. As water forms during the reaction, its vapors and those of the reaction solvent condense inside the reflux condenser and drip down into the water separator. The organic solvent overflows through the sidearm and returns to the reaction flask, while the water collects at the bottom of the separator. The theoretical yield of water from the reaction can be calculated, so the volume of water in the separator is monitored to determine when the reaction is nearing completion.

The parts from a standard scale organic lab kit can be assembled (as shown in Figure E14) so that the 25-mL flask, still head, and vacuum adapter together function like a Dean–Stark trap. When you assemble this apparatus, clamp both flasks securely and close the vacuum adapter outlet with a rubber bulb from a medicine dropper. Use a funnel to fill the water separator with the organic solvent to a level just below the bottom of the sidearm. Heat the reaction mixture under gentle reflux, being careful that the adapter

The Operations

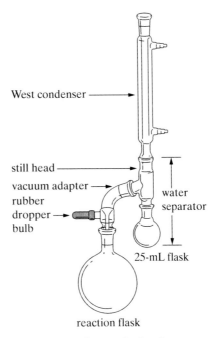

Figure E14 Apparatus for standard scale water separation

drip tip does not become flooded with liquid. When disassembling the apparatus after the reaction, leave the water separator clamped while the other components are removed; then cautiously tilt the water separator to pour liquid from its sidearm into a beaker.

For microscale work, a Hickman still can function as a water separator in an apparatus such as one pictured in Figure E11. Before you begin heating, either (1) fill the well with the solvent used or (2) add an amount of excess solvent equal to the well's capacity (1–2 mL) to the pot. During the reaction, the well fills with distillate and the organic solvent overflows into the pot while water remains in the bottom of the well.

The Operations

F. Measuring Physical Constants

OPERATION **30**   ## Melting Point

Principles and Applications

The melting point of a pure substance is defined as the temperature at which the solid and liquid phases of the substance are in equilibrium at a pressure of 1 atmosphere. At a temperature slightly lower than the melting point, a mixture of the two phases solidifies; at a temperature slightly above the melting point, the mixture liquefies. Melting points can be used to characterize organic compounds and to assess their purity. The melting point of a pure compound is a unique property of that compound, which is essentially independent of its source and method of purification. This is not to say that no two compounds will have the same melting point; many compounds have melting points that differ by no more than a fraction of a degree. If two pure samples have *different* melting points, however, they are almost certainly different compounds.

The melting point of an organic solid is usually measured by grinding the solid to a powder and packing the powder inside a *melting-point tube*, a capillary tube that is closed at one end. The melting-point tube is then placed in an appropriate heating device and the *melting-point range* of the sample—the range of temperatures over which the solid is converted to a liquid—is observed and recorded. A pure substance usually melts within a range of no more than 1–2°C; that is, the transition from a crystalline solid to a clear, mobile liquid occurs within a degree or two if the rate of heating is sufficiently slow and the sample is properly prepared.

The presence of impurities in a substance *lowers* its melting point and *broadens* its melting-point range. To better understand the effects of impurities on melting points, consider the phase diagram for phenol (P) and diphenylamine (D) in Figure F1.

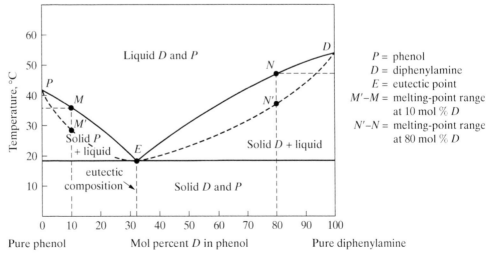

Figure F1 Phase diagram for the phenol–diphenylamine system

Pure phenol melts at 41°C and pure diphenylamine at 53°C. If a sample of phenol contains a small amount of diphenylamine as an impurity, its melting point will decrease in approximate proportion to the mole percent of diphenylamine present; likewise, the melting point of diphenylamine will decrease on addition of phenol. For example, the melting point of a mixture containing 10 mol % diphenylamine in phenol is given by point M; that of 20 mol% phenol in diphenylamine is given by point N.

Pure phenol and diphenylamine both have sharp melting points. Mixtures of the two (except the *eutectic mixture* at the minimum in the diagram) exhibit broader melting-point ranges that depend on their composition. The approximate melting-point range for a mixture is given by the distance between the broken line connecting points P and E or points E and D and the solid lines connecting the same points. For example, the melting-point range of a 10 mol% diphenylamine mixture is given in the figure by the distance between M' and M, and for an 80 mol% mixture by the distance between N' and N.

Since the melting point decreases in a nearly linear fashion as the amount of impurity increases (up to a point, at least), the difference between the observed and expected values may make it possible to estimate a compound's purity. The melting-point lowering effect can also be used to confirm the identity of a substance, such as the product of a reaction, when it is thought to be a certain known compound. The compound in question is mixed with a sample of the known compound, and the melting point of the mixture is measured. If the two compounds are identical, the mixture melting point will be essentially the same as that for the known compound measured separately. If they are not identical, the known compound will act as an impurity in the unknown, so the melting point of the mixture will be lower and its range broader than for the known compound.

Experimental Considerations

Melting Behavior. The melting-point range of a sample is reported as the range between (1) the temperature at which the sample first begins to liquefy and (2) the temperature at which it is completely liquid, called the *liquefaction point*. When a single melting point is to be reported, the liquefaction point is generally used, although a compound may also be charactized by its *meniscus point*, the temperature at which the liquid meniscus is barely clear of the solid below it. Some automatic melting-point devices report melting points that are closer to the meniscus point than to the liquefaction point.

If traces of solvent remain in a sample because of insufficient drying or other causes, you may observe "sweating" of solvent from the sample or bubbles in the molten sample, which may resolidify when all of the solvent is driven off. If a sample does show this behavior, it should be dried and the melting point remeasured. Even a dry sample will tend to soften and shrink before it begins to liquefy; this process begins at the *eutectic temperature* (point E in Figure F1.) In any case, softening, shrinking, and sweating should not be mistaken for melting behavior. The melting-point range does not begin until the first free liquid is clearly visible, at which time you should see movement of both solid and liquid in the melting-point tube.

Some compounds sublime—change directly from the solid to the vapor state—when they are heated in an open container. Sublimation can be detected during a melting-point determination by a pronounced shrinking of the sample, accompanied by the appearance of crystals higher up inside the melting-point tube (see Figure F2). The melting point of a sample that

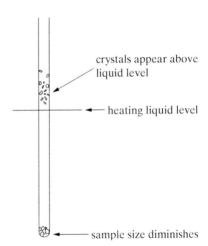

crystals appear above liquid level

heating liquid level

sample size diminishes

Figure F2 Sublimation of a sample in a melting-point tube

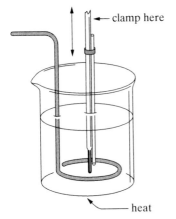

clamp here

heat

Stir with a gentle, up-and-down motion.

Figure F3 Stirred heating bath

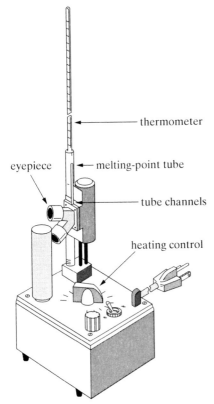

thermometer

eyepiece

melting-point tube

tube channels

heating control

Figure F4 Apparatus for measuring melting points (Mel-Temp method)

sublimes at or below its melting temperature can be measured using a sealed melting-point tube. An ordinary melting-point tube should be cut (see OP-3) short enough so that it does not project above the block of a melting-point apparatus, such as the one in Figure F4, or so that it can be entirely immersed in a heating-bath liquid. The sample is introduced and the open end is sealed in a burner flame (see OP-3). Then the melting point is measured by one of the methods described next.

If a sample becomes discolored and liquefies over an unusually broad range during a melting-point determination, it is probably undergoing thermal decomposition. Compounds that decompose on heating usually melt at temperatures that vary with the rate of heating. The approximate melting point (or *decomposition point*) of such a compound should be measured by heating the melting-point apparatus to within a few degrees of the expected melting temperature before inserting the sample, and then raising the temperature at a rate of about 3–6°C per minute.

Apparatus for Measuring Melting Points. Melting points can be determined with good accuracy using a special glass tube (Thiele tube or Thiele–Dennis tube) filled with a heating-bath liquid such as mineral oil (see OP-7a), as illustrated in Figure F5. The design of such tubes promotes good circulation of the heating liquid without stirring. A melting-point tube containing the solid is secured to a thermometer, which is then immersed in the bath liquid. The solid is observed carefully for evidence of melting as the apparatus is heated. Melting points can also be measured in an ordinary beaker if the bath liquid is stirred constantly (Figure F3), either manually or with a magnetic stirrer [OP-10].

Commercial melting-point instruments that use capillary melting-point tubes are available, such as the Mel-Temp illustrated in Figure 4. Such melting-point devices are quite accurate if operated properly, and they can be used to make several measurements at once. This feature is useful when a mixture melting point is being determined, since the melting points of the unknown compound, the known, and the mixture can be measured and compared at the same time. The heating rate is adjusted by a dial controlling the voltage input to a heating coil. The dial reading required to attain the desired heating rate at the melting point of the sample can be estimated from a heating-rate chart furnished with the instrument. The dial is initially set higher than this to bring the temperature within 20°C or so of the expected melting point, and then reduced to the estimated value.

Either kind of apparatus can be used for both standard scale and microscale experiments, but commercial melting-point instruments are preferred because they are easier to use and allow more precise temperature control.

Melting-Point Corrections. The observed melting point of a compound may be inaccurate because of defects in the thermometer used or because of the "emergent stem error" that results when a thermometer is not immersed in a heating bath to its intended depth. Many thermometers are designed to be immersed to the depth indicated by an engraved line on the stem, usually 76 mm from the bottom of the bulb; slight deviations from this depth will not result in serious error. Other thermometers are designed for total immersion; if they are used under other circumstances, the temperature readings will be in error. Such an error can be compensated for by placing the bulb of a second thermometer opposite the middle of the exposed part of the thermometer's mercury column when the sample is melting, recording the temperature readings of both thermometers, and calculating an *emergent stem correction* with the following equation:

$$\text{emergent stem correction} = 0.00017 \cdot N(t_1 - t_2)$$

where

N = length in degrees of exposed mercury column
t_1 = observed melting temperature
t_2 = temperature at middle of exposed column

The emergent stem correction is added to the observed melting temperature, t_1. Melting points that have been corrected in this way should be reported as, for example, "m.p. 123–124° (corr.)."

Errors arising from either thermometer defects or an emergent stem can be corrected by *calibrating* the thermometer under the conditions in which it is to be used. A thermometer used for melting-point determinations, for example, is calibrated by measuring the melting points of a series of known compounds, subtracting the observed melting point from the true melting point of each compound, and plotting this correction as a function of temperature. The correction at the melting point of any other compound is then read from the graph and added to its observed value. A list of pure compounds that can be used for melting-point calibrations is given in Table F1. Sets of pure calibration substances are available from chemical supply houses.

Table F1 Substances used for melting-point calibrations

Substance	m.p., °C
ice	0
diphenylamine	54
m-dinitrobenzene	90
benzoic acid	122.5
salicylic acid	159
3,5-dinitrobenzoic acid	205

Mixture Melting Points. A mixture melting point is obtained by grinding together approximately equal quantities of two solids (a few milligrams of each) until they are thoroughly intermixed, then measuring the melting point of the mixture by the usual method. Usually one of the compounds (X) is an "unknown" that is believed to be identical to a known compound, Y. A sample of pure Y is mixed with X and the melting points of this mixture and of pure Y (and sometimes of X as well) are measured. If the melting points of pure Y and of the mixture are the same, to within a degree or so, then X is probably identical to Y. If the mixture melts at a lower temperature and over a broader range than pure Y, then X and Y are different compounds.

General Directions for Melting-Point Measurement

Mineral oil begins to smoke and discolor below 200°C and can burst into flames at higher temperatures. Oil fires can be extinguished with solid-chemical fire extinguishers or powdered sodium bicarbonate.

Safety Notes

 Standard Scale and Microscale

Equipment and Supplies (Starred items are for method B only)

Mel-Temp (method A only)
watch glass
flat-bottomed stirring rod or flat-bladed spatula

The Operations

1-m length of glass tubing
thermometer
capillary melting-point tube
*Thiele or Thiele–Dennis tube
*clamp, ring stand
*heating oil
*burner
*cut-away cork
*3-mm slice of rubber tubing

A melting-point tube can be constructed by sealing one end of a 10-cm length of 1-mm (i.d.) capillary tubing.

Put a few milligrams of the dry solid on a small watch glass and grind it to a fine powder with a flat-bottomed stirring rod or a flat-bladed spatula. Use a spatula to make a small pile of powder near the middle of the watch glass. Press the open end of a capillary melting-point tube into the pile until enough has entered the tube to form a column 1–2 mm high. Using too much sample can result in a melting-point range that is too broad and a melting-point value that is too high. Tap the closed end of the tube gently on the bench top (or rub its sides with a small file); then drop it (open end up) through a 1-meter length of small-diameter glass tubing onto a hard surface, such as the bench top. Repeat the process several times to pack the sample firmly into the bottom of the tube. Use one of the methods that follow to measure the melting-point range of the sample. If you don't know the sample's expected melting point, determine its approximate value with rapid heating (6°C per minute or more); then carry out a more accurate melting-point measurement with a second sample as described here.

A. Mel-Temp Method.   Place the melting-point tube (sealed side down) in one of the channels on the Mel-Temp's heating block. Use the heating-rate chart to estimate the dial setting that will cause the temperature to rise at a rate of 1–2°C per minute at the expected melting point of the sample. If the thermometer reading is well below the expected melting point, adjust the dial setting to raise the temperature quite rapidly until it is about 20°C below the expected value, and then reduce the dial setting so that the temperature is rising no more than 2°C/minute (preferably 1°C/minute) by the time it is within a few degrees of the expected melting point. Continue heating at that rate as you observe the sample through the magnifying lens in the observation port, and record (as the limits of the melting-point range) the temperatures (1) when the first free liquid appears in the melting-point tube and (2) when the sample is completely liquid. For best results, do at least two measurements on each compound. Let the block cool to 15–20°C below the melting point before you do another measurement. Cooling can be accelerated by passing an air stream over the block.

B. Thiele-Tube Method.   (You can use a similar method with other melting-point baths, such as the one shown in Figure F3, but stirring and a hot plate or other flameless heat source will be required in that case.) Clamp the Thiele or Thiele–Dennis tube securely to a ring stand and add enough mineral oil (or other appropriate bath liquid) to just cover the top of the sidearm outlet, as shown in Figure F5A. Secure the melting-point tube to a broad-range thermometer as follows:

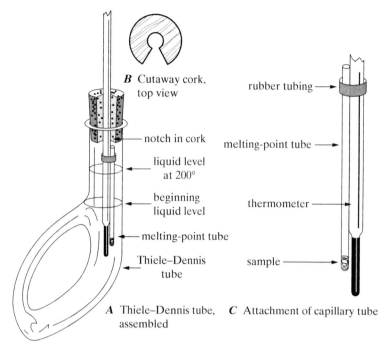

B Cutaway cork, top view

rubber tubing

notch in cork

melting-point tube

liquid level at 200°

thermometer

beginning liquid level

melting-point tube

Thiele–Dennis tube

sample

A Thiele–Dennis tube, assembled

C Attachment of capillary tube

Figure F5 Apparatus for measuring melting points (Thiele-tube method)

1 Cut a 3-mm-thick rubber band from $\frac{1}{4}$-inch i.d. thin-walled rubber tubing (rubber bands may be provided).
2 Place the rubber band around the thermometer about 9 cm from its bulb end.
3 Pinch the rubber band between your fingers to create a gap and insert the open end of the melting-point tube into the gap.
4 Move the melting-point tube until the sample is adjacent to the middle of the thermometer bulb (see Figure F5C).

Snap the thermometer into the center of a cutaway cork (Figure F5B) at a point above the rubber band, with the capillary tube and the degree markings on the same side as the opening in the cork. Insert this assembly into the bath liquid and move the thermometer, if necessary, so that its bulb is centered in the tube about 3 cm below the sidearm junction and the temperature can be read through the opening in the cork (Figure F5A). The rubber band should be 2–3 cm above the liquid level so that the bath liquid, as it expands on heating, will not contact it. If the hot oil covers the rubber band, it may soften and allow the capillary tube to drop out.

   If the expected melting point of the compound is known, heat the bottom of the Thiele tube with a burner flame (or a microburner, for more precise control) until the temperature is about 15°C below the expected value. Turn down the flame and apply it at the sidearm to reduce the heating rate so that the temperature is rising no more than 2°C/minute (preferably 1°C/minute) by the time it is within a few degrees of the expected melting point. Continue heating at that rate as you observe the sample closely, and record (as the limits of the melting-point range) the temperatures (1) when

The cork is bored out to accommodate the thermometer, and then cut with a single-edged razor blade or a sharp knife so that the thermometer can be snapped into place from the side rather than inserted from the top.

The Operations

the first free liquid appears in the melting-point tube and (2) when the sample is completely liquid. For best results, do at least two measurements on each compound. Let the heating bath cool to 15–20°C below the melting point before you do another measurement. Cooling can be accelerated by passing an air stream over the tube. Clean up the apparatus and either place the oil in a container for recycling or, if the oil is not too dark, store it in the Thiele tube. Mineral oil can be removed from glassware by rinsing the glassware with petroleum ether, followed by acetone, and then washing it with a detergent and water.

Summary

1 Assemble apparatus for melting-point determination.
2 Grind solid to powder, fill melting-point tube(s) to depth of 1–2 mm.
IF you are using method **B**, GO TO 4.
3 Insert sample in Mel-Temp heating block. GO TO 5.
4 Secure melting-point tube to thermometer; insert assembly in heating bath.
5 Heat rapidly to ~15–20°C below m.p.; then reduce heating rate to 1–2°C/min.
6 Observe and record melting-point range.
7 Disassemble apparatus, clean up.

OPERATION **31**

Boiling Point

The boiling point of a liquid is defined as the temperature at which the vapor pressure of the liquid is equal to the external pressure at the surface of the liquid, and also as the temperature at which the liquid is in equilibrium with its vapor phase at that pressure. These definitions are the basis for various standard scale and small-scale methods for measuring boiling points. For example, the boiling point of a liquid can be determined by distilling a small quantity of the liquid and observing the temperature at the still head, where the liquid and its vapors are assumed to be in equilibrium. It can also be determined by measuring the temperature at which the liquid's vapor, trapped inside a capillary tube immersed in the liquid, exerts a pressure equal to the external pressure. Like the melting point of a solid, the boiling point of a liquid can be used to help identify it and assess its purity.

Boiling-Point Corrections.   The *normal boiling point* of a liquid is its boiling point at an external pressure of 1 atmosphere (760 torr, 101.3 kPa). Since the atmospheric pressure at the time of a boiling-point determination is seldom exactly 760 torr, observed boiling points may differ somewhat from values reported in the literature and should be corrected. If a laboratory boiling-point determination is carried out at a location reasonably close to sea level, atmospheric pressure will rarely vary by more than 30 torr from 760. For deviations of this magnitude, a *boiling-point correction*, Δt, can be estimated using Equation **1**.

$$\Delta t \approx y(760 - P)(273.1 + t) \tag{1}$$

Δt = temperature correction, to be added to observed boiling point
P = barometric pressure, in torr
t = observed boiling point (°C)

The value 1.0×10^{-4} is used for the constant y if the liquid is water, an alcohol, a carboxylic acid, or another associated liquid; otherwise, y is assigned the value 1.2×10^{-4}. For example, the boiling point of water at 730 torr is 98.9°C. Use of Equation **1** leads to a correction factor of $\left[(1.0 \times 10^{-4})(760 - 730) (273.1 + 98.9)\right]$ °C = 1.1°C, which yields the correct normal boiling point of 100.0°C.

At high altitudes, the atmospheric pressure may be considerably lower than 1 atmosphere, resulting in observed boiling points substantially lower than the normal values. For example, water boils at 93°C on the campus of the University of Wyoming at Laramie (elevation 7520 feet). For major deviations from atmospheric pressure, Equation **2** can be used in conjunction with approximate entropy of vaporization values obtained from the section "Correction of Boiling Points to Standard Pressure" in older editions of the *CRC Handbook of Chemistry and Physics*.

*Equation **2** is a simplified form of the Hass–Newton equation found in the CRC Handbook, 64th edition, p. D-189.*

$$\Delta t \approx \frac{(273 + t)}{\phi} \log \frac{760}{P} \tag{2}$$

ϕ = (entropy of vaporization at normal boiling point)$/2.303R$

For example, hexane boils at 49.6°C at 400 torr; the value of ϕ for alkanes is found (from the *CRC Handbook*) to be about 4.65 at that temperature. Substituting into Equation **2**, we obtain a correction factor of

$$\Delta t \approx \frac{(273°C + 49.6°C)}{4.65} \log \frac{760 \text{ torr}}{400 \text{ torr}} = 19.3°C$$

which gives a normal boiling point of 68.9°C. This compares very favorably with the reported value of 68.7°C. (A second approximation, using the value of ϕ at the corrected boiling point, gives 68.8°C.) As in melting-point determinations, it may be necessary to correct the boiling point for thermometer error, especially when working with high-boiling liquids. See OP-30 for details.

a. Distillation Boiling Point

During a carefully performed distillation of a pure liquid, the vapors surrounding the thermometer bulb are in equilibrium (or nearly so) with the liquid condensing on the bulb. Thus, the still-head temperature recorded during the distillation of a pure liquid should equal its boiling point. If the liquid is contaminated by impurities, the distillation boiling point may be either too high or too low, depending on the nature of the impurity. Volatile impurities in a liquid lower its boiling point, whereas nonvolatile impurities raise it; in either case, the distillation boiling-point range will be broadened. Therefore, if there is any doubt about the purity of a liquid, it should be distilled or otherwise purified prior to a boiling-point determination.

General Directions for Distillation Boiling-Point Measurement

 Standard Scale and Microscale

For standard scale work, assemble the compact distillation apparatus pictured in Figure E9 [OP-27] using a 25-mL round-bottom flask and placing the thermometer as shown in Figure E8. For microscale work, assemble an apparatus

The Operations

pictured in Figure E11 [OP-27] using a conical vial or 10-mL round-bottom flask and placing the thermometer as shown in Figure E12. For high-boiling liquids, be sure that the still head or Hickman still is well insulated from the heat source to prevent superheating of the vapors. Add 5–10 mL (SS) or 2–5 mL (μS) of the pure liquid to the flask or conical vial and drop in a boiling chip or two, or use a stirring device. Distill the liquid slowly, recording the temperature readings when approximately 5%, 50%, and 95% of the liquid has distilled. The first and last readings represent the boiling-point range, and the middle reading is the *median boiling point.* The median value should provide the best estimate of the actual boiling point. A boiling-point range greater than 2°C suggests that the liquid may need to be purified before further work is done. Record the barometric pressure so that you can make a pressure correction, if necessary.

b. Capillary Tube Boiling Point

When a liquid is heated to its boiling point, the pressure exerted by its vapor becomes just equal to the external pressure at the liquid's surface. If a tube that is closed at one end is filled with a liquid and immersed (open end down) in a reservoir containing the same liquid, the tube will begin to fill with vapor as the liquid is heated to its boiling point. At the boiling point, the vapor pressure inside the tube will balance the pressure exerted on the liquid surface by the surrounding atmosphere, so that the liquid levels inside and outside the tube will be equal. If the temperature is raised above the boiling point, vapor will escape in the form of bubbles; if the temperature is lowered below the boiling point, the tube will begin to fill with liquid.

This behavior is the basis of semimicroscale and microscale methods for measuring boiling points. The semimicroscale method, which requires 2–4 drops of liquid, is suitable for standard scale and some microscale work. It requires an inverted capillary tube or "bell" that can be made by cutting [OP-3] an ordinary melting-point tube in half. The open end of the bell is placed in a small amount of liquid in a boiling tube (prepared as described in Minilab 1) for the boiling-point measurement. The microscale method, which requires only about 5 μL of liquid, is similar in practice except that a melting-point tube is used as the boiling tube and the bell is constructed from a micropipet. Two or three bells can be made by cutting a 10-μL micropipet (such as a Drummond Microcap) in half or in thirds and sealing one open end of each tube (see OP-3).

Avoid overheating during the boiling-point measurement or the liquid will boil away; it may be necessary to add more liquid if the sample is very volatile. If the bell moves up the capillary tube when the liquid boils, try using a longer, heavier bell. For best results, you should repeat the boiling-point measurement. If repeated determinations on the same sample give appreciably different (usually higher) values for the boiling point, the sample is probably impure and should be distilled.

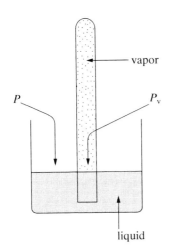

Figure F6 Boiling-point principle. At the boiling point, $P_v = P$, where P_v = pressure exerted by vapor on liquid surface, and P = pressure exerted by atmosphere on liquid surface.

General Directions for Boiling-Point Measurement

 Semimicroscale

Equipment and Supplies

> boiling tube
> bell (made from m.p. tube)
> thermometer
> rubber band
> Thiele tube
> mineral oil
> burner

Add 2–4 drops of the liquid to a boiling tube constructed of a 10-cm length of 4–5 mm o.d. glass tubing sealed at one end (see OP-3). Insert a bell cut from a capillary melting-point tube into the boiling tube with its open end down, and secure the assembly to a thermometer by means of a rubber band cut from thin-walled rubber tubing, as illustrated in Figure F7. Insert this assembly into a Thiele tube as for a melting-point determination (see Figure F5), with the rubber band 2 cm or more above the liquid level. Heat the Thiele tube until a *rapid, continuous* stream of bubbles emerges from the bell at a temperature near the expected boiling point of the liquid, if it is known. (The expansion of heated air in the bell will cause a slow evolution of bubbles; if you stop heating before rapid bubbling occurs, your reported boiling point will be too low.) Immediately remove the heat source and let the bath cool slowly until the bubbling stops; then record the temperature when liquid *just* begins to enter the bell. Let the temperature drop a few degrees so that the liquid partly fills the bell. Then heat very slowly until the first bubble of vapor emerges from the mouth of the bell. Record the temperature at this point also. The two temperatures represent the boiling-point range; they should be within a degree or two of each other. Record the barometric pressure so that a pressure correction can be made. Clean and dry the boiling tube, saving it for future boiling-point measurements. (See Summary.)

 Microscale

Equipment and Supplies

> boiling tube (capillary melting-point tube)
> bell (made from 10-μL micropipet)
> syringe
> Mel-Temp (or other capillary melting-point apparatus)

Construct a pair of bells by cutting a 10-μL micropipet in half using a sharp triangular file or glass-scoring tool, trying to cut it as squarely as possible. Using a burner flame, carefully seal [OP-3] the cut end of each half. Use a

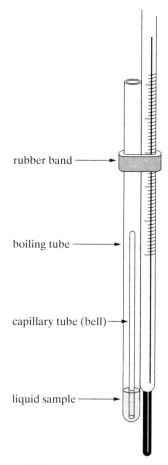

rubber band ⟶

boiling tube ⟶

capillary tube (bell) ⟶

liquid sample ⟶

Figure F7 Semimicroscale boiling-point assembly

Sometimes the capillary tube will stick to the bottom of the boiling tube. This can be prevented by cutting a small nick in the open end of the capillary tube with a triangular file.

The Operations

syringe with a thin needle to introduce enough liquid into the boiling tube (a melting-point capillary) to fill it to a depth of approximately 5 mm. Holding the open end of the boiling tube securely, carefully "shake down" the liquid, as you would shake down the mercury column in a clinical thermometer, until it is all at the bottom of the tube and there are no air bubbles. (Alternatively, you can secure the boiling tube in a centrifuge tube with glass-wool packing and centrifuge it.) Insert a bell, open end down, into the boiling tube, pushing it all the way to the bottom as shown in Figure F8 (use a thin copper wire if necessary). Insert the boiling tube into a Mel-Temp or other capillary melting-point apparatus, or use a Thiele tube as for a semimicroscale boiling-point determination. Heat until a *rapid, continuous* stream of bubbles emerges from the bell at a temperature near the expected boiling point of the liquid, if it is known. (The expansion of heated air in the bell will cause a slow evolution of bubbles; if you stop heating before rapid bubbling occurs, your reported boiling point will be too low.) Immediately remove the heat source, let the apparatus cool slowly until the bubbling stops, and record the temperature when liquid *just* begins to enter the bell. Then heat very slowly until the first bubble of vapor emerges from the mouth of the bell. Record the temperature at that point also. The two temperatures represent the boiling-point range; they should be within a degree or two of each other. Record the barometric pressure so that a pressure correction can be made.

Summary

1 Construct boiling-point bell.
2 Add liquid to boiling tube, insert inverted bell.
3 Place assembly in Thiele tube or Mel-Temp.

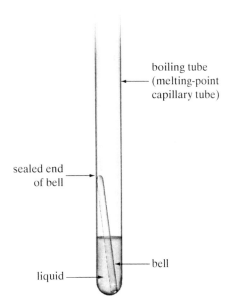

boiling tube (melting-point capillary tube)

sealed end of bell

liquid

bell

Figure F8 Microscale boiling-point assembly

4 Heat until continuous stream of bubbles emerges from bell, stop heating.
5 Record temperature when liquid just enters bell.
6 Heat slowly until first vapor bubble emerges from bell; record temperature.
7 Let cool below boiling point.
  IF another measurement is needed, add more liquid if necessary, GO TO 4.
  IF not, CONTINUE.
8 Record barometric pressure, correct observed boiling point.
9 Disassemble apparatus, clean up.

Refractive Index   OPERATION **32**

The *refractive index* (index of refraction) of a substance is defined as the ratio of the speed of light in a vacuum to its speed in the substance in question. When a beam of light passes into a liquid, its velocity is reduced, causing it to bend downward. The refractive index is related to the angles that the incident and refracted beams make with a line perpendicular to the liquid surface, as shown in Equation **1**,

$$n^t_\lambda = \frac{c_{vac}}{c_{liq}} = \frac{\sin \theta_{vac}}{\sin \theta_{liq}} \qquad \textbf{(1)}$$

where

  n^t_λ = refractive index at temperature t using light of wavelength λ

  c = velocity of light

The refractive index is a unique physical property that can be measured with great accuracy (up to eight decimal places), and it is thus very useful for characterizing pure organic compounds. Refractive-index measurements are also used to assess the purity of known liquids and to determine the composition of solutions.

Experimental Considerations

It is much easier to make measurements in air than in a vacuum, so most refractive-index measurements are made in air, which has a refractive index of 1.0003, and the small difference is corrected by the instrument. Refractive-index values depend on both the wavelength of the light used for their measurement and the density of the liquid, which varies with its temperature. Most values are reported with reference to light from the yellow D line of the sodium emission spectrum, which has a wavelength of 589.3 nm. Thus, a refractive-index value may be reported as n_D^{20} = 1.3330, for example, where the superscript is the temperature in °C and "D" refers to the sodium D line. Since most refractive index readings are made at or corrected to this wavelength, the "D" is sometimes omitted. If another light source is used, its wavelength is specified in nanometers.

  The Abbe refractometer (Figure F10) is a widely used instrument for measuring refractive indexes of liquids. It measures the *critical angle* (the

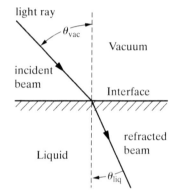

Figure F9 Refraction of light in a liquid

The Operations

smallest angle at which a light beam is completely reflected from a surface) at the boundary between the liquid and a glass prism and converts it to a refractive-index value. The instrument employs a set of compensating prisms so that white light can be used to give refractive-index values corresponding to the sodium D line. A properly calibrated Abbe-3L refractometer should be accurate to within ±0.0002. The calibration of the instrument can be checked by measuring the refractive index of distilled water, which should be 1.3330 at 20°C and 1.3325 at 25°C.

The sample block of an Abbe refractometer can be kept at a constant temperature of 20.0°C by water pumped through it from a thermostatted water bath. If a refractive index is measured at a temperature other than 20.0°C, the temperature should be read from the thermometer on the instrument and the refractive index corrected by using the following equation:

$$\Delta n = 0.00045 \times (t - 20.0)$$

where t is the temperature of the measurement in °C. The correction factor (including its sign) is added to the observed refractive index. For example, if the refractive index of an unknown liquid is found to be 1.3874 at 25.1°C, its refractive index at 20.0°C should be about $1.3874 + [0.00045 \times (25.1 - 20.0)] = 1.3897$. Alternatively, the refractive index of a reference liquid similar in structure and properties to the unknown liquid can be measured at the same temperature (t) as the unknown, and a correction factor calculated from the equation

$$\Delta n = n^{20} - n^t$$

where n^t is the measured refractive index of the reference liquid at temperature t and n^{20} is the reported value of its refractive index at 20°C. The correction factor is then added to the measured refractive index of the unknown at temperature t. This method can correct for experimental errors (improper calibration of the instrument, etc.) as well as temperature differences.

Small amounts of impurities can cause substantial errors in the refractive index. For example, the presence of just 1% (by mass) of acetone in chloroform reduces the refractive index of the latter by 0.0015. Such errors can be critical when refractive-index values are being used for qualitative analysis, so it is essential that an unknown liquid be pure when its refractive index is measured.

General Directions for Refractive-Index Measurements

 ### Standard Scale and Microscale

These directions apply to the B&L Abbe-3L refractometer; if you are using a different instrument, your instructor will demonstrate its operation.

Equipment and Supplies

Abbe-3L refractometer
dropper
washing liquid
soft tissues

Raise the *hinged prism* of the Abbe refractometer and, using an eyedropper, place 2–3 drops of the sample in the middle of the *fixed prism* below it.

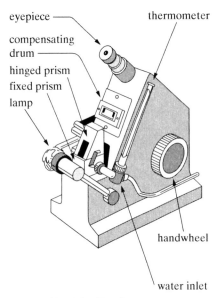

eyepiece
compensating drum
hinged prism
fixed prism
lamp
thermometer
handwheel
water inlet

Figure F10 Abbe-3L refractometer

Never allow the tip of a dropper or another hard object to touch the prisms—they are easily damaged. If the liquid is volatile and free flowing, it may be introduced into the channel alongside the closed prisms. With the prism assembly closed, switch on the *lamp* and move it toward the prisms to illuminate the visual field as viewed through the eyepiece. Rotate the *handwheel* until two distinct fields (light and dark) are visible in the eyepiece, and reposition the lamp for the best contrast and definition at the borderline between the fields. Rotate the *compensating drum* on the front of the instrument until the borderline is sharp and achromatic (black and white) where it intersects an inscribed vertical line. If the borderline cannot be made sharp and achromatic, the sample may have evaporated. Rotate the handwheel (or the fine adjustment knob, if there is one) to center the borderline exactly on the crosshairs (Figure F11).

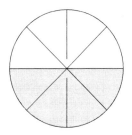

Figure F11 Visual field for properly adjusted refractometer

Depress and hold down the *display switch* on the left side of the instrument to display an optical scale in the eyepiece. Read the refractive index from this scale (estimate the fourth decimal place), and record the temperature if it is different from 20.0°C. Open the prism assembly and remove the sample by gently *blotting* it with a soft tissue (do not rub!). Wash the prisms by moistening a tissue or cotton ball with a suitable solvent (acetone, methanol, etc.) and blotting them gently. When the residual solvent has evaporated, close the prism assembly and turn off the instrument.

Summary

1 Insert sample between prisms.
2 Switch on and position lamp.
3 Rotate handwheel until two fields are visible; reposition lamp for best contrast.
4 Rotate compensating drum until borderline is sharp and achromatic.
5 Rotate handwheel or fine-adjustment knob until line is centered on crosshairs.

The Operations

6 Depress display switch to display optical scale, estimate refractive index to four decimal places, record temperature.
7 Clean and dry prisms, close prism assembly.
8 Make temperature correction if necessary.

Optical Rotation

Principles and Applications

Light can be considered a wave phenomenon with vibrations occurring in an infinite number of planes perpendicular to the direction of propagation. When a beam of ordinary light passes through a *polarizer*, such as a Nicol prism, only the light-wave components that are parallel to the plane of the polarizer can pass through. The resulting beam of *plane-polarized light* has light waves whose vibrations are restricted to a single plane (see Figure F12). When a beam of plane-polarized light passes through an optically active substance, molecules of the substance interact with the light so as to rotate its plane of polarization. The angle by which a sample of an optically active substance rotates the plane of that beam is called its *observed rotation, α*. The observed rotation of a sample depends on the length of the light path through the sample and the concentration of the sample, as well as its identity. The first two are not intrinsic properties of the sample itself, so the observed rotation is divided by these factors to yield its *specific rotation, [α]*, as shown in this equation.

$$[\alpha] = \frac{\alpha}{lc} \tag{1}$$

$[\alpha]$ = specific rotation
α = observed rotation
l = length of sample, in decimeters (dm)
c = concentration of solution, in grams of solute per milliliter solution (for a neat liquid, substitute the density in g/mL)

The specific rotation of a pure substance is an intrinsic property of the substance and can be used to characterize it.

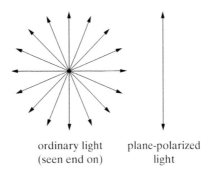

ordinary light
(seen end on)

plane-polarized
light

Figure F12 Schematic representations of ordinary and plane-polarized light

The composition of a mixture of two optically active substances can be calculated from its specific rotation, using the equation

$$[\alpha] = [\alpha]_A X_A + [\alpha]_B (1 - X_A) \qquad (2)$$

In this equation, $[\alpha]$ is the specific rotation of the mixture, $[\alpha]_A$ the specific rotation of component A, X_A the mole fraction of component A, and $[\alpha]_B$ the specific rotation of component B. For example, an equilibrium mixture of α-D-glucose ($[\alpha] = 112°$) and β-D-glucose ($[\alpha] = 18.7°$) has a specific rotation of 52.7°. The mole fraction of α-D-glucose in the mixture can be calculated by substituting these values into Equation **2** and solving for X_A.

$$52.7° = (112°)X_A + (18.7°)(1 - X_A)$$
$$X_A = 0.364$$

Since both forms of glucose have the same molecular weight, the equilibrium mixture contains 36.4% α-D-glucose and 63.6% β-D-glucose by mass.

Experimental Considerations

The specific rotation of an optically active sample can be determined using an instrument called a *polarimeter*. A polarimeter consists of a polarizer, a *sample cell* to hold the sample, and an *analyzer*—a second polarizing prism that can be rotated at an angle to the polarizer. When the axis of the analyzer is perpendicular to that of the polarized light, it blocks out the light completely; this condition is called the *extinction point*. In a precision polarimeter, the analyzer contains two or more prisms set at a small angle to each other, and it is rotated until the prisms bracket the extinction point, transmitting dim light of equal intensity. This feature is necessary because it is easier for the human eye to match two intensities than to estimate a point of minimum intensity. The angle by which the analyzer must be rotated to reach this point equals the angle at which the sample rotated the beam of plane-polarized light, its observed rotation, α. Using Equation **1**, we can covert the observed rotation of the sample to its specific rotation given the sample's concentration and the length of the sample cell (usually 1 or 2 dm).

The optical rotation of a substance is usually measured in solution. Water and ethanol are common solvents for polar compounds, and dichloromethane can be used for less polar ones. Often a suitable solvent will be listed in the literature, along with the light source and temperature used for the measurement. The volume of solution required depends on the size of the polarimeter cell, but 10–25 mL is usually sufficient. A solution for polarimetry

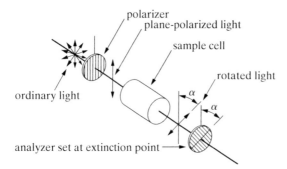

Figure F13 Schematic diagram of a polarimeter

The Operations

ordinarily contains about 1–10 g of solute per 100 mL of solution and should be prepared using an accurate balance and a volumetric flask. If the solution contains particles of dust or other solid impurities, it should be filtered [OP-12]. When possible, the concentration should be comparable to that reported in the literature. For example, the *CRC Handbook of Chemistry and Physics* reports the specific rotation of (+)-menthol as "+49.2 (al, *c* = 5)," where the concentration (*c*) is given in grams per 100 mL of an alcoholic (al) solution (*c* is defined differently here than in Equation **1**). Thus, a menthol solution for polarimetry can be prepared by accurately weighing about 1.25 g of (+)-menthol, dissolving it in ethyl alcohol in a 25-mL volumetric flask, and adding more alcohol up to the calibration mark.

General Directions for Polarimetry

 Standard Scale and Microscale

This procedure applies to a Zeiss-type polarimeter with a split-field image. Experimental details may vary somewhat for different instruments. For standard scale work, you can prepare about 25 mL of solution and use a 2-dm sample cell. For microscale work, prepare about 10 mL of solution and use a 1-dm or smaller sample cell.

Remove the screw cap and glass end plate from one end of a clean sample cell (do not get fingerprints on the end plate) and rinse the cell with a small amount of the solution to be analyzed (for microscale work, rinse it with the solvent used to prepare the solution and let it dry). Stand the polarimeter cell vertically on the bench top and fill it with the solution, rocking the cell if necessary to shake loose any air bubbles. Add the last milliliter or so with a dropper so that the liquid surface is convex. Carefully slide on the glass end plate so that there are no air bubbles trapped beneath it. If the cell has a bulge at one end, a small bubble can be tolerated; in that case, the cell should be tilted so that the bubble migrates to the bulge and stays out of the light path. Screw on the cap just tightly enough to provide a leakproof seal—overtightening it may strain the glass and cause erroneous readings.

If the light source is a sodium lamp, make sure it has ample time to warm up (some require 30 minutes or more). Place the sample cell in the polarimeter trough, close the cover, see that the light source is oriented to provide maximum illumination in the eyepiece, and focus the eyepiece if necessary. Set the analyzer scale to zero and (if necessary) rotate it a few degrees in either direction until a dark and a light field are clearly visible. You may see a vertical bar down the middle and a background field on both sides, as shown in Figure F14, or two fields divided down the middle.

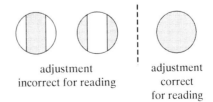

adjustment
incorrect for reading

adjustment
correct
for reading

Figure F14 Split-field image of polarimeter

Focus the eyepiece so that the line(s) separating the fields are as sharp as possible. Starting from zero, rotate the analyzer scale about 10° (more if necessary) in either direction until you reach a point at which both fields are of nearly equal intensity. Then back off a degree or so toward zero, and use the fine-adjustment knob (if there is one) to rotate the scale *away* from zero until the entire visual field is as uniform as possible and the dividing lines between fields have all but disappeared. (If the field is very bright and a slight turn of the knob has little effect on it, you are probably 90° off. Rotate the scale 90° back toward zero.) If you overshoot the final reading, move the scale back a few degrees so that you again approach it going away from zero. Read the rotation angle from the analyzer scale, using the Vernier scale (if there is one) to read fractions of a degree, and record the direction of rotation, + for clockwise or − for counterclockwise. Obtain another reading of the rotation angle, this time approaching the final reading going *toward* zero. For accurate work, you should take a half-dozen readings or more, reversing direction each time to compensate for mechanical play in the instrument, and average them.

Rinse the cell with the solvent used in preparing the solution. Fill the cell with that solvent (or use a solvent blank provided) and determine the solvent's rotation angle by the same procedure as before. Remove the solvent and let the cell drain dry, or clean it as directed by your instructor. Subtract the average rotation angle of the solvent blank (note + and − signs) from that of the sample to obtain the observed rotation of the sample, and calculate its specific rotation using Equation **1**. In reporting the specific rotation, specify the temperature, light source, solvent, and concentration.

Summary

1 Prepare solution of compound to be analyzed.
2 Rinse sample cell and fill with solution, place in polarimeter.
3 Adjust light source, focus eyepiece.
4 Rotate analyzer scale until optical field is uniform, read rotation angle.
5 Repeat Step 4 several times, reversing direction each time, and average readings.
    IF solvent blank has been run, GO TO 7.
    IF not, GO TO 6.
6 Place solvent blank in polarimeter, GO TO 4.
7 Clean cell, drain dry, dispose of solution and solvent as directed.
8 Calculate observed rotation and specific rotation of sample.

The Operations

G. Instrumental Analysis

OPERATION 34 ## Gas Chromatography

Gas chromatography (GC) is a powerful method for the separation of volatile components of mixtures. Like all chromatographic methods, its operation is based on the distribution of the sample components between a mobile phase and a stationary phase. *Gas–liquid chromatography* is the most common form of gas chromatography; *gas–solid chromatography* has limited application and will not be discussed here. The mobile phase for gas–liquid chromatography is an unreactive *carrier gas* such as helium, and the stationary phase consists of a high-boiling liquid on a solid support, contained within a heated column. The components of the sample must have a reasonably high vapor pressure so that their molecules will spend enough time in the vapor phase to travel through the column with the carrier gas. Thus gas chromatography can be used only for mixtures of (1) gases, (2) liquids that are volatile enough to vaporize without decomposing when heated, and (3) some volatile solids, which must first be dissolved in a suitable solvent. Mixtures of solids and less volatile liquids can be separated by high-performance liquid chromatography [OP-35].

Preparative gas chromatography is used to separate the components of a mixture and recover the pure components, or to purify a major component of a mixture. Because even a large GC column will not accommodate sample sizes greater than about 0.5 mL, preparative GC cannot be used to separate large volumes of liquids. In the undergraduate organic chemistry lab, it is most useful for purifying the products of reactions conducted at the microscale level. *Analytical gas chromatography* is used for the qualititative and quantitative analysis of mixtures; that is, to identify the components of a mixture and find out how much of each component is present. An analytical gas chromatograph requires only a tiny amount of sample, usually a microliter or so.

Principles and Applications

In gas–liquid chromatography, the components of a mixture are distributed between a liquid stationary phase and a gaseous mobile phase, the carrier gas. The time it takes for a component to pass through the column, called its *retention time*, depends on its relative concentrations in the stationary and mobile phases. While the molecules of a component are in the gas phase, they pass through the column at the speed of the carrier gas. While they are in the liquid phase, they remain stationary. The more time a component spends in the vapor phase, the sooner it will get through the column, and the lower its retention time will be. The more time a component spends in the liquid phase, the longer its retention time will be. The time a component spends in the gas phase depends on its volatility (and thus on its boiling point) and on the temperature of the column. The time it spends in the liquid phase depends on the strength of the attractive forces between its molecules and the molecules of the liquid phase.

In order for any two components of a mixture to be separated sharply, they must have significantly different retention times, and their bands (the regions of the column they occupy) must be narrow enough so that they do not overlap appreciably. The degree of separation depends on a number of factors, including the length and efficiency of the column, the carrier-gas flow rate, and the temperature at which the separation is carried out. Modern gas chromatographs provide the means to vary these factors precisely, and they offer an almost endless variety of applications, from analyzing automobile emissions for noxious gases to detecting PCBs in lake trout.

There are several important differences between gas–liquid chromatography and liquid–solid chromatographic methods such as column chromatography [OP-18] and thin-layer chromatography [OP-19]. Unlike the mobile phase in a liquid–solid separation, the mobile phase in gas chromatography does not interact with the molecules of the sample; its only purpose is to carry them through the column. Thus, the separation of the components of a mixture depend on (1) how strongly they are attracted to the stationary phase and (2) how volatile they are. If the components have similar polarities, they will be attracted to the stationary phase to about the same extent, so they will tend to be separated in order of relative volatility, with the lower-boiling components having the shorter retention times. If the components have different polarities, their retention times will depend on their relative polarities and the polarity of the stationary phase. A polar stationary phase will attract polar components more strongly than nonpolar ones, giving polar components longer retention times than nonpolar components. A nonpolar stationary phase will attract nonpolar components more strongly, giving them the longer retention times.

A column chromatography or TLC separation is usually conducted at room temperature, and the temperature stays about the same throughout the separation. By contrast, a GC separation is usually carried out at an elevated temperature, and the temperature can be changed throughout the separation according to a preset program. Increasing the temperature of the column increases the fraction of each component in the gas phase, thus decreasing its retention time. The column temperature also affects the separation efficiency, since, at excessively high temperatures, components will tend to spend most of their time in the vapor phase, causing their bands to overlap.

Instrumentation

In addition to the column and carrier gas, a gas chromatograph must have some means of vaporizing the sample, controlling the temperature of the separation, detecting each constituent of the sample as it leaves the column, and recording data from which the composition of the sample can be determined. A typical gas chromatograph includes the components diagrammed in Figure 1 and described here.

Injection Port. The injection port is the starting point for a sample's passage through the column. The sample, in a microliter syringe, is injected into the column by inserting the needle through a rubber or silicone septum and depressing the plunger. The sample size for a packed column is typically about 1–2 μL, but may vary from a few tenths of a microliter to 20 μL. With an open tubular column (described later), a sample splitter

The Operations

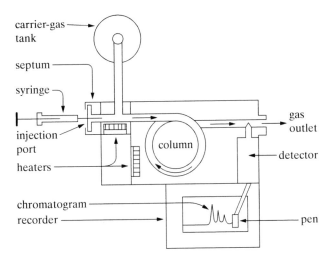

Figure G1 Schematic diagram of a gas chromatograph

delivers about 1 nL (10^{-3} μL) of the injected sample to the column; the rest is discarded. The injector port is heated to a temperature sufficient to vaporize the sample, usually about 50°C above the boiling point of its least volatile component.

Packed Columns. A packed column is a long tube packed with an inert solid support that is coated with the high-boiling liquid phase. The tube is usually made of stainless steel or glass. A typical column may be 1.5–3.0 meters long with an inner diameter of 2–4 mm ($\frac{1}{8}$–$\frac{1}{4}$ inch o.d.), and is usually bent into a coil to fit inside a column oven, where its temperature is controlled. Although such columns can be packed by the user, most columns are purchased ready-made. The column is packed with a finely ground support medium such as Chromosorb W, whose particles are previously coated with the liquid phase. The composition of the packing is described on a tag attached to each column. For example, a column packing described as "10% DEGS/Chromosorb W 80/100" contains 10% by mass of a diethylene glycol succinate liquid phase on a Chromosorb W support having a particle-size range from 80 to 100 mesh (0.17 to 0.15 mm). As for a distillation column [OP-29], the efficiency of a chromatography column can be measured in terms of the number of theoretical plates it provides. Most packed columns have efficiencies ranging from 500 to 1000 theoretical plates per meter.

Open Tubular Columns. An *open tubular column* or *capillary column* consists of an open tube coated on the inside with the liquid phase. A very thin film of the liquid phase (ranging from 0.05 μm to 1.0 μm or more) is adsorbed on or chemically bonded to the inner wall of the column, which is a long capillary tube made of glass or fused silica. Fused silica open tubular (FSOT) columns are flexible enough to be bent into coils 15 cm or so in diameter. The columns range in size from "microbore" columns that may have an i.d. of 0.05–0.10 mm and a length of 20 meters to "megabore" columns having an i.d. of about 0.50 mm and a length of 100 meters or more. Packed columns are generally cheaper, less fragile, and easier to use than open tubular columns, and they accommodate much larger sample sizes. But

The mesh number is the number of meshes per inch in the finest sieve that will let the particles pass through.

open tubular columns are faster and less likely to react with the sample, and they provide unparalled resolution of sample components—a microbore column may have an efficiency of more than 10,000 theoretical plates per meter. Since a capillary column may be 20–50 times longer than a typical packed column, the capillary column is usually hundreds of times more efficient than a packed column containing the same liquid phase.

Column Oven.   The column is mounted inside a heated chamber, the *column oven*, that controls its temperature. Under *isothermal operation*, the oven temperature is kept constant throughout a separation; under *program operation*, it is varied according to a programmed sequence. As a general rule, the column temperature for isothermal operation should be approximately equal to or slightly above the average boiling point of the sample. If the sample has a broad boiling range, it may be separated by program operation. The more volatile components are ordinarily eluted during the low-temperature end of the program, and less volatile components are eluted at its high-temperature end.

Carrier Gas.   A chemically unreactive gas is used to sweep the sample through the column. Helium is the most widely used carrier gas, although nitrogen and argon are also used with some detectors. Carrier gases usually come in pressurized gas cylinders, and various devices are used to measure and control their flow rates.

Detector.   The detector is a device that detects the presence of each component as it leaves the column and sends an electronic signal to a recorder or other output device. A separate oven is used to heat the detector enclosure so that the sample molecules remain in the vapor phase as they pass the detector. The most widely used detectors for routine gas chromatography are *thermal conductivity (TC)* detectors and *flame ionization (FI)* detectors. A TC detector responds to changes in the thermal conductivity of the carrier-gas stream as molecules of the sample pass through. With an FI detector, the component molecules are pyrolyzed in a hydrogen–oxygen flame, producing short-lived ions that are captured and used to generate an electrical current. Thermal conductivity detectors are comparatively simple and inexpensive, and they respond to a wide variety of organic and inorganic species. Flame ionization detectors are much more sensitive than thermal conductivity detectors, so they are used with open tubular columns (for which TC detectors are unsuited) as well as packed columns. An FI detector is somewhat inconvenient to use because it requires hydrogen and air to produce the flame, and it cannot be used for preparative gas chromatography because it destroys the sample.

Data Display.   A typical gas chromatograph intended for student use may have a mechanical *recorder* that records a peak on moving chart paper as each component band passes the detector. The resulting *gas chromatogram* consists of a series of peaks of different sizes, each produced by a different component of the mixture. The recorder may be provided with an *integrator* that measures the area under each component peak. Modern research-grade gas chromatographs are interfaced with computers and other hardware devices that display the peaks on a monitor screen, print or plot copies of the gas chromatogram, and provide digital readouts of peak areas, retention times, and various instrumental parameters.

The Operations

Liquid Phases

The factor that most often determines the success or failure of a gas chromatographic separation is the choice of the liquid phase. In general, polar liquid phases are best for separating polar compounds, and nonpolar liquid phases are best for separating nonpolar compounds. However, there are hundreds of liquid phases available, and choosing the right one for a particular separation may not be an easy task. Some typical liquid phases and their maximum operating temperatures are listed in Table G1 in order of polarity (lower to higher). General-purpose liquid phases such as dimethylpolysiloxane (dimethylsilicone) can separate a variety of compounds successfully, usually in approximate order of their boiling points. Other liquid phases have more specialized applications; for example, diethylene glycol succinate is a high-boiling ester used mainly to separate the esters of long-chain fatty acids.

Heating a column above its maximum operating temperature will cause the liquid phase to vaporize.

Table G1 Selected liquid phases for gas chromatography

Stationary phase	Maximum T, °C	X'	Y'	Z'
squalane	150	0	0	0
dimethylpolysiloxane (OV-1)	350	16	55	44
diphenyl/dimethylpolysiloxane (OV-17)	350	119	158	162
polyethylene glycol (Carbowax 20M)	250	322	536	368
diethylene glycol succinate (DEGS)	225	496	746	590
dicyanoallylpolysiloxane (OV-275)	275	629	872	763

Note: McReynold's numbers (X', Y', Z') apply to the commercial stationary phase in parentheses. Commercial designations for the same kind of stationary phase vary widely; for example, AT-1, DB-1, Rtx-1, SE-30, and DC-200 are all similar to OV-1.

The selection of a liquid phase can be facilitated by the use of *McReynolds numbers*, which indicate the affinity of a liquid phase for different types of compounds; the higher the number, the greater is the affinity. X' is a McReynolds number measuring the relative affinity of a liquid phase for aromatic compounds and alkenes; Y' measures its affinity for alcohols, phenols, and carboxylic acids; and Z' measures its affinity for aldehydes, ketones, ethers, esters, and related compounds. For example, the polar liquid phase DEGS has a much higher Z' value (590) than dimethylpolysiloxane (44), so it will retain an ester much longer. McReynolds numbers are particularly useful for selecting a liquid phase to separate compounds of different chemical classes, such as alcohols from esters. Thus, a Carbowax 20M column should separate isoamyl acetate from isoamyl alcohol satisfactorily because its Y' and Z' values are very different; but an OV-17 column would not be a good choice for such a separation. Chromatography supply companies often provide detailed information about the kinds of separations their columns can accomplish.

Qualitative Analysis

The retention time of a component is the time it spends on the column, from the time of injection to the time its concentration at the detector reaches a maximum. The retention time corresponds to the distance on the chromatogram, along a line parallel to the baseline, from the injection point to the top of the component's peak, as shown in Figure G2. This distance can be

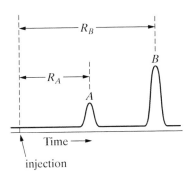

Figure G2 Retention times of two components, A and B

converted to units of time if the chart speed is known. If all instrumental parameters (temperature, column, flow rate, etc.) are kept constant, the retention time of a component will be characteristic of that compound and may be used to identify it. You can seldom (if ever) identify a compound with certainty from its retention time alone, but you can sometimes use retention times to confirm the identity of a compound whose identity you suspect. For example, if a known compound and an unknown have identical retention times on two or more different stationary phases under the same operating conditions, the compounds are probably identical.

When you carry out a reaction and obtain a gas chromatogram of the product mixture, you may be able to guess which GC peak corresponds to which product, especially if the products have significantly different boiling points and the stationary phase is known to separate compounds in order of boiling point. It is always a good idea to back up your guess with proof, however. One way to identify the components of a product mixture is to "spike" the mixture with an authentic sample of a possible component and see which GC peak increases in relative area after spiking. For example, suppose that you carry out the Fischer esterification of acetic acid by ethanol and record a gas chromatogram of the product mixture.

$$\underset{\text{acetic acid}}{CH_3COOH} + \underset{\text{ethanol}}{CH_3CH_2OH} \rightleftharpoons \underset{\text{ethyl acetate}}{CH_3COOCH_2CH_3} + H_2O$$

Since this is an equilibrium reaction, the product mixture would be expected to contain some unreacted starting materials as well as the product. To detect the presence of unreacted ethanol, you can add a small amount of pure ethanol to the sample and record a second gas chromatogram. The peak that increases in relative area is the ethanol peak, as shown in Figure G3. The process can be repeated using different pure compounds to identify the other components, if necessary.

Another way to identify the components of a mixture using GC is to obtain spectra of the components after they pass through the column. As described in OP-39, a mass spectrometer coupled to a gas chromatograph can act as a "superdetector," identifying the components as they come off the column. When the GC column in use has a large enough capacity that individual components can be collected at the column outlet, they can often be identified from their IR or NMR spectra.

Quantitative Analysis

The use of gas chromatography for quantitative analysis is based on the fact that, over a wide range of concentrations, a detector's response to a given component is proportional to the amount of that component in the sample. Thus, the area under a component's peak can be used to determine its mass percentage in the sample. If a peak on a gas chromatogram is symmetrical, its area can be calculated with fair accuracy by multiplying its height (h) in millimeters (measured from the baseline) by its width at a point exactly halfway between the top of the peak and the baseline ($w_{1/2}$), as shown in Figure G4.

$$\text{approximate peak area} = h \times w_{1/2}$$

Many gas chromatographs are equipped with an integrator that automatically calculates the peak areas and displays them digitally. Peak areas can also be

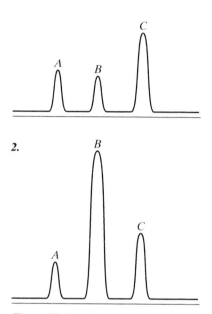

1.

2.

Figure G3 Use of gas chromatography for qualitative analysis: (1) chromatogram before adding ethanol; (2) chromatogram after adding ethanol

The Operations

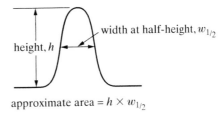

height, h

width at half-height, $w_{1/2}$

approximate area $= h \times w_{1/2}$

Figure G4 Measurement of approximate peak area

measured by making a photocopy of the chromatogram, accurately cutting out each peak with a sharp knife or razor blade (using a ruler to cut a straight line along the baseline), and weighing the peaks to the nearest milligram (or tenth of a milligram) on an accurate balance.

From the peak areas for a sample, you can sometimes estimate the percentage of each component in the mixture by dividing its area by the sum of the areas and multiplying by 100%. For example, suppose a gas chromatogram has three peaks (corresponding to three components A, B, and C) and the area of peak A is 1227 mm^2, the area of peak B is 214 mm^2, and the area of peak C is 635 mm^2. The sum of the areas is 2076 mm^2, so the mass percentages of the components are approximately

$$\%A = \frac{1227}{2076} \times 100\% = 59.1\%$$

$$\%B = \frac{214}{2076} \times 100\% = 10.3\%$$

$$\%C = \frac{635}{2076} \times 100\% = \underline{30.6\%}$$

$$100.0\%$$

This kind of calculation is accurate only if the detector responds in the same way to each component. This may be true (or nearly so) if you are analyzing a mixture of very similar compounds, such as a series of long-chain fatty acid esters. In many cases, however, the same mass of two different components will not necessarily result in the same detector response. Flame ionization detectors respond mainly to ions produced by certain reduced carbon atoms, such as those in methyl and methylene groups. Because an ethanol molecule contains about three-fifths as much carbon by weight as a heptane molecule does, the response of an FI detector to a gram of ethanol is only about three-fifths as great as its response to a gram of heptane. Thermal conductivity detectors also respond differently to different substances, but the variations are usually not as large as with FI detectors.

For accurate quantitative analysis of most mixtures, you should multiply each peak area by a *detector response factor* to obtain a corrected area that is proportional to its mass. Detector response factors can be obtained from the literature in some cases, or by direct measurement. For example, detector response factors for cyclohexane and toluene using a TC detector are reported to be 0.942 and 1.02, respectively (relative to benzene). Suppose that the chromatogram of a distillation fraction is recorded using such a detector and has relative peak areas of 78.0 mm^2 for cyclohexane and 14.6 mm^2 for toluene. The corrected peak areas are then $(0.942 \times 78.0 \text{ mm}^2) = 73.5 \text{ mm}^2$ for cyclohexane and $(1.02 \times 14.6 \text{ mm}^2) = 14.9 \text{ mm}^2$ for toluene. Dividing each corrected area by the sum of the corrected areas and multiplying by 100 gives mass percentages of 83.1% for cyclohexane and 16.9% for toluene.

If detector response factors for the components of a mixture are not known, you can determine them by the following method, which is described for two components, A and R. Component R is a reference compound, arbitrarily assigned a detector response factor of 1.00.

- Obtain a gas chromatogram of a mixture containing carefully weighed amounts of A and R
- Measure the peak area for each component
- Calculate the detector response factor for A using the following relationship:

$$\text{detector response factor for A} = \frac{\text{mass}_A}{\text{area}_A} \times \frac{\text{area}_R}{\text{mass}_R}$$

This method can be used to calculate detector response factors for any number of components simultaneously if their peaks are well resolved. Each component (including the reference compound) is carefully weighed, a gas chromatogram of the mixture is recorded, all of the peak areas are measured, and the detector response factors are calculated from the resulting masses and areas using the previous equation.

Preparative Gas Chromatography

Most preparative gas chromatographs are too expensive to be used routinely in undergraduate laboratories, but some inexpensive analytical gas chromatographs, such as the Gow-Mac 69-350, can be operated with preparative columns using a metal adapter that is connected to the exit port on the gas chromatograph. A special GC collection tube, provided in some microscale lab kits, is inserted into the adapter just before the desired compound's peak begins to appear on the chromatogram and removed just after the end of the component's peak has been recorded. The condensed liquid is then transferred to a small ($\sim 100 \ \mu\text{L}$) conical vial by centrifugation and can be used to obtain an IR or NMR spectrum of the compound. Cotton packing is used to support the conical vial and to center the top of the collection tube in the centrifuge tube. Additional components can be collected in other collection tubes.

If an adapter and specialized collection glassware are not available, a 3-inch, 2-mm o.d. glass tube can be packed with glass wool and inserted into the GC exit port while the desired component's peak is being recorded. The component should condense on the surface of the glass wool, from which it can be washed off with a small amount of solvent (if the component is quite volatile, the tube can be chilled first). An infrared or NMR spectrum of the compound can then be obtained in a solution of the solvent used, or the solvent can be evaporated.

General Directions for Recording a Gas Chromatogram

 ## Standard Scale and Microscale

Do not attempt to operate the instrument without prior instruction and proper supervision. The directions that follow are for a typical student-grade gas chromatograph connected to a mechanical recorder. For other kinds of instruments, follow your instructor's directions. Consult the instructor if the instrument does not seem to be working properly or if you have questions about its operation. It will be assumed that all instrumental parameters have been preset, that an appropriate column has been installed, and that the column oven will be operated isothermally. If not, the instructor will show you what to do. Before you begin, be sure you have read the section in OP-5 about the use of syringes.

If the sample is a volatile solid, dissolve it in the minimum volume of a suitable low-boiling solvent; otherwise, use the neat liquid. Rinse a microsyringe with the sample a few times, and then partially fill it with the sample. A microsyringe is a very delicate instrument, so handle it carefully and avoid using excessive force that might bend the needle or plunger. If there are air bubbles inside the syringe, tap the barrel with the needle pointing up, or eject the sample and refill the syringe more slowly. Hold the syringe with the needle pointing up and expel excess liquid until the desired volume of sample (usually 1–2 μL) is left inside. Wipe the needle dry with a tissue, and pull the plunger back a centimeter or so to prevent prevaporization of the sample.

Set the chart speed, if necessary, and switch on the recorder-chart drive (and the integrator, if there is one). Carefully insert the syringe needle into the injection port by holding the needle with its tip at the center of the septum and pushing the barrel slowly, but firmly, with the other hand until the needle is as far inside the port as it will go. Inject the sample by *gently* pushing the plunger all the way in just as the recorder pen crosses a chart line (the starting line); use as little force as possible to avoid bending the plunger. Withdraw the needle and mark the starting line, from which all retention times will be measured. Let the recorder run until all of the anticipated component peaks have appeared. Then turn off the chart drive and tear off the chart paper using a straightedge. Inspect the chromatogram carefully; if it is unsuitable because the significant peaks are too small, poorly resolved, or off-scale, repeat the analysis after taking measures to remedy the problem. If there is evidence of prevaporization (as indicated by an extraneous small peak preceding each major peak at a fixed interval), be sure that the plunger is pulled back before you inject the sample for the next run. Injecting the sample immediately after you insert the needle in the injector port will also prevent prevaporization, but this technique requires good timing.

Take Care! The injection port is hot! Don't touch it.

Before you analyze a different sample, clean the syringe and rinse it thoroughly with that sample. When you are finished, rinse the syringe with an appropriate low-boiling solvent such as methanol or dichloromethane, remove the plunger, and set it on a clean surface to dry.

Summary

1 Rinse syringe, fill with designated volume of sample.
2 Start chart drive and integrator (if applicable).
3 Insert syringe needle into injector port, inject sample when pen crosses a chart line.
4 Withdraw needle; mark starting line.
5 Stop chart drive after last peak is recorded.
6 Remove chromatogram, clean and dry syringe.

High-Performance Liquid Chromatography

Principles and Applications

High-performance liquid chromatography (HPLC) can be regarded as a hybrid of column chromatography and gas chromatography, sharing some features of both methods. As in column chromatography, the mobile phase is a liquid that carries the sample through a column packed with fine particles that interact with the components of the sample to different extents, causing them to separate. As in gas chromatography, the sample is usually injected onto the column and detected as it leaves the column, and its passage through the column is recorded as a series of peaks on a chromatogram. The stationary phase may be a solid adsorbent, as in column chromatography, but it is more often an organic phase that is bonded to tiny beads of silica gel. The silica beads are, in effect, coated with a very thin layer of a liquid organic phase. Each component of the sample is partitioned between a liquid mobile phase and the liquid stationary phase according to a ratio—the *partition coefficient*—that depends on its solubility in each liquid. The components of a mixture generally have different partition coefficients in the liquid phases, so they pass down the column at different rates.

Instrumentation

HPLC was developed as a means of improving the efficiency of a column chromatographic separation by reducing the particle size. Most column chromatography packings contain particles with diameters in the $75–175$-μm range, while most modern HPLC packings have particle sizes in the $3–10$-μm range, increasing separation efficiency dramatically. But solvents will not easily flow through such small particles by gravity alone. Thus, a powerful pump is needed to force eluents through the column at pressures up to 6000 psi (~ 400 atm).

The basic components of an HPLC system are diagrammed in Figure G5. The instrument ordinarily has several large solvent reservoirs, each of which can be filled with a different solvent. *Isocratic elution* is elution using a single solvent. *Gradient elution* utilizes two or more solvents of different polarity and varies the solvent ratio throughout a separation according to a programmed sequence. Gradient elution can reduce the time needed for a separation and increase the separation efficiency.

Preparative HPLC systems, which require special wide-bore columns, are equipped with fraction collectors to collect the eluent as it comes off the column; the fractions are evaporated to yield the pure components. Analytical HPLC systems, which are used to determine the compositions of mixtures, require much smaller samples and the components are not recovered. A typical analytical HPLC column is constructed of stainless steel, with a length of 10–25 cm and an i.d. of 2.1–4.6 mm. A microbore analytical column may have an i.d. of 1 mm, while a large preparative column may have an i.d. of up to 50 mm or so. Samples are introduced onto the column by means of a syringe or sampling valve and are carried through it by the pressurized eluent mixture. Because the particles of the stationary phase are so small, a column can easily be plugged by particulate matter or adherent solutes

The Operations

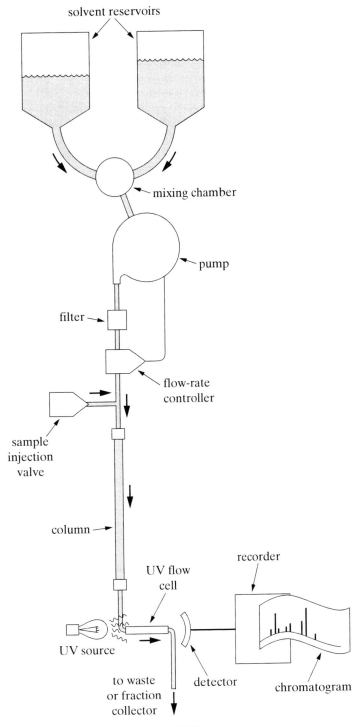

Figure G5 Schematic diagram of HPLC system

introduced by either the eluent or the sample. To remove anything that might harm the column, the eluent is forced through one or more filters and the sample may be introduced through a short *guard column*.

As each component of a sample leaves the column, the detector responds to some property of the component, such as its ability to absorb ultraviolet radiation. The detector then sends an electronic signal to a recorder, which traces the component's peak on a chart. The resulting chromatogram is a graph of some property of the components, such as UV absorbance, plotted against the volume of the mobile phase. Because different solutes may have greatly different UV absorptivities at the wavelength used by an *ultraviolet absorbance detector*, for example, a detector response factor (see OP-34) must be determined for each component before its percentage in the mixture can be calculated. Components that do not absorb ultraviolet radiation will not be detected by a UV detector; in that case, a different type of detector can be used, or the components can be converted to derivatives that are UV active. Any component whose refractive index is different from that of the eluent can be detected by a *refractive index (RI) detector*, but RI detectors have a lower sensitivity than UV detectors.

High-performance liquid chromatography can be used to separate mixtures containing proteins, nucleic acids, steroids, antibiotics, pesticides, inorganic compounds, and many other substances whose volatilities are too low for gas chromatography. Because HPLC separations can be run at room temperature, there is little danger of decomposition reactions or other chemical changes that sometimes occur in the heated column of a gas chromatograph. These advantages have made HPLC the fastest growing separation technique in chemistry, but its use in undergraduate laboratories is limited because of the high cost of the instruments, columns, and high-purity solvents required (HPLC-grade water costs about $50 a gallon!).

Stationary Phases

Some HPLC columns contain a solid adsorbent such as silica gel or alumina. Such a stationary phase is much more polar than the eluent, so nonpolar components are eluted faster than polar ones. Most modern HPLC columns contain a *bonded liquid phase*—an organic phase that is chemically bonded to particles of silica gel. Silica gel contains silanol ($-Si-OH$) groups to which long hydrocarbon chains, such as octadecyl groups, can be attached by reactions such as the following:

$$-Si-OH \xrightarrow{R_2SiCl_2} -Si-O-\underset{\underset{R}{|}}{\overset{\overset{R}{|}}{Si}}-Cl \xrightarrow{H_2O} \xrightarrow{(CH_3)_3SiCl}$$

$$-Si-O-\underset{\underset{R}{|}}{\overset{\overset{R}{|}}{Si}}-O-Si(CH_3)_3 \qquad R = CH_3(CH_2)_{17}- \text{ (octadecyl)}$$

The Operations

The bonded stationary phase in this example is *less* polar than the eluent, which may be a mixture of water with another solvent such as methanol, acetonitrile, or tetrahydrofuran. Thus, polar components will spend more time in the eluent than in the stationary phase and will be eluted faster than nonpolar ones, reversing the usual order of elution. This mode of separation is called *reverse-phase chromatography*.

Other stationary phases operate by still different mechanisms. The stationary phase for *size-exclusion chromatography* is a porous solid that separates molecules based on their effective size and shape in solution. Small molecules can enter even the narrowest openings in the porous structure, larger molecules find fewer openings they can get into, and still larger molecules may be completely excluded from the solid phase. Thus large, bulky molecules pass down the column faster than smaller molecules. A stationary phase for *ion-exchange chromatography* has ionizable functional groups that carry a negative or positive charge over a suitable pH range, attracting ionic solutes from solution. In organic chemistry, such stationary phases are used mainly to separate ionizable organic compounds such as carboxylic acids, amines, and amino acids. Chiral stationary phases that can separate enantiomers and determine their optical purity are also available.

Hundreds of different stationary phases are used for HPLC separations. Some of the most popular reverse-phase packings contain silica gel bonded to methyl ($-CH_3$), phenyl ($-C_6H_5$), octyl [$-(CH_2)_7CH_3$], octadecyl [$-(CH_2)_{17}CH_3$], cyanopropyl [$-(CH_2)_3CN$], and aminopropyl [$-(CH_2)_3NH_2$] groups. Size-exclusion stationary phases contain silica, glass, and polymeric gels of varying porosity. Ion-exchange stationary phases include (a) styrene-divinylbenzene copolymers to which ionizable functional groups (such as $-SO_3H$ and $-NR_4^+OH^-$) are attached, (b) beads with a thin surface layer of ion-exchange material, and (c) bonded phases on silica particles.

General Directions for HPLC

 ## Standard Scale and Microscale

Do not attempt to operate the instrument without prior instruction and proper supervision. Because HPLC systems vary widely in construction and operation, only a very general outline of the procedure is provided here. It will be assumed that all instrumental parameters have been preset, that an appropriate reverse-phase column has been installed, and that the elution will be isocratic. If not, the instructor will provide additional directions.

Prepare an approximately 0.1% stock solution of the sample in the same solvent or solvent mixture as the one being used for the elution, and dilute an aliquot of this solution further, if necessary. Be certain that you are using HPLC-grade solvents for preparing the solution and eluting it through the column. The solvents should be purged with helium prior to elution to remove dissolved gases. Filter the solution through a 1.0-μm membrane filter to remove any particulate matter. Degas it, if necessary, as directed by your instructor. Inject the sample (10 μm unless otherwise directed) through the injection port, or use a sampling valve to introduce it into the system. Using a guard column to protect the analytical column from particles is advisable. Once the sample is injected, a microprocessor will control all aspects of the

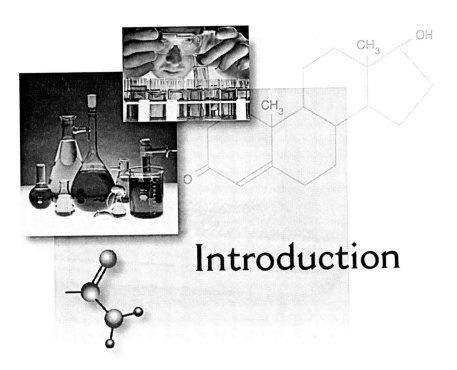

Introduction

Welcome to Organic Chemistry Laboratory, Chemistry 225. This course is designed to teach basic organic chemistry laboratory techniques and to illustrate some of the topics covered in organic chemistry lecture courses through experiments. This text was compiled by combining portions of an existing text with materials developed here at Loyola University Chicago. In some experiments, you will be developing new skills and techniques for working with organic compounds. In particular, we must learn to isolate, purify and characterize organic molecules. Armed with these abilities, we will move on to performing chemical reactions intended to transform organic compounds into completely new molecules—this is sometimes called synthesis and is a major activity of organic chemists. Good luck, be safe and, once again, welcome to the world of organic chemistry!

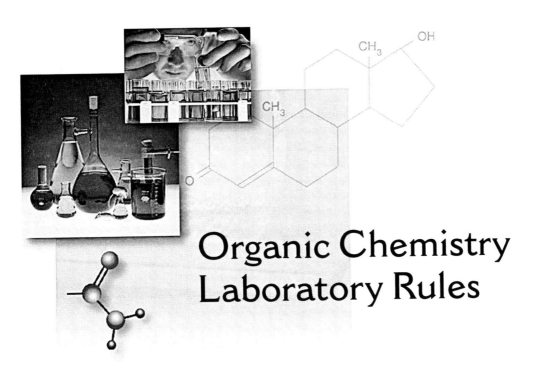

Organic Chemistry Laboratory Rules

An organic chemistry laboratory is a potentially dangerous place. However, accidents usually result from simple carelessness and inattention to detail. Being aware of and taking precautions against potential hazards is the best way to PREVENT ACCIDENTS BEFORE THEY HAPPEN. In particular, following the safety rules outlined below can help to ensure your safety and the safety of those around you. Since these safety rules are to ensure everyone's protection, anyone who violates them will not be allowed to remain in the laboratory.

1. **Wear eye protection at all times.** In any chemistry lab, it is your eyes that are the most vulnerable to permanent damage. Do not remove your eye protection even for a brief moment. Historically, it has been exactly at the moment when a student has removed his/her eye protection to 'get a better look' at something when a chemical splash or explosion has happened right in the student's unprotected face. Some of the chemicals used in lab can cause serious burns to your skin—just think of the damage they can do to your eyes!

   If anything should get into your eyes, go directly to the eye wash station. Wash your eyes with large amounts of water—a brief rinse is not enough. While at the eyewash, call out for help. Do not remove your eyes from the eyewash until your teaching assistant has assisted you.

   While in organic lab, also do not wear contact lenses. They can trap chemicals against your eyes.

2. **Know the location of fire extinguishers.** Since most organic solvents are flammable, fire is a constant threat. Bunsen burners should only be used in the fume hood and only when there are no flammable solvents in the area.

   If your clothing catches on fire, roll on the floor to smother the flames. In the event of a fire, clear the area and notify your teaching assistant at once. Your personal safety and that of others around you should be your first concern.

3. **Know the location of the laboratory safety showers.** Chemicals should be washed from your skin immediately with large amounts of water. If you get a small amount of a chemical on your hands or

the lower parts or your arms, this can be accomplished in a sink. For larger spills, however, the safety shower should be used. If in doubt, use the safety shower. Any contaminated clothing should be removed.

4. **Do not eat, drink or smoke in the laboratory.** Do not even bring these items into the room. Also, never taste any reagents.

5. **Do not take chemicals or equipment out of the laboratory.** Do not remove any starting materials, products or other chemicals from the laboratory. Do not bring any chemicals into the laboratory from outside sources.

6. **Do not keep coats, backpacks or books on the floor or in the aisles.** There must be a clear path to the doors in case of an emergency.

7. **Bare feet and sandals are not permitted.** This is due to the large amount of broken glass generated.

8. **Wear clothing that does not expose your skin to chemical contact.** Any part of your skin that cannot be quickly rinsed off in the sink should be covered. Specifically, do not wear shorts or other items that do not cover your legs. Shirts should cover at least the midsection, chest and shoulders. Also, it is a good idea to wear an apron or lab coat to protect your clothing and gloves to protect your hands.

9. **Never work alone in the laboratory.**

10. **Do not perform unauthorized experiments.**

11. **Do not pipette by mouth.**

12. **"Horseplay" will not be tolerated.**

13. **Do not contaminate reagents.** First, make every effort to take only what you need. If you take too much, any excess should then be shared with you neighbors or discarded.

14. **Waste chemicals should be placed in the appropriate containers.** If you are unsure what to do with your chemical waste, consult your teaching assistant.

15. **Cleanliness.** A work area that is not clean is often also not safe. Spills should be cleaned up immediately. Do not allow used paper towels, broken glass, litmus paper, labels, etc. to accumulate at your desk or in the sink. Before you leave, be sure to clean your area, wipe off the desktop and return any equipment you may have used to the place where you found it.

16. **Maintain a quiet environment.** In the event of an emergency, it is very important that everyone be able to hear the instructions of the Teaching Assistant. Therefore, radios, televisions, computer games, etc. are not allowed in lab.

Safety Pre Lab

A major part of the first pre-lab is to prepare yourself for the your first experiment. At a bare minimum that means buying the textbook, a notebook and eye protection; and planning ahead for what you are going to wear.

WARNING: Anyone not wearing the proper attire will not be allowed to enter the lab!

1. Bring your lab goggles/ safety glasses!

2. Why is it important to wear eye protection while working in a chemistry laboratory?

3. Why is it not wise to eat, drink or smoke in the lab?

4. During an experiment, a student washes and rinses out a 10 mL graduated cylinder. The student then takes the cylinder to the fume hood to acquire 5 mL of starting material for the reaction. However, the student accidentally measures out 7 mL. What should be done with the extra 2 mL of starting material?

Safety Results

1. Indicate where at least one *of each* of the following safety items can be found in the lab (FH-204) by placing the corresponding letters on the appropriate places on the map below.

   a. Fire Extinguisher   d. Fire blanket

   b. Eye wash   e. Emergency exit

   c. Safety shower   f. Waste Solvent Container

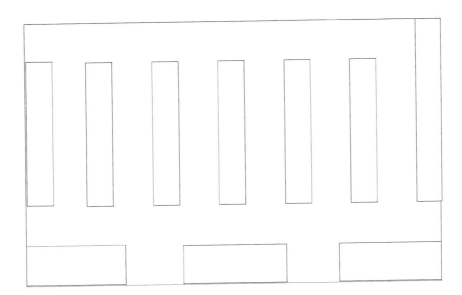

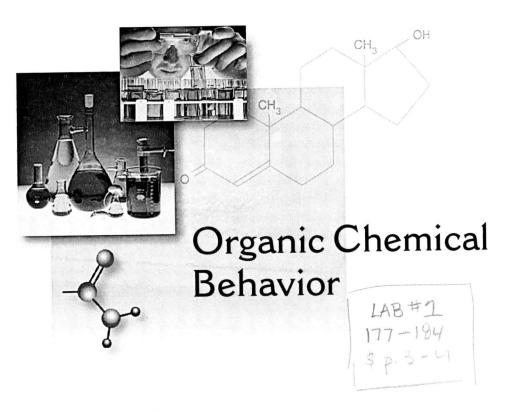

Organic Chemical Behavior

LAB #1
177-184
$ p. 3-4

Background

Early in its history, organic chemistry was defined as the chemistry of compounds derived from living organisms. Since these compounds came from living things, it was thought that there must be something special about them—that they possessed some type of 'vital force'. This type of thinking was central to the theory of 'vitalism', which was prevalent at the beginning of the nineteenth century. Ultimately, it was a chemist, Friedrich Wöhler, who disproved the vitalist theory by synthesizing an organic compound, urea, from an inorganic compound, ammonium cyanate, in 1828. Once chemists discovered that they could make organic compounds in the laboratory, organic chemistry was free to expand beyond those compounds that could be isolated from natural sources. As the concepts of vitalism began to fade from scientific thought, the definition of organic chemistry was altered and extended to include all compounds that contain carbon. This change in definition didn't alter the actual science of organic chemistry much, though, since most of the compounds derived from living organisms contained carbon anyway.

In fact, in the hundred years or so since Wöhler's discovery, chemists have discovered that most organic compounds are made up of a very limited number of elements. The most commonly found elements in organic compounds are carbon, hydrogen, oxygen and nitrogen. But that's not to say organic compounds are boring! Even though they originate from a small number of elements, there is still an almost endless variety of ways to put those elements together. Just think of all of the different proteins, carbohydrates, and lipids in the human body! These compounds are very different from one another and, yet, they still all consist of essentially the same elements.

So far, chemists have isolated over 10 million compounds that contain only carbon, hydrogen, oxygen and nitrogen. Of course, studying 10 million compounds would be an impossible undertaking for a single chemist. In order to understand the chemistry of organic compounds, we need to break that large group of compounds down into smaller groups. One way to do that is to divide compounds into groups that have similar chemical properties. This idea is very similar to something you've seen before: In general chemistry you learned that there are groups of elements with similar properties. These properties depended on the electronic structure of the element—both the total number of electrons and the number of valence electrons. Very similarly, there are groups of organic compounds with very similar chemical properties. The trick, then, is to identify the key factor that will systematically allow us to predict the properties of an organic compound, as electronic structure did for the elements.

Organic compounds tend to be grouped together and studied by functional groups. A functional group is structural unit that contains *other than* carbon-carbon and carbon-hydrogen single bonds. Since carbon and hydrogen have very similar electronegativities, carbon-carbon and carbon-hydrogen single bonds are almost purely covalent and are, thus, relatively inert. If an organic compound is going to undergo a reaction, the reaction will probably take place somewhere else in the molecule other than at the carbon-carbon and carbon-hydrogen single bonds. Those other places are the functional groups and they include things such as carbon-carbon multiple bonds and bonds between carbon and other elements.

In this experiment, you will explore a few of the properties of several kinds of organic compounds. Each of the following tests is used to identify a particular characteristic of an organic compound—water solubility, the presence of a particular functional group (a halogen, a carbon-carbon double bond, etc.), the presence of an aromatic ring, etc. Since there are so many organic compounds, we will obviously not be able to test them all. We won't even be able to test for all of the different possible functional groups. However, we will test some representative compounds from each of the following major functional groups, which you have covered or will soon discuss in Chemistry 223:

   A. Aliphatic Hydrocarbons.
   B. Aromatic Hydrocarbons.
   C. Halogenated Aliphatic Compounds.
   D. Halogenated Aromatic Compounds.
   E. Low-molecular-weight alcohols.
   F. High-molecular weight alcohols.

[handwritten: 7,10,11 do not react with bromine only one should]

Experimental

Since you will be doing such a large number of tests, you should probably use a grid—similar to the one at the end of the experiment—to summarize your results.

I. Test for Water Solubility *[handwritten: (X 11) use deionized]*

Anyone who has ever tried to make salad dressing knows that sometimes two liquids will dissolve in one another (i.e.; the liquids are *miscible*) and sometimes they won't (the liquids are *immiscible*). "Oil and water don't mix." Ethanol and water, however, are miscible—as anyone who has ever consumed an alcoholic beverage knows. But why is this? Why are some organic compounds soluble in water while others are not? The answer lies in the physical properties of the compounds. We have already mentioned that, of the over ten million possible compounds made from carbon, hydrogen, oxygen and nitrogen, not all of the compounds have the same properties. The key property here is something called polarity.

You learned in general chemistry that some molecules have charge or a net dipole moment. This is the result of ionic or polar covalent bonds in the molecule, respectively. Molecules with a charge or a net dipole moment are said to be 'polar'. In the liquid phase, polar molecules tend to line up with the more negative part of one molecule adjacent to the more positive part of another molecule. This ionic interaction is very favorable and results in strong interactions between molecules. In order to dissolve a compound into a polar solvent, some of the interactions between the polar molecules must be disturbed. Disrupting these interactions is unfavorable, however, the situation is not so bad if the original interactions can be replaced by new strong interactions—that is, if the original molecule is replaced by another polar molecule. If you tried to replace a polar molecule with a nonpolar one, the nonpolar molecule would not be able to line up with the polar molecules and would just get pushed aside in favor of the original molecule.

The overall result can be summarized in the general rule of thumb: 'like dissolves like'. Liquids of similar polarity will dissolve in each other. Polar liquids will dissolve polar liquids; nonpolar liquids will dissolve non-polar liquids. Since water is a very polar liquid, we would expect other polar liquids to dissolve in it. (Note: You many recall from general chemistry that water is very polar because of the polar covalent nature of the bonds between hydrogen and the very electronegative element, oxygen.)

Procedure: Place 10 drops of the organic compound in a small test tube. Add 2 mL of tap water. Shake the test tube from side to side to thoroughly mix the contents. Determine if the compound has dissolved. The compound is soluble if a homogeneous solution results. If two layers or droplets form, the compound is not soluble. Mix the contents again and set the test tube aside for about five minutes and then check it again. On your grid, label compounds that dissolved immediately as soluble (+); compounds that dissolved after five minutes as slightly soluble (+/–); and compounds which did not dissolve at all as insoluble (–).

II. Test for Solubility in Hexane (x 11)

The above discussion for solubility in water also applies to solubility in hexane. The only difference is that the hexane is nonpolar. Therefore, many very nonpolar organic compounds, which are not soluble in water, will be soluble in hexane.

Procedure: Place 10 drops of the organic compound in a small test tube. Add 2 mL of hexane. Shake the test tube from side to side to thoroughly mix the contents. Determine if the compound has dissolved. The compound is soluble if a homogeneous solution results. If two layers or droplets form, the compound is not soluble. Mix the contents again and set the test tube aside for about five minutes and then check it again. On your grid, label compounds that dissolved immediately as soluble (+); compounds that dissolved after five minutes as slightly soluble (+/–); and compounds which did not dissolve at all as insoluble (–).

III. Test for the Presence of an Isolated Double Bond

We now move on to our first direct test for the presence of a functional group. The bromination test indicates the presence of a carbon-carbon double or triple bond. A compound which contains one of these types of bonds will react; other compounds will not react. This is because double and triple bonds are electron rich and, therefore, susceptible to attack by electrophilic ("electron-loving") reagents. After all, for a reaction to take place, bonds have to broken and formed. A bond is shared electrons. So, to make or break a bond, you have to convince electrons to move. The easiest and most common way to do this is to bring together a species which has too much electron density and a species which doesn't have enough. The former is called a nucleophile ("nucleus lover") since it is in search of positive charge to balance out its excess negative charge. The latter is called an electrophile ("electron lover") since it is seeking out electrons to help balance out its excess positive charge. One has too many electrons; one does have enough. So, if these two species are brought together, electrons will flow and bonds will be formed and broken.

A solution of bromine, Br_2, in dichloromethane (a solvent) has a deep-orange color. Since bromine is a halogen, it is very electronegative (electron hungry). Thus, it will react with electron-rich functional groups, such as isolated carbon-carbon double and triple bonds. (Later on in your organic chemistry lecture course, you will learn that this reaction proceeds via an electrophilic addition mechanism.) As the reaction proceeds, the orange color will fade as the Br_2 is consumed. However, bromine will not react with the double bonds in an aromatic ring (because of the special stability of aromatic rings mentioned below) or carbon-oxygen double bonds (i.e.; ketones and aldehydes).

CAUTION: Bromine is very corrosive and will cause severe burns. Avoid breathing its vapors by keeping containers closed and in the fume hood as much as possible. Wear rubber gloves.

Procedure: Place 10 drops of the organic compound in a small test tube. Add 10 drops of the provided bromine in dichloromethane solution. Immediately shake the test tube from side to side to thoroughly mix the contents. Record the results. Mix the contents again and set the test tube aside from about five minutes and then check it again.

IV. Test for the Presence of an Aromatic Ring

An aromatic ring is typically a six-membered ring that contains three double bonds. At first glance, aromatic rings look very much like a normal cycloalkene. However, this pattern of bonding results in a structure which is much more stable than one would ordinarily predict. You will talk about this in detail later on in your lecture course. But, for now, you should realize that the bonds in an aromatic ring behave differently than isolated double bonds. We will test for the presence of an aromatic ring by using an ultraviolet (UV) lamp.

Procedure: Obtain a Thin-Layer Chromatography (TLC) plate from your Teaching Assistant. This plate is treated with a dye that will cause the aromatic compounds to appear under an ultraviolet light. *Using a pencil,* make a grid on the surface of plate. Your grid should have points for each of the compounds and should be labeled so that you can clearly identify which compound is which. In the fume hood, you will find small bottles of each of the compounds. Attached to each bottle should be a small (microliter) spotter. Open the bottle and immerse the end of the spotter into the liquid. A small amount of liquid should be drawn up into the spotter by capillary action. Transfer this liquid to your TLC plate by touching the end of the spotter on to the desired spot on your grid. Again, capillary action will draw the liquid out of the spotter and on to the plate. Return the spotter to its carrier and *close the bottle. It is very important that you return the spotter to the appropriate bottle to prevent contamination.* Repeat this process until you have spotted all of the compounds. Once you have spotted all of the compounds, visualize your plate by holding under the ultraviolet lamp. Use a pencil to mark the compounds that appear.

CAUTION: Do not look directly into the UV lamp and do not shine the UV light directly on your skin.

Test for the Presence of a Halogen

To test for the presence of a halogen, you will perform a Beilstein test by burning a small amount of compound on the surface of a copper wire. When a halogen is present, a reaction will occur between the halogenated compound and the copper and the flame will turn green. Be careful, though. The Beilstein test is very sensitive and will give a false positive if the copper wire contacts salts (NaCl) from your fingers or from the bench top.

CAUTION: The compounds you are working with are flammable. Be sure to keep the Bunsen burners in an isolated fume hood. Keep reagent bottles out of the hood and away from the Bunsen burners.

Procedure: Place 10 drops of the organic compound in a small test tube. Obtain a copper wire. Carry the test tube and the copper wire to the fume hood which has been designated for Bunsen burner use. Heat the tip of the copper wire in a Bunsen burner flame until flame around the wire is no longer green. Allow the wire to cool to room temperature. Be sure not to touch the wire! It is hot and the sodium chloride from your fingers will interfere with your results. Dip the cooled wire into the organic compound and immediately place the tip of the wire into the Bunsen burner flame to ignite the compound. Record whether the flame was momentarily green or consistently yellow.

Organic Chemical Behavior
Pre-Lab Exercises

1. Of the compounds listed on the Results Table below, predict which ones would fall into the classes given here. (Note: Some compounds may fit into more than one class.)

   A. Aliphatic (i.e.; Non-aromatic) Hydrocarbons.

   B. Aromatic Hydrocarbons.

   C. Halogenated Aliphatic Compounds.

   D. Halogenated Aromatic Compounds.

   E. Low-molecular-weight (<100 g/mol) alcohols.

   F. High-molecular-weight (>100 g/mol) alcohols.

2. Predict the solubility of butane in:

   A. Water

   B. Hexane

3. Predict the color you would observe upon adding a solution of bromine in dichloromethane to benzene. Is this result consistent with a compound containing three double bonds? Explain.

4. If you were given two liquids, 1-hexanol and benzyl alcohol, how could you differentiate between the two based on the tests outlined in this experiment?

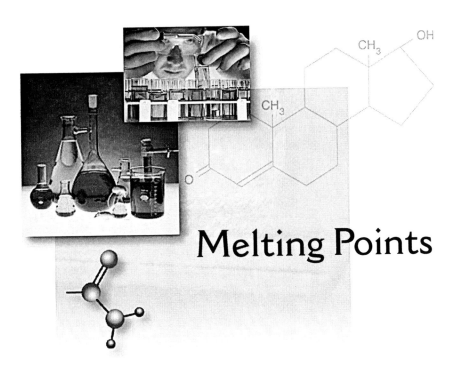

Melting Points

Background

The first physical property of organic compounds that we will explore quantitatively is the melting point. Colloquially, we perceive the melting point as the temperature at which a solid is changed into a liquid. This is a good working definition, but the actual formal definition of the melting point is the temperature at which the solid and the liquid phase are in equilibrium. That is, the melting point is the temperature at which the combined vapor pressure of the solid and liquid equals atmospheric pressure.

As a physical property, melting points are useful because they tend to be unique. Compounds with different structures will usually have different melting points. This is fortunate for chemists because it allows us to do a couple of very important things. First, it allows us to determine the identity of an unknown sample. Measuring the melting point of an unknown and comparing it to tables of known melting points can accomplish this. Unfortunately, however, there are some melting points that coincidentally overlap. So, taking the melting point of the pure unknown alone cannot always uniquely determine its identity. This brings up the second important thing melting points allow us to do. Taking a melting point allows us to determine the purity of a sample since the presence of an impurity will cause a melting point to change.

A solid consists of molecules that are aligned in a regular pattern. They maintain this arrangement because the molecules have attractive forces holding them together. For many inorganic compounds these intermolecular forces are ionic and, hence, quite strong. Thus, it can be difficult to melt inorganic compounds. Ordinary table salt, sodium chloride, has a melting point range of 801°C. Most organic molecules that are not salts (i.e.; which are not ionic), however, are not held together this tightly. The intermolecular forces at work are things like van der Waals forces and, perhaps, hydrogen bonds. As a result, organic compounds have lower melting points—typically under 300°C.

Regardless of the types of interactions that hold them together in the solid state, molecules are always in motion (i.e.; they always have at least some kinetic energy). For solids, this motion is limited to a small fixed space in the vicinity of nearby molecules. By supplying enough heat energy, it is possible for the motion of the molecules to overcome some the attractive forces that exist between them. The result is that the molecules are no longer limited to a fixed space and they are free to slip over and between other molecules. The attractive forces have not been completely destroyed; its just that the molecules are moving more freely and some of the structure of the solid state is gone. This state where enough energy has been added to cause disorder but when there are still some attractive forces between the molecules is the liquid state. If even more energy is added to the liquid it is possible to overcome the remaining attractive forces. This highly disordered state is called a gas.

For any state—solid, liquid or gas—not all molecules of a substance have the same energy at a given temperature. Some molecules can be very energetic, while others are more lethargic. Therefore, even though a substance may be below its melting point, some molecules may posses enough energy to behave as though they were part of a liquid. These very energetic molecules can transfer their energy when they collide with other molecules or with the walls of the container. If they lose enough energy, the intermolecular attractive forces take over and the molecules start to behave as a solid again. Below the melting point range, the rate of solidification is far greater than the rate of melting. When you are at the melting point, the rate of melting equals the rate of freezing—that is, the solid state and the liquid state are in equilibrium. Heating the sample further can cause the all of it to liquefy.

Also because of this distribution of energies, the melting point is not a point at all. Rather, it is a range. Experimentally, we will measure the melting point as the temperature range from when the sample first begins to melt to the temperature when the last remaining bit of solid sample just disappears. This is the melting point range. The exact temperatures and the size of the range both reflect the purity of the sample.

This is because the presence of an impurity disrupts some of the attractive forces which hold the solid together.

In this experiment you will explore the melting points of known compounds and determine identity of an unknown based on its melting point behavior.

Experimental

1. *Choose two compounds.* Each of the knowns and unknowns for this experiment will be from the following list:

Compound	Melting Point (°C)
Benzamide	128–129
trans-Cinnamic acid	133–134
Urea	133–135
Maleic acid	134–136
Benzoin	134–136
Malonic acid	135–137
Salicylic acid	158–160
L-arabinose	160–163
Triphenylcarbinol	160–163
Benzanilide	162–164
Sulfanilamide	165–167
Itaconic acid	166–167

Obtain a small amount (pea-sized) of each of two compounds on a piece of paper. Make sure to mark which is which.

2. *Prepare a sample.* Place a small amount of sample on a watch glass. Crush and grind the sample with a spatula until it is a fine powder. Using the spatula, push a small amount of the solid into the open end of a capillary tube. (Note: Be sure you are using a capillary tube that is only open on one end—not both ends—or your sample will fall out!). Gently scratch the tube with a file. The vibrations should cause the solid to fall to the bottom of the tube. Once the sample is at the bottom of the tube, pack the sample by dropping the capillary tube down a piece of glass tubing and letting it bounce. Do this several times until the sample is very well packed.

3. *Set up a melting point apparatus.* For this experiment, we will be using a Melt-Temp® apparatus. These devices have three slots for samples and another opening for a thermometer. Because of the temperature ranges we require, the thermometer contains mercury and must be treated with caution. DO NOT REMOVE THE THERMOMETER from the Melt-Temp®.

4. *Take a melting point.* Slowly heat the sample. A heating curve that correlates the rate of temperature to the setting on the control knob is posted in lab. Allow the temperature to rise fairly rapidly to within 15 to 20 degrees below the expected melting point of the sample. Then, as you approach the expected value, adjust your heating so that the temperature rises no more than 2–3 degrees per minute near the expected melting point. Record the melting point range as the temperature from when the sample first begins to show signs of a liquid (it softens, appears moist, or forms a tiny drip of liquid) to when the entire sample is a liquid. Repeat for your other known compound.

5. *Take a Mixture Melting Point.* Take approximately equal amounts of the two compounds for which you have already determined melting points and grind them together very thoroughly on a watch glass. Prepare a capillary tube with this mixture and determine its melting point. Pay particular attention to how the melting point range changes.

6. *Choose an unknown.* Determine its melting point as described above. You may want to do a very quick melting point first in order to determine approximately where the melting point range is. You can then repeat the melting point determination more carefully.

7. *Make a preliminary assignment.* Based on the melting point you determine for your unknown, choose some compounds from the list which may be the same as your sample. Prepare mixtures of your unknown and each of the compounds which you suspect may be the same as your sample. Some of the compounds on the list have very similar melting points, so a mixture melting point is the only to decide between two close choices.

8. *Determine the melting point of each mixture.* If the melting point of your unknown is depressed and broadened, you know that the known sample was not the same as your unknown. The identity of your unknown is whatever compound for which the melting point range remains unchanged.

Melting Point
Pre-Lab Exercises

1. Define the term melting point.

2. Suppose that two different organic compounds, M and N, have about the same melting point and that you are given an unknown organic compound, X, which also has the same melting point and is suspected of being identical with either M or N. Describe a procedure for identifying X and state the results you would obtain in each of the following situations.

   a. X is identical with M

   b. X is identical with N

   c. X is not identical with either M or N

Melting Point

Results Table

Name: _____

Section: _____

I. Known compounds:

_____
Compound 1

_____
Melting Point

_____
Compound 2

_____
Melting Point

_____
Mixture

_____
Melting Point

II. Unknown:

_____
Approximate
Melting Point

_____
Accurate
Melting Point

Possible compounds: _____

Mixture Melting Points

Compound in Mixture	Melting Point

Identity of Unknown: _____

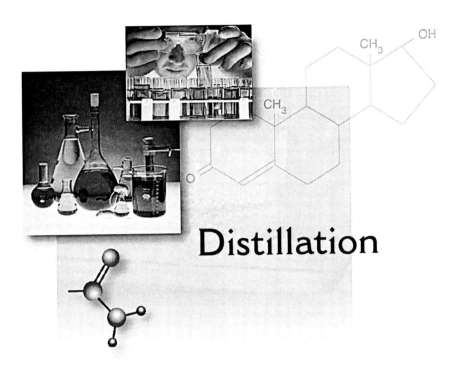

Distillation

Molecules in a liquid are in constant motion. Even at temperatures far below the boiling point, some of these molecules can escape from the surface and become gaseous molecules. (We know this phenomenon as evaporation.) As heat is added to the liquid, more and more molecules can escape from the surface. Eventually, we reach a point where the pressure of the gaseous molecules escaping from the surface (the vapor pressure) equals atmospheric pressure. This is the boiling point. We have already seen how the boiling point can be a useful physical property to measure for pure liquids. It also turns out that boiling a sample is a useful way to separate a mixture of two miscible liquids that have different boiling points.

When a mixture boils, the vapor is enriched in the compound with the lower boiling point. Intuitively, this makes senses since the liquid with the lower boiling point 'boils easier'. What is actually happening is that the liquid with the lower boiling point is making a larger contribution to the total pressure. Thus, its mole fraction is larger in the vapor. If the hot vapor that is formed by boiling a mixture is cooled down until a liquid re-forms, the new liquid will contain a larger percentage of the compound with the lower boiling point. This process of separating two liquids by repeated vaporization followed by condensation is known as distillation.

For this experiment, you will determine the boiling point of a pure liquid by distillation. You will also separate a mixture of ethanol and 1-butanol using simple distillation (a distillation where there is essentially only one transition from liquid to vapor and back again) and fractional distillation (a distillation where there are multiple transitions from liquid to vapor and back again.) You will then be able to compare the efficiency of simple versus fractional distillation.

Experimental

1. **Assemble your distillation apparatus.** To perform a distillation, you will need a round-bottomed flask, a three-way adapter, a condenser, a vacuum adapter, a neoprene adapter, a thermometer and a thermometer adapter. These items should be assembled as shown in the diagram in the textbook. The size of the round-bottom flask will vary depending on the size of the sample to be purified by distillation. As a

general rule, the flask should be at least one-third full but not more than two-thirds full. This prevents losses due to 'dead' volume and prevents the boiling liquid from escaping out of the flask.

2. Distillation of a pure compound. Place 10 mL of pure ethanol into a 25 mL round-bottom flask using a clean, dry funnel. After adding one or two boiling chips, attach the round-bottom to distillation apparatus. Make sure all of the connections are tight to prevent the loss of sample due to vapor leakage. Also, replace the receiving round-bottom flask with a graduated cylinder so that the volume of distillate collected can be easily measured. Heat the flask gently using a heating mantle until the sample begins to boil. Adjust the heating rate until the ring of vapor condensation rises out of the flask and past the thermometer in to the condenser. Record the temperature when the first few drops of distillate are collected. Continue to distill the liquid and record the temperature for each 2 mL of distillate collected.

3. Sample preparation. Obtain 50 mL of a 50% solution of ethanol in 1-butanol. Determine the refractive index of the mixture. For an ideal system, the refractive index of the solution is a linear combination of the refractive index of the components.

4. Simple distillation. Place 25 mL of the ethanol/1-butanol solution into a clean, dry 50 mL round-bottom flask using a clean, dry funnel. After adding one or two boiling chips, attach the round-bottom to distillation apparatus. Make sure all of the connections are tight to prevent the loss of sample due to vapor leakage. Also, replace the receiving round-bottom flask with a graduated cylinder so that the volume of distillate collected can be easily measured. Heat the flask gently using a heating mantle until the sample begins to boil. Adjust the heating rate until the ring of vapor condensation rises out of the flask and past the thermometer into the condenser. Record the temperature when the first few drops of distillate are collected. Continue to distill the liquid and record the temperature for each 2 mL of distillate collected.

5. Plot the data. Make a graph that plots the distilling temperature on the vertical axis versus the total volume of distillate on the horizontal axis for each distillation. Try to determine what points on the graph correspond to pure ethanol, pure 1-butanol or mixtures of 1-butanol and ethanol.

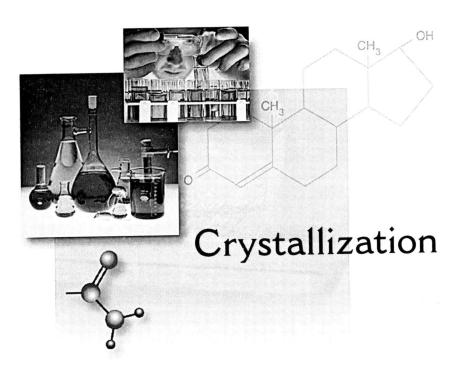

Crystallization

Last week, we performed a common organic procedure used for purifying compounds that are liquids at room temperature, distillation. This week, we will extend our purification techniques to include compounds that are solids at room temperature. The most common method for purifying a solid is recrystallization.

In general, a recrystallization takes advantage of the fact that different compounds have differing degrees of solubility and that solubility changes with temperature. For instance, a compound may be only slightly soluble in dichloromethane but it may contain an impurity which is much more soluble. In this case, the sample is dissolved in just enough hot solvent to form a saturated solution. The solution is then allowed to cool. As the temperature of the solution goes down, the solubility of the sample also goes down. Thus, if the solution was already saturated at the higher temperature, it is now 'supersaturated'. That is, the solution contains more dissolved solid than it should at the lower temperature. This 'extra' material has to go somewhere and, if the solution is cooled slowly and the conditions are just right, crystals will form. Since the impurities were more soluble than the desired solid, they remain in solution. The final result is a solid which is more pure than the original sample.

Recrystallization can also be utilized to remove insoluble impurities (sand, dust, boiling chips, etc.). To remove such materials, one simply has to filter the hot, saturated solution before it is allowed to cool. This must be done quickly and carefully, however, to prevent the loss of too much solvent and the premature formation of crystals.

A recrystallization consists of the following steps:

1. Dissolve the substance in a minimum amount of hot solvent.

2. Filter the hot solution to remove any insoluble material. *OPTIONAL*

3. Allow the hot solution to cool and produce crystals.

4. Filter the cool solution.

5. Wash the collected crystals.

6. Dry the crystals to remove any remaining solvent.

Experimental

_10 mL_

1. Crystallization of Sodium Acetate

Place about 20 mL of distilled water in a small beaker (100 mL). Heat the water on a hot plate to approximately 50° to 60°C (Don't boil off the water!). While keeping the beaker in contact with the hot plate, add a small amount of sodium acetate. Swirl the beaker until all of the sodium acetate dissolves. (It may take a moment.) Repeat this procedure until it is not possible to dissolve any more sodium acetate. (At this point, you have created a saturated solution by adding more and more solid to a fixed amount of solvent. Ordinarily, for a recrystallization, you will create a saturated solution by adding a minimum amount of hot solvent to a fixed amount of solid. Either way, the idea is to create a solution that is saturated at an elevated temperature. As this solution cools, it will then produce crystals.) Pour the solution onto a watch glass. As the solution cools and some of the solvent evaporates, needle-like crystals of sodium acetate should form.

2. Recrystallization of Benzoic Acid   _Just "wet" crystals_

Begin heating about 100 mL of water in a 250 mL Erlenmeyer flask. Heating the water in an Erlenmeyer flask helps to condense the water vapor which is formed to prevent the loss of too much solvent. In general, when doing a recrystallization, you want the solvent to be as hot as possible. This will cause the solubility to be as large as possible and create the maximum difference between the hot solvent and room temperature. Essentially, this means that the solvent from which the solid is to be recrystallized should be boiling.

Obtain a sample of about 1.0 g of impure benzoic acid for recrystallization. Place a small amount of sample in a capillary tube for a melting point determination. Transfer the remainder of the sample into a 125 mL Erlenmeyer flask. Add about 20 mL of boiling water to the solid and place the Erlenmeyer on the hot plate. At this point, you should have two flasks on the hot plate: one containing your sample and one containing a reservoir of boiling solvent. While swirling, heat the benzoic acid/water mixture to boiling. If the sample does not all dissolve, slowly add small portions of hot water and continue to swirl. Keep everything hot! Once the benzoic acid has completely dissolved, add 2–4 mL of additional hot solvent. (This extra solvent is in anticipation of solvent that will be lost to evaporation as the sample cools. Remember, too, that there has to be enough solvent to carry away an soluble impurities.)

Prepare a piece of fluted filter paper (your TA will show you how to fold it). Wet the filter paper and place it into your glass funnel. Warm the funnel and the paper by placing the funnel into the top of the Erlenmeyer which contains the boiling water. The hot water vapor from that flask should heat up the funnel and prevent your sample solution from cooling too quickly and producing crystals prematurely.

Pour the sample solution through the warmed funnel and into a small beaker (100 mL). If not all of the solution can be filtered at once, be sure to return the sample back to the hot plate to keep it warm while you are waiting. Once all of the hot solution has been filtered, place a watch glass over the top of the beaker and set it in a place where it will not be disturbed. Allow the solution in the beaker to cool slowly and form crystals.

When the filtrate has cooled to room temperature, collect the crystals by vacuum filtration using your Büchner funnel. While the crystals are on the filter paper in the Büchner funnel, wash them twice with a little cold water and hen press them as dry as possible on the funnel with a spatula. Transfer the crystals onto a watch glass and dry them i the oven. Once the crystals are dry, determine the mass and the melting point of the purified product.

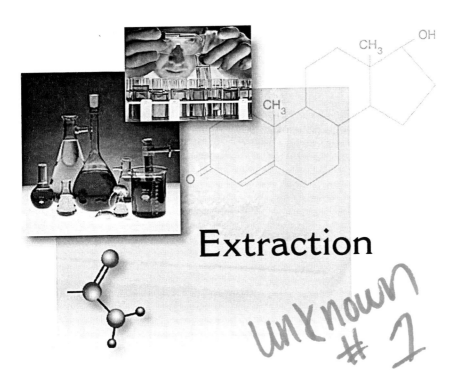

Extraction

unknown #2

Last week, we took advantage of differences in solubility to purify a solid by recrystallization. This week, we will again use differences in solubility to separate and isolate organic compounds. This time, however, the compounds will not leave solution to form a solid. Instead, they will partition themselves between two immiscible solvents which are in contact with each other. This separation technique is called liquid-liquid extraction.

An extraction of a mixture is carried out by dissolving the mixture in an organic solvent and shaking the resulting solution with an aqueous solution. Since the organic solvent and the water are not miscible, two layers will form. And, since different compounds have different degrees of solubility in each of the two solvents, the compounds will partition themselves between the two layers. The more polar compounds will move into the more polar solvent, the water layer, and the more nonpolar compounds will move into the more nonpolar solvent, the organic layer. Since we can physically separate the two layers in a separatory funnel, the net result is a separation of the compounds in the mixture.

In addition to separating compounds based on their solubility, extraction is also useful because certain types of compounds can be extracted very readily. In particular, organic acid and organic amines can be extracted very easily because they contain functional groups which can be made more or less polar by an acid-base reaction. For instance, an organic acid such as benzoic acid is normally not very water soluble at room temperature. By deprotonating benzoic acid, however, we can convert it into a compound which has charge. It is, therefore, much more polar and much more soluble in water.

Neutral
Not very water soluble

Charged
Very water soluble

$+ H_2O$

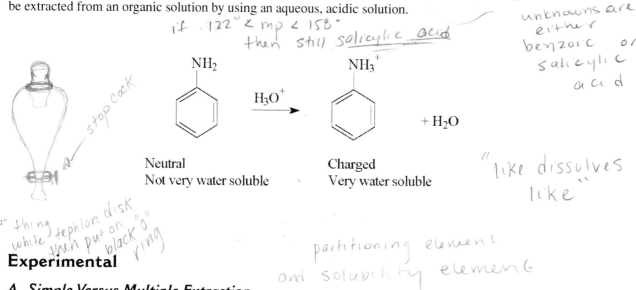

208

[handwritten: smells like moth balls] napthalene
[handwritten: neutral comp.] *[handwritten: ①]* benzoic acid *[handwritten: 122° m.p.]*
[handwritten: neutral comp.] biphenyl *[handwritten: 1a]*
[handwritten: ②] salicylic acid *[handwritten: 158° m.p.]*

Thus, if we had a mixture in an organic solvent which contained benzoic acid, we could selectively 'pull out' the benzoic acid by performing an extraction with a solution of aqueous base. Similarly, an organic amine can be extracted from an organic solution by using an aqueous, acidic solution.

[handwritten: if 122° < mp < 158° then still salicylic acid]

[handwritten: unknowns are either benzoic or salicylic acid]

Neutral
Not very water soluble

Charged
Very water soluble

[handwritten: "like dissolves like"]

[handwritten: stop cock]

[handwritten: 1st thing tephlon disk (white then put on "o" black ring)]

[handwritten: partitioning element and solubility element]

Experimental

A. Simple Versus Multiple Extraction

The purpose of this experiment is to compare the effectiveness of a single extraction with a fixed volume of solvent against two extractions which are each done with one half the fixed volume of solvent. An aqueous solution of an intensely purple dye (crystal violet) will be extracted into dichloromethane, in which the dye is somewhat more soluble.

[handwritten: Don't just shake to mix! (emulsion) = bad. just want two layer seperation. Just turn it upside down → remember to vent]

1. Simple Extraction.

Place 10 mL of the stock aqueous solution of crystal violet into a 125 mL separatory funnel and extract the solution with 10 mL of dichloromethane as follows: Stopper the separatory funnel and shake gently by rocking the funnel. While tightly holding the stopper between two fingers, turn the funnel upside down and open the stopcock to release any pressure. Be careful not to point the stem of the funnel at anyone when you release the pressure—any liquid in the stem may be ejected forcefully. Once the pressure has been released, close the stopcock and gently shake the funnel by rocking it again. Repeat this procedure four or five times, each time remembering to hold the stopper tightly and to vent the pressure regularly.

[handwritten: H-C-Cl, Cl on bottom, H₂O on top]

After shaking, place the separatory funnel in a ring stand and allow it to stand undisturbed. When the two layers have separated, open the stopcock and allow the lower dichloromethane layer to drain out into a small Erlenmeyer flask. Transfer the upper aqueous layer into a test tube by pouring it out through the top of the separatory funnel. In general, this is a rule you should always remember—'bottom layer out through the bottom (the stopcock), top layer out through the top.'

[handwritten: less dense layer rises to top. density of solution ≈ density of solvent]

2. Multiple Extraction.

Clean out your separatory funnel well with water and place into it a second 10 mL of the stock solution of crystal violet. As described in part 1, extract the solution with 5 mL of dichloromethane. After separating the two layers, extract the aqueous solution which remains in the separatory funnel with a second 5 mL of dichloromethane. Combine the two organic layers. As before, transfer the remaining aqueous layer into a test tube.

[handwritten (left margin, vertical): More soluble in organic solvent]
[handwritten: should more successful extraction method]
[handwritten: remember to break vaccuum by pulling out stopper 1st then opening stop cock]

look up melting point

more purple color = less successful extraction

in 2nd part ether layer is ~~on top~~ H_2O layer on bottom

3. Comparison of Simple versus Multiple Extraction.

Compare the effectiveness of the two different extraction procedures by examining the intensity of the color remaining in the aqueous layer. The difference will be more noticeable if you look down the mouth of the test tube and if the volume of aqueous solution is the same in each test tube. The procedure which resulted in the extraction of the most dye from the aqueous solution is the one which leaves the least amount of purple color behind.

B. Separating An Organic Acid From A Neutral Compound

"Reactive Extraction" utilizes acid-base chemistry

1. Extracting the Acidic Component

You will be given an unknown consisting of one acidic component (benzoic acid or salicylic acid) and one neutral compound (naphthalene or biphenyl). Weigh out approximately 1 gram of the unknown and dissolve it in 15 mL of ether. Pour the solution into a 125 mL separatory funnel. If the entire sample does not dissolve, transfer any remaining solid to the funnel with another 5 mL of ether.

Extract the ether solution twice with 10 mL portions of an aqueous 5% sodium hydroxide solution. Be sure to vent frequently to prevent the build-up of pressure! Combine the aqueous layers in a small beaker. At this point, the organic acid is in the water layer and is present as its salt, sodium benzoate or sodium salicylate. In order to recover the acid, we must do another acid-base reaction to regenerate the neutral compound. To do this, add 12 M aqueous hydrochloric acid until a persistent white precipitate forms. Then add more HCl slowly until the solution is distinctly acidic to litmus paper. The solid which forms is the original organic acid. Cool the slurry, filter it, rinse the filter cake with cold water, and let the sample dry in the oven.

Once the sample is dry, determine the identity of the organic acid by measuring its melting point. If you wish, you may recrystallize the acid from water to improve the melting point.

take melting point temps 1st

2. Isolation of the Neutral Component.

The ether solution which remains in your separatory funnel should contain the neutral component. Decant the ether solution out the top of the separatory funnel into a clean, *dry* beaker. There should be no visible droplets of water present. Dry the ether layer using anhydrous magnesium sulfate. When the solution is dry, filter it through a small plug of cotton which has been gently poked into the stem of a dry glass funnel. Collect the filtrate in a small beaker or flask. *In the fume hood,* pour the solution out onto a watch glass and allow the ether to evaporate. The solid residue which is left behind is your neutral component. When it is dry, determine its melting point and the identity of your unknown.

Salts more polar = more water soluble

benzoic acid not soluble in H_2O
sodium benzoate very soluble
extract by adding a base

protonate amines with acid

Benzoic Acid

$$\text{C} \overset{O}{\underset{}{\parallel}} \text{OH}$$

+

biphenyl

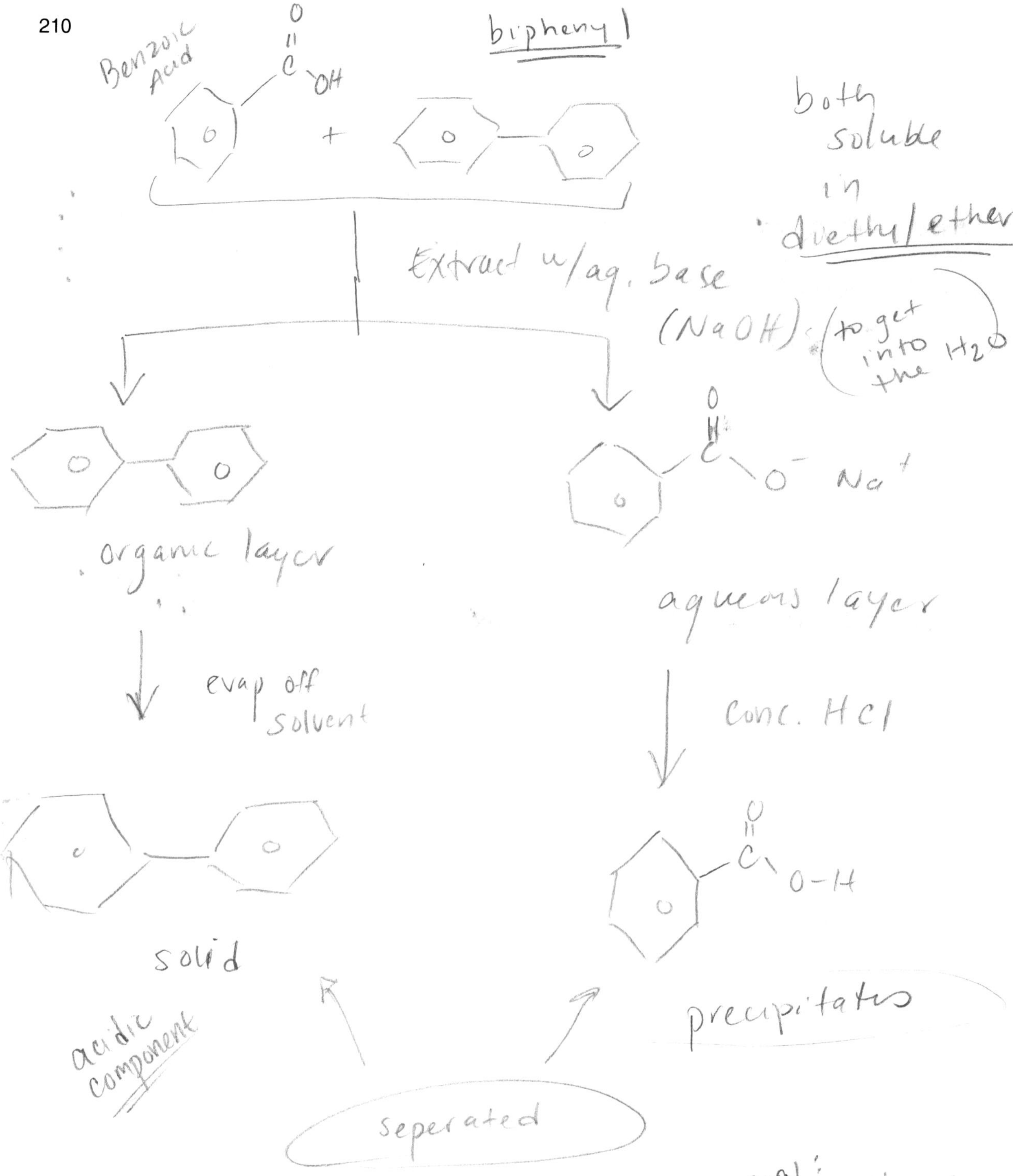

both
soluble
in
diethyl ether, so dissolve
in
the
diethyl
ether

Extract w/ aq. base
(NaOH) (to get
into H₂O
the

$$\text{C} \overset{O}{\underset{}{\parallel}} \text{O}^- \text{Na}^+$$

organic layer

aqueous layer

↓ evap off solvent

↓ Conc. HCl

$$\text{C} \overset{O}{\underset{}{\parallel}} \text{O-H}$$

solid

precipitates

acidic
component

↗   ↗

(seperated)

goal:
get pH
below pKa
to fully
precipitate

use "congo red" =
opposite of
litmus
red → blue =
acidic

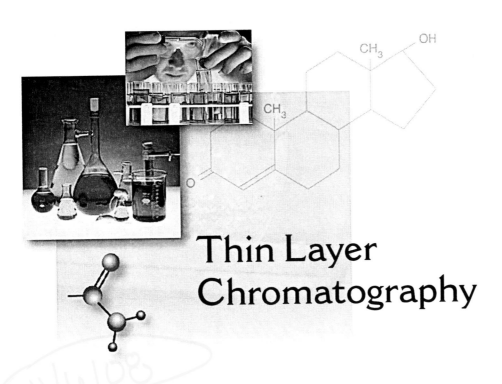

Thin Layer Chromatography

Thin Layer Chromatography (TLC) is an incredibly useful technique in organic chemistry. It is by far the most common method by which organic chemists monitor reactions. An organic chemist can easily run dozens of TLC plates in the course of a day—it is almost second nature.

Chromatography is the separation of the components of a mixture by distribution between two phases. One phase is stationary and the other phase is mobile. Chromatographic techniques are classified on the basis of the type of stationary and mobile phases used. In gas chromatography, for example, the stationary phase is a viscous liquid on the inside of a column and the mobile phase is a nitrogen carrier gas. Gas chromatography is often also abbreviated GLC, for gas-liquid chromatography. TLC is an example of solid-liquid chromatography where a solid (also called an absorbent) is the stationary phase and the liquid is the mobile phase.

Solid absorbents commonly used in thin-layer chromatography are silica gel ($SiO_2 \times H_2O$) or alumina ($Al_2O_3 \times H_2O$). As they are carried along by the mobile phase through the stationary phase, different compounds (solutes) have different affinities for the solid phase. The sources of this affinity may include hydrogen bonding, dipole-dipole interactions, or Van der Waals attractions. Since "like dissolves like," polar compounds have a stronger affinity for polar stationary phases. Because of this affinity, compounds are held (adsorbed) by the stationary phase. In addition to the solute-adsorbent interactions, there are also interactions between the mobile phase (the solvent) and both the solute and the adsorbent. This gives rise to solute-solvent and solvent-adsorbent interactions. The adsorbent and the solvent compete for the solute. Also, since the solvent itself can adsorb on the stationary phase, the solvent can displace less polar compounds which were previously adsorbed. This means that polar solvents cause compounds to move further through the stationary phase.

Since the adsorbent is very polar, certain solvents should be avoided when using TLC plates made of silica gel or alumina. In particular pyridine, methanol, water, and acetic acid dissolve and remove some of the adsorbent itself. Generally, solvents more polar than acetone or ethyl acetate should be avoided with this type of plate.

A list of solvents numbered from least polar to most polar is given below. If the solvent is too nonpolar, none of the compounds will move up the plate. If too polar a solvent is used, all of the compounds will move up the plate without separation. To get a solvent of just the right polarity, mixtures of solvents are often used.

Common chromatography solvents

1. Petroleum Ether (Hexanes)
2. Carbon Tetrachloride
3. Benzene
4. Methylene Chloride
5. Chloroform
6. Diethyl Ether
7. Ethyl Acetate
8. Acetone
9. Ethanol
10. Methanol
11. Water
12. Acetic Acid

In thin layer chromatography, the solutes separate in an upward direction as the solvent ascends the plate by capillary action. For a given type of adsorbent and solvent system, a solute should be the same relative distance from the baseline and solvent front each time a chromatogram is run. This can be defined mathematically in what are called R_f values.

$$R_f = \text{distance compound traveled/distance solvent traveled}$$

To calculate the R_f, you will need to measure the distance from the line where the compound was spotted to the center of the visualized spot. The distance the solvent traveled is the distance from the spotting line to where the solvent front had reached at the time the plate was removed from the developing chamber.

Usual R_f order of compounds, highest to lowest, when separated by TLC:

1. Hydrocarbons
2. Olefins
3. Ethers
4. Halocarbons
5. Aromatics
6. Ketones
7. Aldehydes
8. Esters
9. Alcohols
10. Amines
11. Acids

This list presupposes that the solutes are of approximately the same molecular weight. Increasing the molecular weight of a compound by adding carbon and hydrogen atoms makes the molecule more like an alkane and less polar. Hence, 3-pentanone would be expected to be less polar and to have a higher R_f than 2-propanone.

TLC can be a very useful tool in the organic laboratory. It can be used for assessing the purity of substances and for identifying compounds. It can also be used for monitoring the progress of a chemical reaction. In fact, reaction monitoring is one of TLC's major uses in research laboratories. The chemist can determine if the reactants are being consumed and whether or not the right products are forming.

In short, TLC is a very useful laboratory technique—one which we will use periodically throughout this course.

Procedure

Obtain a TLC plate and a developing chamber from your Teaching Assistant. Fill the developing chamber with a small amount of developing solution. The level of the liquid in the chamber should be less than 1 cm. Lightly draw a line in pencil 1 cm from the bottom of the plate. This will be your spotting line. Be careful not to gauge the adsorbent when drawing the line. Mark the line with 5 different starting points. Using the provided glass capillaries, transfer a small amount of each known solution and your unknown solution onto the plate. Each solution should get its own lane.

Make sure the level of the solvent in the developing chamber will not be above your pencil line (Remove some solvent if necessary.). After the plate has been spotted, carefully put the plate into the developing chamber. You want the solvent to rise up the plate in a uniform, even line. If the plate is placed into the chamber recklessly, the compounds may run together and the results will be useless. Try to place the plate in the chamber so that only the bottom edge touches the solvent and that all portions of the bottom edge contact the solvent simultaneously. Once the plate has been properly placed in the developing chamber, do not move or otherwise disturb the developing chamber.

Allow the solvent to rise up the plate to within 1.0 cm of the upper edge. Do not let the solvent touch the top of the plate. When the solvent reaches the desired height, carefully remove the plate and *immediately* mark the solvent front line with your pencil. After allowing the plate to air dry, visualize the plate using a UV lamp in the fume hood.

Identification of an Unknown

You will be given a known solution of each of the following compounds: acetylsalicylic acid (aspirin), *p*-methoxybenzophenone, biphenyl, and acetaminophen. You will also be given an unknown solution which contains one of these compounds. Your task is to use TLC to determine the identity of the unknown.

Record your unknown number. Prepare the developing chamber by adding about 10 mL of ethyl acetate/petroleum ether solution (4:6) to the jar and promptly replacing the cover. Use a separate toothpick for each, apply the four known solutions and the unknown solution at different points along the spotting line. (Make sure you know which spot is which!) Develop the plate and visualize it under a UV lamp in the fume hood. Be careful to note the color and appearance of the spot in addition to its location.

Calculate the R_f's for each spot. Based on the calculated R_f's and the appearance of the spots, identify your unknown.

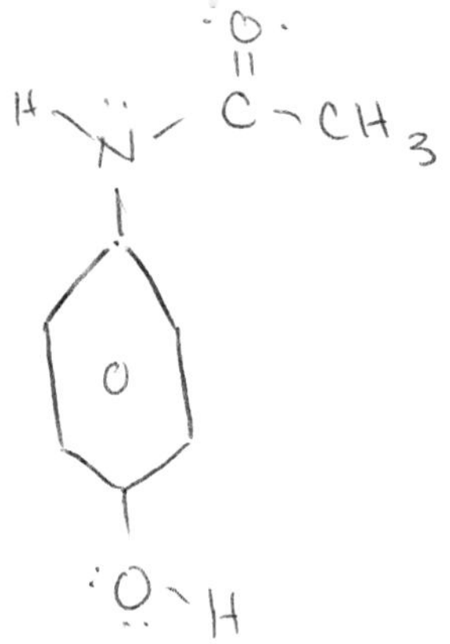

4-acetaminophenol

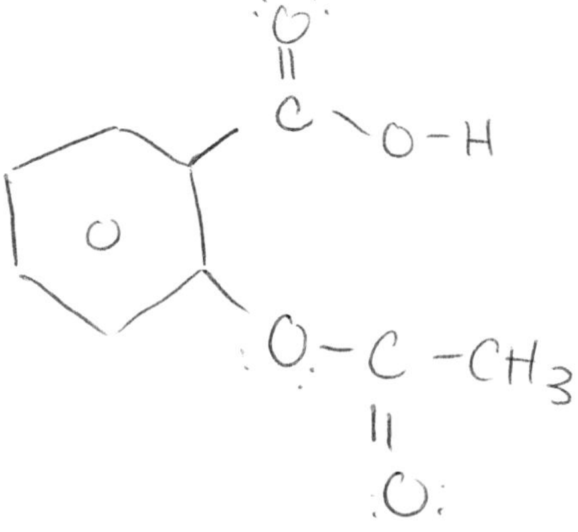

acetylsalicylic acid

(1)

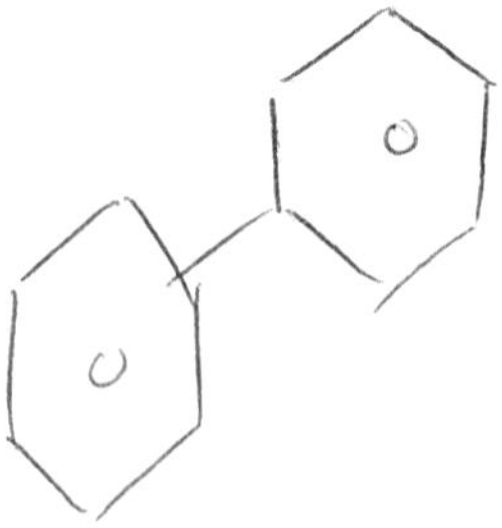

biphenyl

travels farthest on plate or

(2)

CH_3O

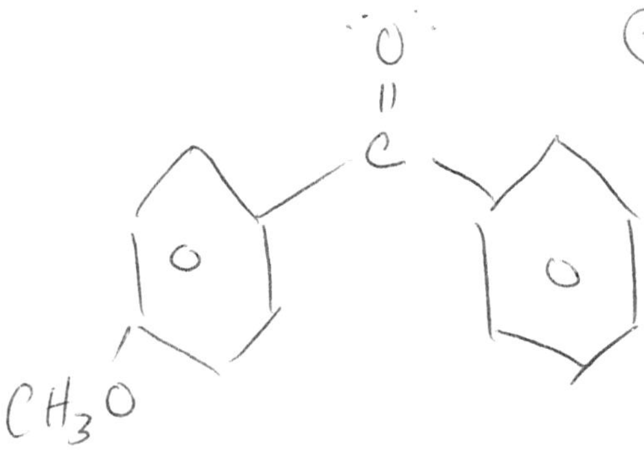

p-methoxybenzophenone

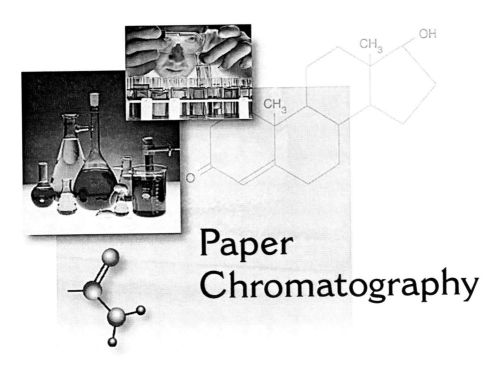

Paper Chromatography

Paper chromatography is of importance in both the identification and in the separation of amino acids. Since its invention in 1944, this technique has been widely used.

Paper chromatography is classified as an example of liquid-liquid chromatography. At first glance, this may seem surprising since solid paper appears to be the stationary phase. However, the stationary phase is actually water which is strongly adsorbed on the cellulose fibers in the paper. The liquid water is so strongly adsorbed that it remains stationary. The mobile phase, or eluting solvent, is usually some mixture of liquids which is carefully chosen to separate the compounds. The adsorbent-solute-solvent interaction principle discussed in the thin layer chromatography experiment apply here as well.

Amino acids are separated based on their differing solubilities in water. That is, they are separated based on their polarity and the different ways in which they interact with water and the eluting solvent. The more water soluble the amino acid is, the more tightly it is held by the stationary water phase and the harder it is for the mobile phase to move it up the paper. There are two factors which affect the solubility of an amino acid in water. The first factor is molecular weight. Increasing the molecular weight of a compound by adding carbon and hydrogen atoms makes the molecule more like an alkane and less polar. Therefore, the compound does not dissolve as readily in water. The second factor is the polarity of the amino acid. The more polar groups the amino acid has, the greater its solubility in water, which is also polar. The polarity factor is usually *more* significant than molecular weight in determining the elution order of amino acids.

Paper chromatography is like TLC in that the solutes separate in an upward direction as the solvent ascends the paper by capillary action. You also calculate R_f values for the solutes the same way. Different amino acids have different solubilities in water. Hence, they travel different distances and have different R_f values.

In this experiment, as in the TLC experiment, you will have to identify the components of an unknown. This will be done by comparing the R_f values of the two components of the unknown with the R_f values you measure for known samples.

Note: Amino acids are colorless. To make them visible to the eye, the paper will be sprayed with ninhydrin. Ninhydrin reacts with amino acids on heating to give bluish compounds. The reaction is irreversible and the amino acids are destroyed.

Procedure

Prepare the developing chamber by placing about 15 mL of the prepared solvent in a 1000 mL beaker. The solvent consists of ammonium hydroxide/2-propanol (1:2). Cover the beaker with a piece of aluminum foil until you are ready to use it.

Obtain a strip of Whatman #1 filter paper (10 cm × 14 cm) from your teaching assistant. *DO NOT TOUCH THE PAPER WITH YOUR FINGERS!* Use a folded piece of scrap paper when handling the filter paper. If you touch the filter paper, you will get extra spots from the amino acids that are on your skin.

Place the paper on a clean sheet of notebook paper and draw a light *pencil* line about 1.5 cm from and parallel to the 14 cm edge of the filter paper. Fold the paper strip into roughly thirds so that it fits more easily into the developing chamber. Place pencil marks along the line at about 1 cm intervals.

The samples should be applied to the paper using toothpicks. These should be dipped into the solution of the amino acid so that the wood is saturated. The tip should then be used to transfer a small spot of sample to the paper. Using a *separate* toothpick for each sample, place at one pencil mark a *small* (0.1 cm) spot of a 0.1 M aqueous solution of one known amino acid.

When spotting the paper, it is essential not to make a big spot. As the chromatogram develops, the compounds diffuse, causing big spots to grow even bigger and to possibly obscure another spot. The known amino acids are glutamic acid, leucine, valine, alanine, β-alanine, glycine, aspartic acid, and lysine. Repeat the above procedure for each of the other knowns at different pencil marks. At one of the pencil marks (preferably near the center of the strip), spot your unknown mixture, which consists of two of the known amino acids. Use your pencil to write in an abbreviation of what you spotted at each pencil mark (e.g.; Leu for leucine, Val for valine, etc.)

Allow the spots to dry and refold the paper into a triangular tube along the previously-made creases. Be careful when placing the paper into the developing chamber. The same considerations as in TLC apply here. After making sure the foil cover is replaced over the top of the beaker, allow the solvent to rise up the paper to within 1.5 cm of the upper edge. Again, do not let the solvent touch the top of the paper. When the solvent reaches the desired point, carefully remove the paper, mark the solvent front line with a pencil and let the paper dry.

Bring your dried chromatogram to your teaching assistant who will spray it lightly with a ninhydrin solution (composed of 400 mg of ninhydrin and 2 mL of pyridine (toxic!) in 100 mL of 95% ethanol). In a fume hood, detect the spots by placing your paper on a hot plate with a low setting. Make sure the hot plate is clean and that you don't overhear the paper.

As soon as the spots appear, make notes on the variations in color, size, and shape of the spots. Valuable information could be lost if this is not done immediately since the quality of the colors tend to fade. You should also outline the spots with your pencil to preserve the detail.

Chromatography

Name:_____

Pre-Lab Exercises

Section: _____

1. Rank the following compounds according to their R_f's (smallest first, largest last) for TLC using silica gel plates and ethyl acetate as a developing solvent.

2. Calculate the R_f for spot on the TLC plate shown below:

3. Each of the compounds used for this experiment is a colorless liquid. How is it possible to see the compounds after they have been separated? (Hint: the TLC and paper experiment as slightly different.)

4. Why is it important not to touch the filter paper used in the paper chromatography experiment with your fingers?

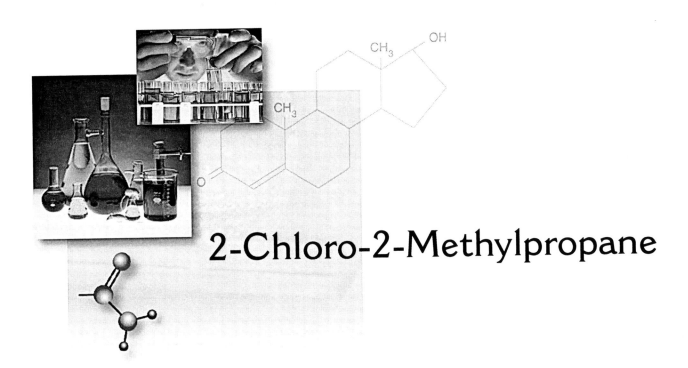

2-Chloro-2-Methylpropane

This is the first experiment in which we will utilize some of the techniques we have covered so far to synthesize a new organic compound. That is, we will begin with one organic compound, 2-methyl-2-propanol. By means of a chemical reaction, we will convert that compound into an entirely different compound, 2-chloro-2-methylpropane. The original compound and the new compound will have completely different physical properties—molecular weights, melting points, boiling points, densities, etc.

$$
\underset{\underset{CH_3}{|}}{\overset{\overset{CH_3}{|}}{CH_3-C-OH}} \quad + \quad HCl \quad \longrightarrow \quad \underset{\underset{CH_3}{|}}{\overset{\overset{CH_3}{|}}{CH_3-C-Cl}} \quad + \quad H_2O
$$

To synthesize 2-chloro-2-methylpropane from 2-methyl-2-propanol, we are going to react the alcohol with hydrochloric acid. This is an example of a unimolecular substitution—an S_N1 reaction. This reaction is called unimolecular because the rate of the reaction is only dependent on the concentration of a single species. The mechanism of this reaction proceeds first via protonation of the alcohol by the strong mineral acid, HCl. The rate-determining step in the mechanism is then the dissociation of the resulting oxonium ion to form a relatively stable tertiary carbocation. This carbocation is then attacked by the nucleophilic chloride anion. If this were a primary or secondary alcohol, bimolecular substitution would probably be favored since the corresponding carbocation would be much less stable.

Experimental

1. **Starting materials.** Obtain a pre-measured sample of 2-methyl-2-propanol (10 mL) from your Teaching Assistant. In order to determine the maximum amount of product which may be formed by a

reaction, we need to do a little stoichiometry. That is, we need to determine which reagent is the limiting reagent as this will tell us how many moles of product can be formed.

After determining the number of moles of the limiting reagent, the next step would ordinarily be to examine the balanced chemical equation to determine the relationship between the number of moles of limiting reagent and the number of moles of product. For this reaction, however, all of the coefficients in the balanced chemical equation are one. Therefore, the maximum number of moles of product is equal to the number of moles of the limiting reagent.

2. Reaction. Cool 30 mL of concentrated (12 M) hydrochloric acid in a 125 mL Erlenmeyer flask. Once the acid has cooled, pour it into a 125 mL separatory funnel. Add the 10 mL of 2-methyl-2-propanol to the separatory funnel and, without a stopper, swirl the contents of the funnel carefully to mix the reactants. When the reactants are well mixed, replace the stopper and shake the mixture gently every three minutes for a total of 15 minutes. REMEMBER TO VENT FREQUENTLY! Let the layers separate and discard the lower aqueous layer.

3. Work-up. Wash the organic layer successively with 10 mL of cold water, then 10 mL of 5% aqueous sodium bicarbonate solution and, finally, with another 10 mL of cold water. (Note: As you are 'working-up' your reaction products, to 'wash' an organic layer means to perform an extraction with a solution and keep the organic layer. The idea is that the wash solution will carry away some contaminant or impurity. In this case, we are trying to get rid of any excess acid or any unreacted alcohol—both of which are water soluble.) Discard the aqueous washes once you are confident that they are not your product. Dry the resulting organic layer over calcium chloride.

4. Purification. Once the product is dry, purify it by doing a simple distillation. During the distillation, remember that the fractions which come off at different temperatures HAVE DIFFERENT COMPOSITIONS. Since you're trying to purify your t-butyl chloride, it is best to collect the fractions which you believe to be your product (i.e.; have a boiling point which is stable and near the literature value).

5. Calculations. You can determine how well the reaction went by comparing the number of moles of product which you actually obtained with the number of moles of product which would have been formed if the reaction went perfectly to convert all of the starting materials to product. This is called the percent yield.

6. Evaluate and dispose of your product. In order to determine if you successfully converted all of the t-butyl alcohol to t-butyl chloride, you should gather as much physical data about your sample as you can. You already know the boiling point from the distillation. Other physical properties, such as the refractive index, will also give you some information about your product.

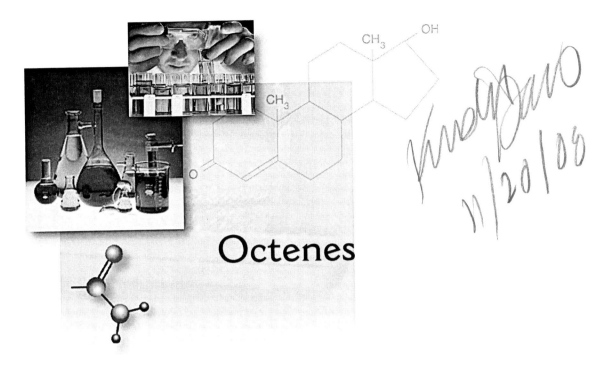

Octenes

In this experiment, we will prepare a mixture of octene isomers via the dimerization of isobutylene. This will be our first example of the use of π-electrons to form bonds. The isobutylene will be produced in the reaction mixture via the dehydration of 2-methyl-2-propanol. A mixture of octene isomers is formed because there are two types of hydrogen atoms that can be removed during the final step of the mechanism.

Procedure

Place 7 mL of water into a clean 50 mL round-bottom flask. To this water, *carefully* add 7 mL of concentrated sulfuric acid. Be careful! The addition of sulfuric acid to water is very exothermic. Don't add the acid so fast that the water boils and starts to splatter. Cool the diluted sulfuric acid solution to about 50° C.

Slowly add 5 g of 2-methyl-2-propanol to the cooled acid solution. (Hint: Since 2-methyl-2-propanol is a liquid, you can weigh it by placing a vial on the balance, re-zeroing the balance, and then adding the liquid drop wise until the desired weight is obtained.) After all of the alcohol has been added, immediately place a reflux condenser into the mouth of the round-bottom and boil the mixture gently for 30 min.

After the reflux period, allow the reaction mixture to cool to room temperature. Transfer the mixture to your separatory funnel and carefully remove the aqueous acid layer. Wash the remaining organic layer with an approximately equal volume of water to remove any unreacted acid. Dry the organic layer with a small amount (ca. 0.5 g) of anhydrous calcium chloride.

After drying the organic layer, transfer it to a round-bottom flask and distill it. Collect the fractions between 100° and 108°C. Determine the mass of the distilled product and calculate the percent yield. Test the product for the presence of an isolated double bond using a bromination test.

Octenes

Name:_____

Section: _____

Pre-Lab Exercises

1. What is the molar mass of 2, 4, 4-trimethyl-2-pentene?

2. What is the molar mass of 2, 4, 4-trimethyl-1-pentene?

3. The two products of this reaction are related to one another. What specific term is used to describe compounds with this relationship?

4. Assuming all of the 2-methyl-2-propanol is converted to a dimer, what is the maximum theoretical yield for this reaction when 5 g of alcohol and an excess of all other reagents is used?

5. Of the two major organic products formed in this reaction, one is formed in greater amount than the other. Which of the two compounds do you expect to predominate and why? (Hint: Use the mechanism of the reaction and make sure you rationalize the number and type of hydrogens involved.)

(more on back)

6. If the reflux is not monitored carefully, the yield of the reaction will be reduced due to lost vapors. Based on the boiling point of the compounds associated with this lab, which vapors are the most likely to escape and why?

7. Another major side reaction for this experiment is the formation of higher-order polymers. Using the curved arrow formalism, draw the reaction mechanism for the acid-catalyzed *tri*merization of 2-methyl-2-propanol.

Table of Reagents

Compound	m.p. ±1°C	b.p. ±1°C	Molar Mass (g/mol)	Density	Safety Precautions
2-methyl-2-propanol	25.5	82.2	74	.786	Flammable
Conc. Sulfuric acid					
CaCl₂					
Bromine					